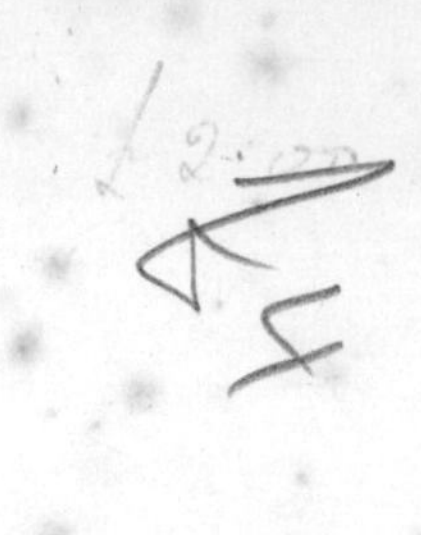

THE CARDIFF REGION

THE CARDIFF REGION

A Survey

Prepared for the meeting of the British Association held in Cardiff 31 August to 7 September 1960

CARDIFF
UNIVERSITY OF WALES PRESS
1960

PRINTED IN GREAT BRITAIN
BY WILLIAM LEWIS (PRINTERS) LIMITED, CARDIFF

EDITORIAL COMMITTEE

PROFESSOR J. G. C. ANDERSON

PROFESSOR JAMES BROUGH

PROFESSOR A. O. H. JARMAN

PROFESSOR W. R. D. JONES

PROFESSOR BRINLEY THOMAS

SIR J. FREDERICK REES (*Chairman*)

CONTRIBUTORS

ALCOCK, LESLIE	Lecturer in Archaeology, University College, Cardiff
ANDERSON, J. G. C.	Professor of Geology, University College, Cardiff
ATKINSON, R. J. C.	Professor of Archaeology, University College, Cardiff
BROUGH, JAMES	Professor of Zoology, University College, Cardiff
DAVIES, EDNA M.	Principal of the College of Domestic Arts, Llandaff
DAVIES, EMLYN	County Agricultural Advisory Officer, Monmouthshire
DAVIES, JOHN	County Agricultural Advisory Officer, Glamorgan
DAVIES, MARGARET	Formerly Lecturer in Geography, University of Manchester
HARVEY, ALEXANDER	Principal of the Welsh College of Advanced Technology, Cardiff
JARMAN, A. O. H.	Professor of Welsh, University College, Cardiff
JEFFERSON, G. T.	Lecturer in Zoology, University College, Cardiff
JOHN, D. DILWYN	Director of the National Museum of Wales, Cardiff
JOHN, WILLIAM H.	Hon. Secretary of the Association of Past Students of University College, Cardiff
JONES, A. TREVOR	Provost of the Welsh National School of Medicine
JONES, LESLIE	Senior Lecturer in Economics and Social Science, University College, Cardiff
JONES, WALTER T.	Principal of the City of Cardiff Training College
LEWIS, C. W.	Lecturer in Welsh, University College, Cardiff
LOYN, H. R.	Lecturer in History, University College, Cardiff
MATHESON, C.	Keeper of Zoology, National Museum of Wales, Cardiff
PEATE, IORWERTH C.	Curator of the Welsh Folk Museum, St. Fagans
PERCIVAL, MARY S.	Senior Lecturer in Botany, University College, Cardiff
PIERCE, G. O.	Lecturer in the History of Wales, University College, Cardiff
PRESSWOOD, ROBERT E.	Director of Education, Cardiff

PROWEL, A. W.	County Agricultural Advisory Officer, Breconshire
REES, SIR J. FREDERICK	Formerly Principal of University College, Cardiff
REES, WILLIAM	Emeritus Professor of History, University College, Cardiff
SALMON, H. MORREY	A Past President of the Cardiff Naturalists' Society
STEEL, ANTHONY B.	Principal of University College, Cardiff
THOMAS, BRINLEY	Professor of Economics and Social Science, University College, Cardiff
THOMAS, R. G.	Senior Lecturer in English, University College, Cardiff
WILLIAMS, GLANMOR	Professor of History, University College, Swansea
WILLIAMS, G. J.	Emeritus Professor of Welsh, University College, Cardiff

PREFACE

THE British Association has met in Cardiff on two occasions. The first time was so long ago as 1891 and the second was in 1920. During the last forty years great changes have occurred in the region and in our detailed knowledge of it. This survey endeavours to record some of these. For the purpose of the investigation, the region has been defined as east Glamorgan, the whole of Monmouthshire and part of Breconshire. Following the usual pattern, special attention has been paid to landscape and climate, geology, botany and zoology. To enable members to appreciate human aspects of the development of the region, contributions have been included on the Welsh language, local place-names, the historical and literary background and the economic structure. Brief accounts of the history of the educational and other cultural institutions in Cardiff have also been included.

The Editorial Committee wishes to express its appreciation of the willing response of those who were invited to contribute to the volume. Special mention must be made to the valuable work done by Dr. Margaret Davies in the general supervision of the maps that add so much to the elucidation of the text. Dr. Elwyn Davies, Secretary of the University of Wales Press Board, has given unremitting attention to the many details that arose during the preparation of the volume. It is interesting to record that William Lewis (Printers) Ltd., Cardiff, were responsible for the production of the Handbook of 1920. The present volume is a further testimony to their craftsmanship.

J. F. REES
Editor

CONTENTS

LIST OF FIGURES IN TEXT

LIST OF PLATES

I

THE CARDIFF REGION

MARGARET DAVIES

LANDSCAPE

CARDIFF is a city of the plain which owes its growth to the mineral wealth of the hills. Lying athwart one of the lowland entries into Wales, its nucleus is a Roman fort by the River Taff. Within the crumbling walls of this fort the Norman conquerors built a strongpoint from which south Glamorgan was administered. A walled medieval borough developed beside the castle and along the navigable Taff (see Fig. 1). By 1801 the town had spread little beyond the bounds of the medieval market town and its population was only 1,870; it is now 253,300.

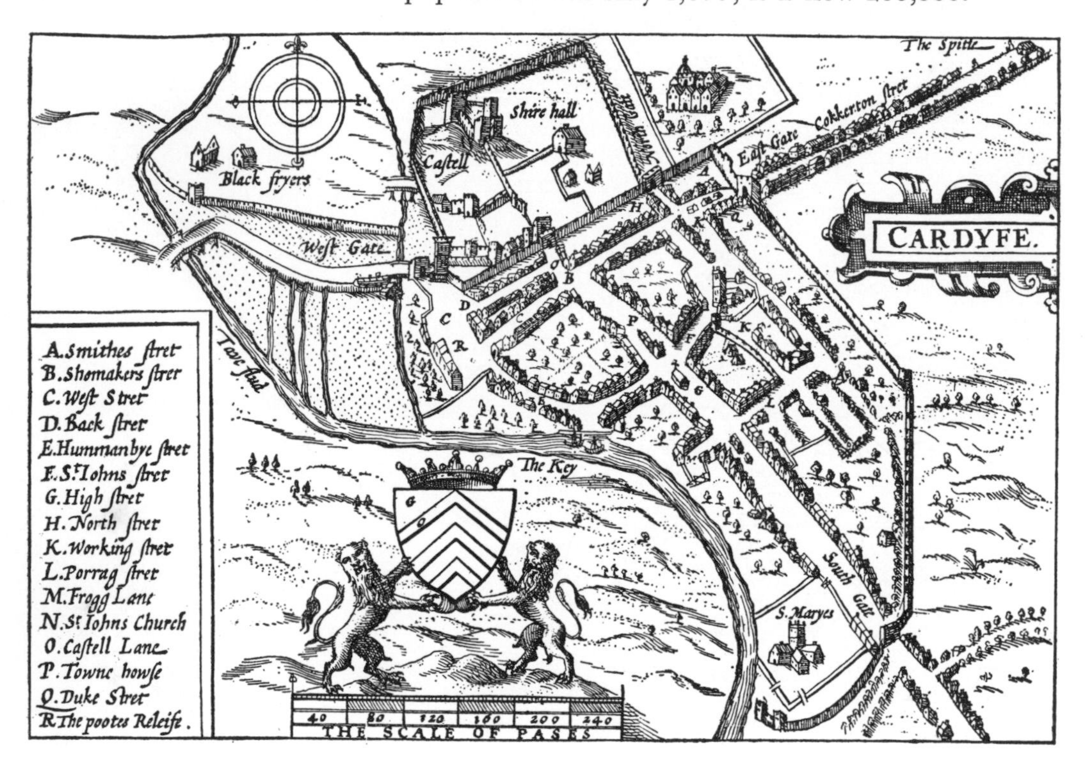

Fig. 1. SPEED'S MAP OF CARDIFF: 1610

The names of some streets have changed, and the course of the Taff has been altered, but the street plan of the heart of Cardiff at the present day is substantially that shown here.

Cardiff is dominated on the north by the sharp line of limestone and red sandstone Border Ridges which here enclose the South Wales Coalfield. One narrow gorge cleaves the barrier at Tongwynlais, and the Glamorganshire Canal, brought through it from Merthyr Tydfil to Cardiff in 1794, initiated the rapid growth of

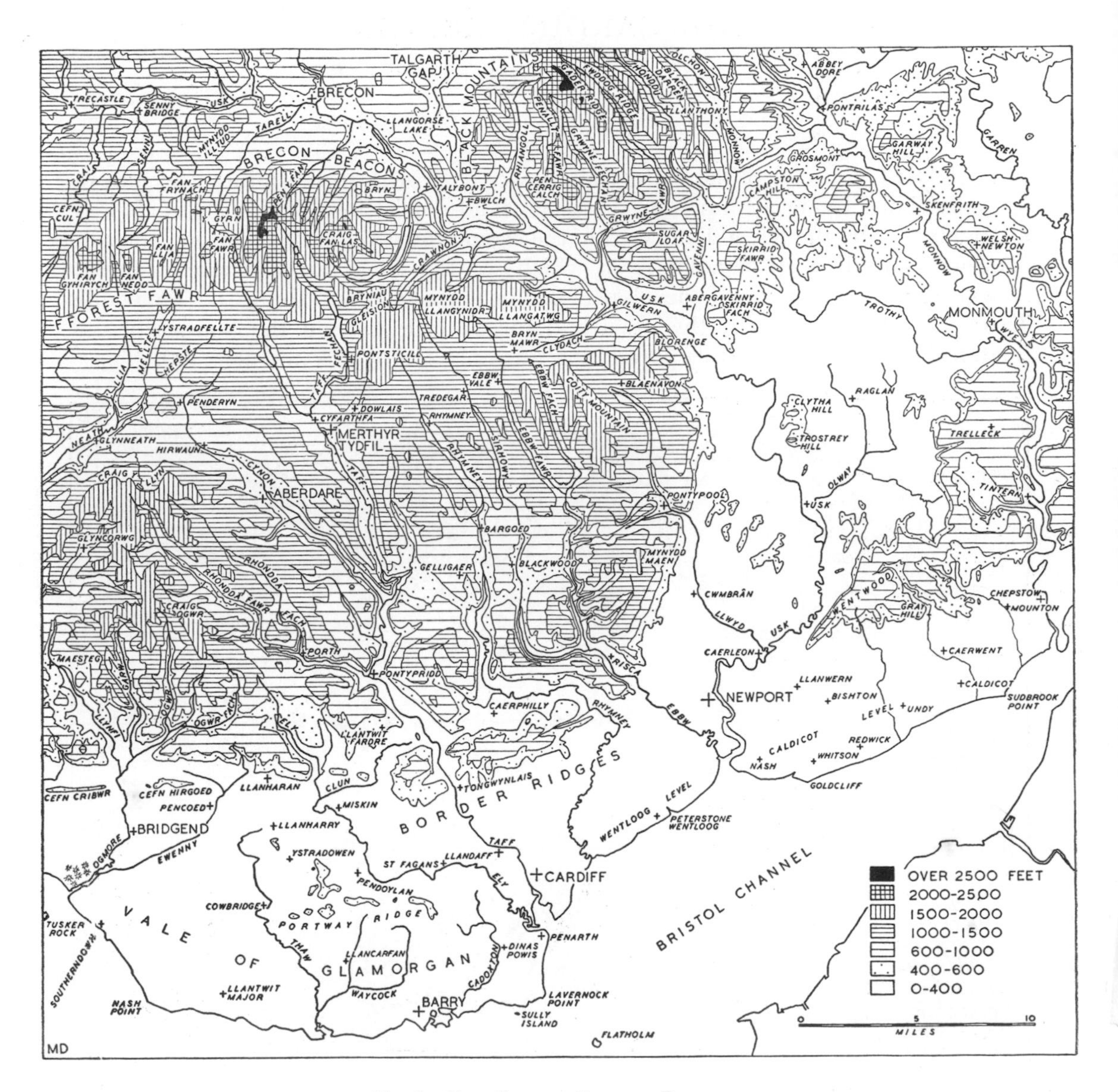

Fig 2. The Cardiff Region: Relief.

the city. To the Taff, the heart of the coalfield is tributary, and through its gorge iron and coal were carried seaward from the iron towns near the northern rim and from the confluent Cynon and Rhondda valleys (Pls. I and II).

Railways were subsequently taken through the gorge and through tunnels in the Border Ridges, and between 1839 and 1907 five docks were built to export coal. The town spread outwards, engulfing old villages such as Canton, Roath, Llandaff and Llanishen, and it now covers most of an area within a five-mile radius of the docks. The built-up area focuses on two distinctive nuclei. The first is the medieval town, which is dominated by the largely rebuilt castle, and which is the market and shopping centre for a large district. Its shopping streets, although widened, are those of Speed's plan of 1610. But the fashionable nineteenth-century street was that which linked the old town with the port at the end of the Glamorganshire Canal. Bute Street led for a mile southward to Lord Bute's docks and to the second nucleus, the commercial centre. Here, from large Victorian office blocks, the coal trade expanded, and merchants and artisans lived in substantial Regency houses and cottages in and around Bute Street and its residential squares. The district is no longer fashionable, nor is it any longer the notorious Tiger Bay of the clamorous days when millions of tons of coal flowed through the docks. Oil imports are replacing coal exports as the largest item in South Wales trade and Swansea is now the leading port. The mixed population of Bute Town is employed, as is that of Cardiff in general, in a variety of modern industries.

Within a radius of 30 miles from Cardiff there is greater variety of landscape than is usual around most British cities. The margins of Fig. 2 cut across several physical units. All or parts of the following are included:

The Plateau and Border Ridges of the South Wales Coalfield;

The Brecon Beacons and Fforest Fawr;

The Black Mountains of Brecknock and Monmouthshire, and the Sugar Loaf;

The Hill Margins of the Monnow, Wye and Usk;

The Caldicot and Wentloog Levels;

The Lower Usk Basin;

The Vale of Glamorgan and Bro Miskin.

Each of the first three regions is traditionally a mountain fastness against which waves of conquest have broken and been dissipated. Pastoralism and dispersed farms are, or were, characteristic. The last three regions provided routeways for invaders and settlers, who mainly came from the east. The Norman Conquest stamped the English manorial pattern and the nucleated village of clustered farms on the landscape of the lowlands. The mountains kept their scattered farms until, in the mid-eighteenth century, industry began to draw the hill people and many other migrants to the coalfield fringes and valleys. Intervisibility with the opposing shores of the narrow Severn Sea has been important in the peopling of the lowlands in particular. The contacts established by the builders of the Severn–Cotswold megalithic tombs have been continued for 4,000 years, and many names of settlements and settlers are now common to both sides of the Bristol Channel.

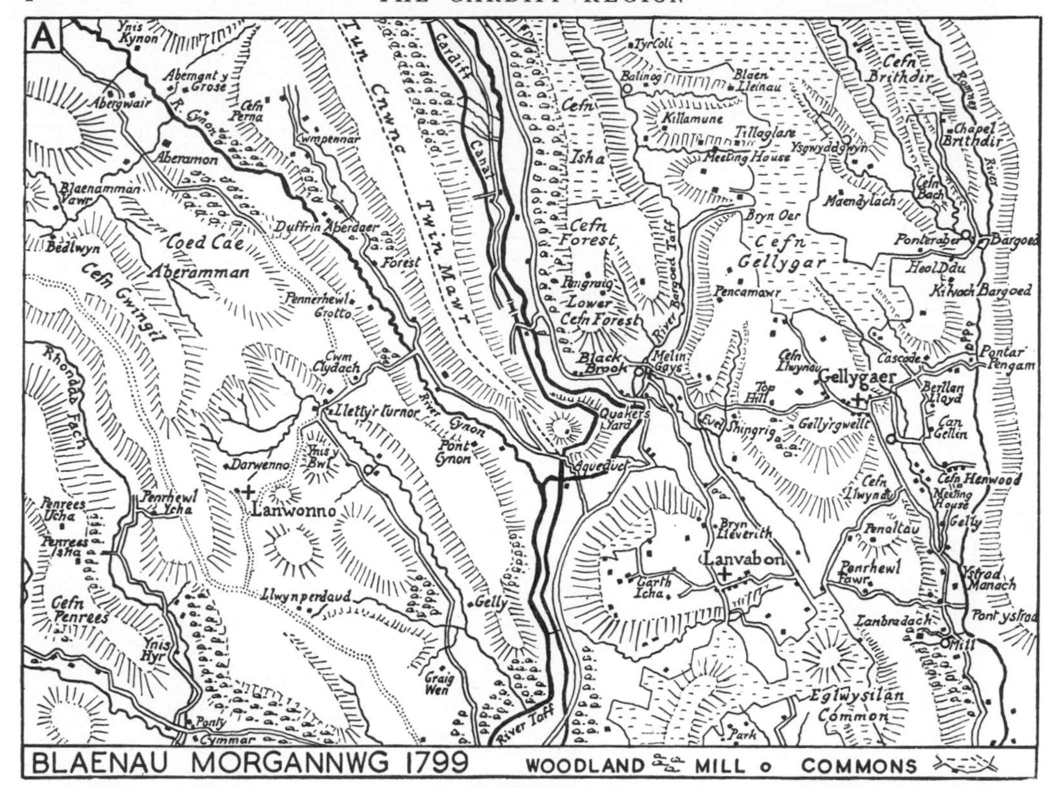

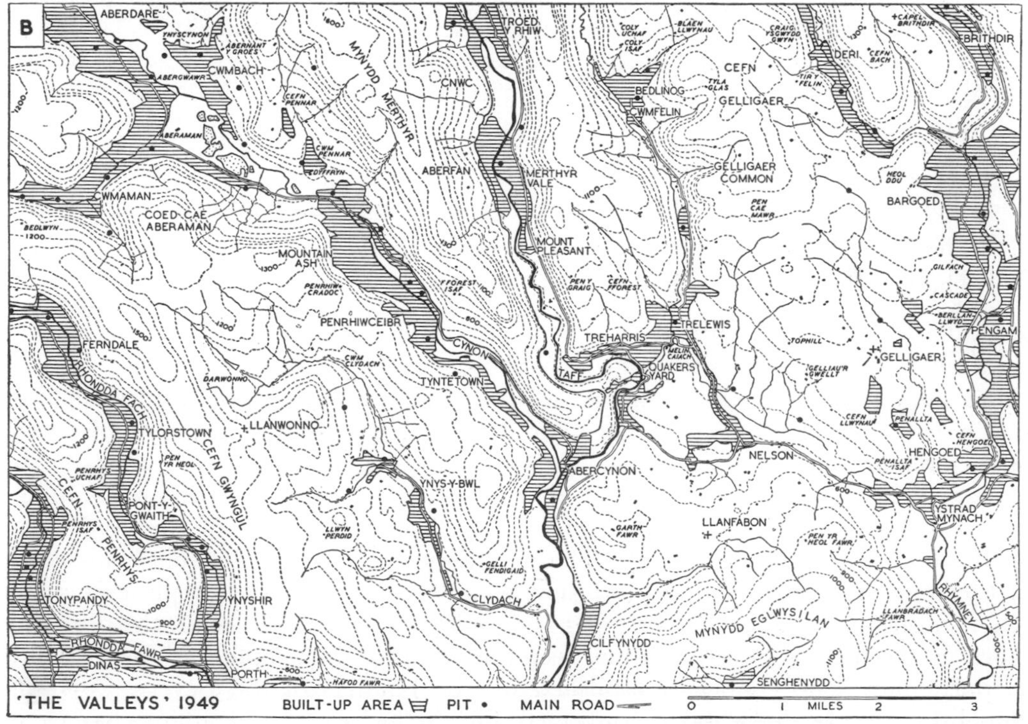

Fig. 3A. The Settlement Pattern in 1799. Based on George Yates's map of Glamorgan. The Taff valley road and the Cardiff Canal were then newly built to take iron goods from Merthyr Tydfil to Cardiff. Some of the former woodlands survive, especially in the Cynon, Taff and Rhymney valleys

Fig. 3B. Settlements in 1949. Farms named in 1799 are indicated where they survive. Some farms shown are deserted and some pits disused. Railways are not shown but they run along all the mining valleys: the canals to Merthyr Tydfil and Aberdare are now partly filled in

THE PLATEAU AND BORDER RIDGES OF THE SOUTH WALES COALFIELD

This unit, the largest shown on Fig. 2, is also the largest upland coalfield in Britain. Its even plateau surfaces are deeply cut by southward-trending valleys; the highest surfaces lie on the knot of ridges between and around Craig y Llyn and Craig Ogwr. These plateau tops retain their original pastoralism and one may look along them for many miles and be unaware of the changed economy and the settlements which are hidden away in the deep valleys.

Industrialization of the coalfield belongs to the past two centuries, but in its centre, where the coal seams lie deep, or on the southern margin where they dip steeply, it has swept through the valleys only in the last hundred years. The pastoral pattern of settlement in the uplands (*blaenau*) of Glamorgan and Monmouthshire is shown on Fig. 3A. It was the culmination of a very gradual increase of cultivation and population which occurred there between the Bronze Age, the only other period when the hills were relatively well peopled, and the modern Iron Age. It produced, throughout the upland areas shown on Fig. 2, a landscape thinly scattered with farmsteads on the valley sides and on the margins of the common grazing land on the plateau tops. Small groups of farmsteads clustered near watermills or ridge-top churches, and the farm people moved along footpaths and ridge-roads as did their Bronze Age ancestors. The valleys were less important as routeways. They contained wooded gorges of great beauty which, though now marred, is not entirely lost, especially in springtime. As late as 1848, a traveller in the Rhondda Fawr could still write: 'The people of this solitudinous and happy valley are a pastoral race, almost entirely dependent on their flocks and herds for support . . . The air is aromatic with wild flowers, and mountain plants—a sabbath stillness reigns' (Cliffe, 1848). (See pl. III.)

Though many farmsteads survive, the emphasis today is not on the *blaenau*, the hills, but on the valleys which cut them. 'The Valleys' are today synonymous with the Coalfield, and all mining, as distinct from opencast working, occurs in some form of valley. The deep river valleys trench through the grit-covered moorlands and often into the Coal Measures. They thus provide easier access to coal seams and a downward gradient to estuaries which (apart from the Ogmore/Ewenny, which has dangerous rocks offshore) were readily dredged and banked and were flanked by flats in which docks could be cut to take a rapidly expanding flow of coal for export. Exported coal is now a minor feature at Cardiff and Newport, but the southward flow of coal continues.

The change wrought by industrialization on the landscape and settlement pattern of the coalfield is illustrated on Fig. 3B. The valley bottoms now house the descendants of a peasantry which came not only from the local hills but from all parts of Wales and much of south-west England and southern Ireland. At first, rows of stone-built houses and one or more chapels arose around each pithead. Now these nuclei have coalesced, and roads, canals, railways, pits, houses and new factories engulf the valley bottoms and lie, e.g. along 10 miles of the Rhondda Fawr, like a bulging petrified snake. Repeated in many valley bottoms, this settlement pattern is unique in Britain. The people of the valleys deserve better living

conditions, but they are surrounded by open moorlands, and not by the built-up areas of large English conurbations (Pl. IV).

Until 1750 the populous part of Glamorgan was *Bro Morgannwg*, the Vale of Glamorgan. In *Blaenau Morgannwg*, the coalfield plateau, Saxton's map of 1578 shows, in the area included on Fig. 2, only eleven villages. With the exception of Glyncorrwg, Ystrad Dyfodwg (in the Rhondda Fawr), Aberdare, and Merthyr Tydfil, they are ridge-top hamlets. All the numerous existing Vale of Glamorgan villages are shown by Saxton, with the unaccountable exception of Flemingston.

The moorlands of the coalfield plateau tops and valley sides are largely underlain by Pennant grits and sandstones which have been widely quarried during the building of the characteristic long terraces which at first housed iron workers and miners. The grits and their glacial clays and gravels carry coarse pasture interrupted by cotton grass in high peaty hollows. This moorland was summer pasture and was often grazed in common by sheep and cattle. Much of it is still common land. Valley meadows provided winter fodder, and sunward slopes were ploughed, until a century ago, to the 1,000-foot level, as can be seen in plough ridges under the turf.

The Caerphilly–Llantwit Fardre and Gelligaer–Blackwood Basins have, on their southward-facing slopes, more arable land than is now usual within the coalfield (Fig. 3B shows the Gelligaer Basin). From Caerphilly Mountain one can look northwards on to a 'coloured coalfield', spread over the hillsides around the Caerphilly Basin. In Monmouthshire, similar Upper Coal Measures country has been extensively replanted and has good coniferous timber.

Below the Pennant grits lie the Lower Coal Measures on which the greater number of South Wales pits are based. These beds are well exposed on the northern margin of the coalfield and dip gently below it. Today the ill-drained marginal land on the North Crop is the main area of opencast coal working. The Lower Coal Measures underlie a broad upland trough which is an important routeway and, as they contain ironstone, they provided the raw material for the first major development, viz. the iron, and subsequently coal, industry of the Hirwaun–Brynmawr–Pontypool belt. Ironstone, valley woodlands, swift rivers and English ironmasters produced ironworks such as Cyfarthfa and Dowlais at Merthyr Tydfil which were lurid scenes by night and made the town the largest in Wales in 1830. It then had a population of 22,000 and by 1935 it had 70,000 of whom 12,000 were unemployed. The iron and steel works have moved to the coast. Ebbw Vale works is an exception. Restarted in 1938, it reaches its Midlands market via the Clydach gorge and Abergavenny. The iron towns have many new factories and some are set on the sites or tips of the old ironworks.

The southern exposure of the Lower Coal Measures is narrow and the South Crop beds turn sharply downwards. Margam monks worked outcrop coal near Cefn Cribwr in the Middle Ages, but the South Crop has had to wait for horizon mining before it could be fully exploited. Settlements such as Llanharan, where this method was initiated in South Wales, are typical. Here are no Border Ridges, no penned-in terraces twisting along the valley below brown crags. These industrial

villages have a nucleus of former farmsteads around an old church, and their industrial accretions are recent. Undulating dairying country spreads southward from their southern margins.

Lower Coal Measures exposed by the Maestêg anticline are worked in the valleys of the upper Llynfi and Ogmore (Ogwr). To north-eastward are the Rhondda valleys. All the valleys which drain from the high plateau of the coalfield have seen nearly a century of the rapid growth of a single industry, which, until its peak in the 1920s, brought an inrush of workers to the valleys. Many of their workers now rush out of and back to the valleys each day. Their livelihood depends on the more varied industries of the Bridgend and Treforest Trading Estates. Roads have been improved for this purpose, but the pre-1930 pattern of communications is unchanged except for some inter-valley roads built across the ridges during the industrial depression of the 'thirties. That which links the Rhondda Fawr with the Hirwaun Trading Estate over the frowning Pennant scarp of Craig y Llyn, is typical.

The Border Ridges of the coalfield are steep upfolds and their higher slopes are mainly given over to grazing and woodland. Along the eastern fringe, in Monmouthshire, they are very thinly peopled moorlands topped with massive Millstone Grit. The Blorenge, a northern outpost of these ridges, looks down on Abergavenny. After being breached by the Risca gorge and wider Rhymney valley, the ridges lose height and form the coalfield border north of Cardiff. Here they present an extensively quarried front of dolomitic limestone on each side of the Taff Gorge. East of the gorge the most southerly ridges are of Devonian sandstone. Their lower slopes have good farmland on which the advancing tide of suburban Cardiff is lapping. Behind are the higher Border Ridges of Caerphilly Mountain and the Garth Hill, sheep country on Millstone and Pennant Grits. West of the Garth Hill the Border Ridges disappear and are only partly replaced by the narrow Millstone Grit ridges of Cefn Hirgoed and Cefn Cribwr.

Millstone Grit and Carboniferous Limestone exposures are narrow along the south and east borders of the coalfield. North of it their gentler dip produces wider tracts of both rocks. Beyond the northern depression between Hirwaun and Gilwern, are grit plateaux given over to sheep and, on their peripheries, to cattle. The higher parts of Mynydd Llangatwg and Mynydd Llangynidr are typical. They take their names from villages in the Usk valley which formerly sent up flocks on to the 'mountain' in summer and had their *hafodau* or shielings there. Stock-rearing and quarrying (for old ironworks and new steelworks) is a feature of the mountain limestone tracts. The Ystradfellte–Penderyn–Glynneath triangle has sweeter pastures and many striking limestone drainage features. South-west of it is the reforested Vale of Neath, splendidly gashed into the anthracite coalfield by tear-faulting.

THE BRECON BEACONS AND FFOREST FAWR

North of a line from Ystradfellte to Pontsticill the long southern slope runs gently up to the summits of Fforest Fawr and the Brecon Beacons. These are deeply dissected Devonian plateaux whose hard conglomerate caps often rise above

2,000 feet. Pen y Fan, south of Brecon, reaches 2,906 feet. Although it is the highest Devonian mountain in Wales, its high flanking ridges are shorter than those of the Black Mountains. Through ways for the Roman army, cattle drovers and travellers by rail and car have been taken through gaps between the plateau blocks. The steep and often precipitous northern scarp commands the Usk valley and is gouged by deep cwms. These contain pockets of marsh flanked by moraines and by sheltered grazing land and big sheepfolds. This landscape is largely given over to sheep and mountain ponies and much of it is unenclosed heathland. The area was a hunting forest, and Fforest Fawr retains the name: the South Wales plateau tops have not had a continuous forest cover since the Bronze Age (Fox and Hyde, 1939).

The run-off of the southern slopes of the Beacons and Fforest Fawr provides soft water which is piped mainly to the ports of the coalfield. The Taff Fawr and Taff Fechan rivers are extensively utilized to feed reservoirs. North of the crest of the Beacons are broad lower ridges such as Mynydd Illtud, where scattered farms lie in a patchwork of arable and good pasture, underlain by Devonian red marls.

Brecon is essentially a market town and lies in a well-tilled undulating lowland between the Brecon Beacons, the Black Mountains and Mynydd Epynt, whose southern margin appears on Fig. 2. Below Talybont the Usk valley narrows and is not an easy routeway. Brecon was established as a Norman stronghold by invaders who used the wider Talgarth Gap leading southward from the Wye. The tortuous way westward from Brecon to the Towy valley has long been in use.

THE BLACK MOUNTAINS AND THE SUGAR LOAF

Across the rich loams east of Brecon lies Llangorse Lake, dammed by a moraine on its north side. From it the Black Mountains scarp rises through a thinning cover of scrub and on through pasture to its plateau top. The almost unbroken scarp is a more formidable barrier than that of the Brecon Beacons. Seen from the north-west it presents as noble a mountain front as any in Britain. This too is Devonian sheep country with a gradual southward tilt, but the valleys are deeper and narrower here. In the south, above Crickhowell, Pen Cerrig Calch, as its name suggests, has a cap of Carboniferous Limestone. The Black Mountains culminate in the Gader Ridge, and their best known valley is the Vale of Ewyas, in which Augustinian canons beautifully set Llanthony Priory. Monks have deserted both the old and the newer monasteries at Llanthony, and many marginal farms and upper field walls lie in ruins in all the valleys.

The Sugar Loaf mass, which rises to a comely bilberry-covered peak, is separated from the Black Mountains by the Grwyne Fawr valley and by a dry valley plugged with rock and drift to the east of it. This valley line is continued by the Honddu and Monnow to Pontrilas. The pre-glacial drainage of all streams except the Rhiangoll seems to have been via the Gavenni to the Usk. This wide valley is now blocked by a moraine barrier, 150 feet high, across the bend of the Honddu at Llanfihangel Crucorney. The Abergavenny–Hereford road and railway pass through it.

The Brecon Beacons, Fforest Fawr, the Black Mountains, and the Black Mountains of Carmarthenshire are mountains of similar formation and great beauty of slope and scarp. Together with the lovely Usk valley, to which they send many swift streams, they now form the Brecon Beacons National Park.

THE HILL MARGINS OF THE MONNOW, WYE AND USK

The lower valleys of the Wye and its tributary the Monnow are incised into relatively low hills which are mainly of Devonian sandstone, though from Tintern to Chepstow the Wye swings under cliffs of Carboniferous Limestone (Miller, 1935). The hills rise steeply from red marl and alluvial lowlands and many of their rounded summits carry remnants of common grazing land. They are often well wooded, and stolid red sandstone and half-timbered cottages are intermixed in the landscape of both hills and plain. English castles were firmly planted along the Wye, Monnow and Usk valleys, but the hills which overlook Grosmont and Skenfrith castles from the west long kept their tribal customs and still have Welsh place-names. Across the Monnow, the red sandstone hills such as Garway Hill are part of the southern scarp of the Hereford Basin.

Monmouth stands high and dignified above its natural moat. It has an important market and access to three valleys. Monmouth commands a lush flood plain and, until the mid-nineteenth century, kept remnants of common arable and common meadow land.

South of Monmouth runs the ridge which curves southwards as Wentwood and rises to Beacon Hill (1,003 feet). It is an area of rolling red sandstone hills, and many of its widely strung settlements are encroachments on common land. Trelleck, the largest village, lies at 600 to 700 feet below Beacon Hill. Wide stretches of the eastern slope of the ridge are now under coniferous timber. Here the Cistercian monks of Tintern had big granges to supplement the produce of the Wye and its water meadows. Tintern lies on one of many deeply incised meanders round which the Wye majestically swings (Pl. XVIII). South of Tintern, Carboniferous Limestone lies above the Devonian rocks and forms a plateau deeply cut by dry valleys and stream courses. The long slopes of these valleys lead up to rounded knolls from 700 to 900 feet high, which are often well wooded. This limestone country has a southward tilt to the Mounton Brook along which are several ruined nineteenth century paper mills.

Wentwood, cut over in wartime and now replanted, presents an unbroken steep face to the Usk valley and a dissected slope, dominated by the asymmetrical Gray Hill, on its southern side. In Wentwood the people of many lowland parishes claimed shares of pasture and timber. It is a thinly-peopled area which was ringed by minor castles and lightly encroached upon only in recent centuries.

The lowland entry into south Monmouthshire is commanded by Chepstow whose old limestone buildings cling to the bedrock from which they are derived (Pl. XIX). The navigable Wye, flowing through productive oak forests and past old-established metal works, made Chepstow a busy port in the days of sail. From

Caerleon and Chepstow an English manorial pattern was imposed on the goodly lowlands of south-east Monmouthshire. The field and village names, like the polder landscape, are often duplicated across the Severn estuary.

THE CALDICOT AND WENTLOOG LEVELS

Some of the best cattle-fattening pasture in Wales lies on both sides of the lower Usk, on marine alluvium reclaimed from the Bristol Channel and protected against its strong tidal flow by sea walls. The shaping of this man-made land dates from the later phases of the Roman occupation, and medieval monks laid out some of the major reens or ditches which carry the water from an intricate drainage network, which serves both uplands and Levels, out under the sea wall.

The Levels attain their maximum breadth of 3 miles between Llanwern and Goldcliff. Their inner margin of solid land runs roughly along the 25-foot contour, and the lowest point of their warped surface lies near this margin. The manorial villages, located at the junction of solid arable land and the rich meadows of the Levels, are therefore flanked on the south by very wet land. This was often left as large village commons; it was useless in wet winters, and at Bishton it is called Rotten Land. The main South Wales railway, taken across it a century ago, complicated drainage and access to the meadows. Six villages (Peterstone Wentloog, St. Bride's Wentloog, Nash, Goldcliff, Whitson and Redwick) stand on the firmer parts of the Levels near the sea wall. Two lie on the Wentloog and four on the Caldicot Level. Their fine churches provide evidence of the prosperity of a considerable medieval and Tudor population. Flood marks well up their towers denote the devastation of the Levels in the winter of 1606–7, a catastrophe from which there was a very slow recovery.

The arable margins of the Levels are underlain by Devonian marls west of Newport, by Keuper marls around Llanwern and east of Caldicot, and by Carboniferous Limestone between these two villages. These rocks and their overlying gravels provide productive and readily worked soils. The arable land lies on the gentler slopes north of the villages, and at Magor, Undy and Caldicot, remnants of open fields survived there until 1850. In the parish of Caldicot, 204 acres of arable lay in unfenced strips in 1842 (Davies, 1955–6). Meadow holdings were also held in strips and are still widely scattered. There was common of pasture alongside the villages, on the saltings outside the sea wall, and in larger commons, such as Caldicot Moor on the Levels, and Earlswood (the east end of Wentwood), to which the tenants of many manors sent their beasts. The wide margins of roads through the Levels were 'street commons', and the name Broadstreet Common survives in both sections of the Levels. Along them lines of scattered cottages, old encroachments nibbled from the road verges, ribbon out from the older farm clusters which surround the churches. In high summer this is a quiet, lush land, a fenland where fat cattle graze between lines of flag iris and pollarded willows. In the depths of winter it is waterlogged, windswept and desolate; but spring comes early. Newport and Cardiff are spreading on to the margins of the Levels, and beefy Herefords have been replaced by dairy Friesians on farms near to these towns.

But the farming pattern of the Levels, so rigidly determined by their delicately balanced drainage, has remained unchanged for centuries. It is now being partly altered by the incursion of heavy industry in the form of a large steel strip mill.

THE LOWER USK BASIN

The estuary of the Usk runs through the Levels, but above Newport there is no comparable development of flat land along its lower course. For three miles south of the town of Usk, the river swings across a mile-wide plain, but this and narrower alluvial belts are closely confined by hills, and, north of Usk, by terraces of glacial gravel. Devonian sandstone underlies the rolling country north of Raglan. West of this historic village are Clytha and Trostrey Hills, masses of Wenlock shale which rise in steep wooded slopes from the Usk valley. This Silurian inlier continues south-westward across the Usk and is deeply etched by well-wooded valleys leading to the main river. The rougher ridge-top pastures were formerly big commons.

The better soils and arable land are found on the Devonian red marls of the rolling lowlands of the lower Usk basin. Here, flanked by orchards, are fine mixed farms whose markets are at Monmouth, Usk and Newport. This is a long-settled and well-tamed countryside whose potentialities as a well-endowed base for further conquest were recognized by the legionaries of Caerleon and by the Norman conquerors. Because of its good soils and relatively dry and warm summers, it has the highest proportion of wheatland in South Wales.

THE VALE OF GLAMORGAN

This deeply dissected coast plateau is not a plain, nor is it comparable to one of the great vales between the calcareous ridges of England. *Bro Morgannwg* is lowlying only in relation to *Blaenau Morgannwg*, the high hills of the coalfield. It is a low plateau covered with good loams, and its lovely and historic villages lie snug in hollows where there are streams and wells. The sides of its little valleys are cut into Lias Limestone and not into Coal Measures, but the narrow roads of the Vale of Glamorgan drop into them as sharply as do roads into the mining valleys. The rivers of the Vale, like those of the coalfield before industrialization, are not through routeways. On the contrary, it is the low plateau surfaces which have the dense network of lanes associated with a well-peopled arable area. They link village and hamlets spaced about a mile apart, and their twists and turns suggest that many were once access roads around open fields. The Vale of Glamorgan, between the Portway (the Cardiff—Ewenny road) and the Bristol Channel, was partitioned among Norman knights who established castles and adjoining villages to house their manorial tenants. Nucleated villages with their characteristic clustering of farms and cottages predominate in the Vale, and the rare isolated buildings, such as Ewenny Priory, were built with strong fortifications until Tudor times. This is a well-tilled countryside, and in its well-tended villages are old churches with strongly built towers, fine manor houses and old inns—grey limestone buildings and lime-washed cottages set in a lime-rich land (Pls. XVI–XVII).

Scattered holdings are often found as a legacy of the open field system (Davies, 1954–5), and the thick grass of a large meadow in the Thaw valley is still grazed in common. This is Llanbethery Moor, which is shown on Fig. 4. Remnants of open arable fields survived in 1840 on the plateau top. The strips and holdings were and are scattered. The arable strips were separated by balks called landshares or lanshers, a name commonly used throughout south-west Britain. The farms are clustered in Llanbethery, one of several hamlets in the large parish of Llancarfan.

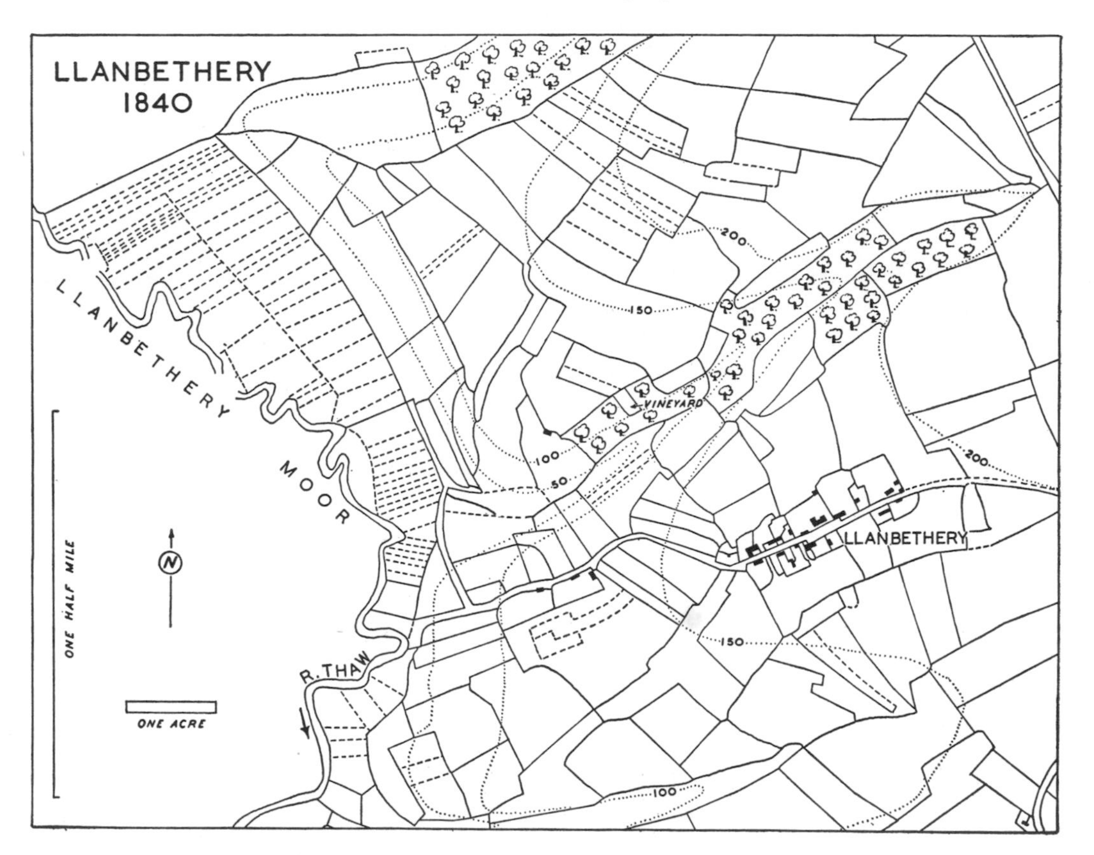

Fig. 4. Field Patterns around Llanbethery, 1840

Based on the tithe map of Llancarfan parish. Continuous lines around fields indicate hedges or walls. Broken lines in open fields probably represent balks in arable fields, but on Llanbethery Moor no boundary would be indicated on the ground apart from mere-stones at the ends of the strips. It is probable that there was formerly a vineyard on the southward-facing slope of the steep valley north of the village. Vines were grown on the sunny fronts of cottages in south Glamorgan in the early nineteenth century, and there were two vineyards there in the early twentieth century

The Vale of Glamorgan coast runs from Southerndown to Nash Point in 150–200 foot cliffs, and thence eastwards to Barry the cliffs are 50 to 100 feet high. These cliffs are formed of horizontally bedded Lias Limestones and vulnerable soft shales, and the Iron Age forts which top them are much reduced by erosion. From Barry to Penarth, Lias and Keuper cliffs alternate, and inland from them the

basin of the Cadoxton River also differs from the Vale of Glamorgan proper. This is an area of Keuper marl lowlands broken by low, but steep-sided, ridges of Carboniferous Limestone. It has much market gardening and quarrying, and Penarth, Barry, Dinas Powis, and Cardiff are all spreading on to the farmland.

The coast plateau of the Vale of Glamorgan rises gently to about 350 feet and has many level stretches. For this reason much land has been acquired for airfields, but it is still the best mixed farming area in Glamorgan. Its good farming changed the Celtic monastic settlement of Llantwit Major (Llanilltud Fawr) into a busy little market town whose merchants built seemly houses and worthily supported their fine church. But the main market of the Vale has always been Cowbridge. Here a long roadside ribbon of limestone houses and coaching inns pushed beyond the medieval walls which enclose the church and Tudor grammar school, and in the eighteenth century the town and market were of greater consequence than Cardiff.

Cowbridge lies on the Portway. This ridge-road is probably prehistoric and, apart from modern diversions, it is certainly Roman. It runs along the 300- to 400-foot ridge of Carboniferous Limestone (the Portway Ridge on Fig. 2) which is the northern border of the Vale of Glamorgan proper. Northward again are the valleys of the Ewenny and Ely rivers, polluted near their sources in the coalfield. These rivers fall sharply until they leave the Border Ridges and then have very gentle falls and ill-drained flood plains. The generally fertile Bro Miskin is thus interrupted by waterlogged pastures along the Ely River near Pendoylan. Between the latter village and Pencoed are low hills of Carboniferous Limestone spread with sands and gravels and with conifer plantations. The mining villages based on the South Crop are scattered along the northern edge of the Ewenny—Ely valleys. Further south, Llanharry is an old village which now depends on the only iron mine in the Cardiff district. Other villages are small and have even decreased in size since their medieval foundation. There are many scattered farms which work consolidated holdings. This is a transition zone between Bro and Blaenau Morgannwg, both in settlement pattern and in economy. It has less arable and more meadowland than the Vale of Glamorgan. Its uneven fertility is reflected in its former heathlands which are modern plantations, but also in some great manor houses, of which St. Fagans Castle is a notable example. Its herds provide much milk for Cardiff and Bridgend and for neighbouring parts of the coalfield.

CLIMATE

Two factors strongly influence the climate of south-east Wales. Its coastlands, lower valleys and ridges have a mild climate and are exposed to winds which are often soft and carry their moisture into the mountains. Proximity to the Bristol Channel ameliorates their climate. Though less favoured than south Pembrokeshire, these coastlands provide drier and sunnier conditions than do other parts of Wales. The high interior of the region, on the other hand, presents the two highest barriers in South Wales to the prevailing south-westerly winds. In consequence nearly 100 inches of rain fall on the average on the highest plateau tops of the coalfield,

between Craig Ogwr and Craig y Llyn, and behind them, the west–east line of Fforest Fawr and the Brecon Beacons, though it does not record quite such high averages, gets from 80 to 90 inches on all its highest slopes. The highest parts of Snowdonia receive twice this total. Temperatures are naturally lower and conditions more rigorous in the mountainous north of the area, which is also more distant from marine influences. The climate of south-east Wales is such that grass, 'the wealth of Wales', is the best crop, but good corn crops are taken off the lowlands. In the mountains coarse grasses and hardy sheep are dominant.

A minor factor is the narrowing of the Severn Sea north-east of Cardiff. This reduces maritime influences and increases the slightly greater 'continentality' of Monmouthshire. The whole area has changeable weather and is strongly influenced by air masses from the Atlantic with their customary changes of wind and weather.

RAINFALL

Fig. 5 shows the annual and monthly average rainfall of forty stations. It must be emphasized that, as in any other maritime climate, there are marked yearly variations from the average figures. Abnormally low spring rainfalls can retard germination, and excessive September rainfalls can ruin the corn harvest. Some falls of rain of rare intensity have been experienced in the area, e.g. 2·9 inches in thirty minutes at Ash Hall, Cowbridge, on 22nd July, 1880, and 2·2 inches also in thirty minutes at The Chain, Abergavenny, on 4th July, 1915. On 11th November, 1929, Lluest Wen reservoir, at the head of the Rhondda Fach, recorded a daily total of 8·31 inches, and on 3rd November, 1931, a gauge near Trecastle in Breconshire recorded 7·25 inches (on this day Lluest Wen had 6·38 inches).

Distribution

Two areas have mean annual totals comparable to those of the eastern lowlands of England or of north-east Wales, i.e. less than 35 inches. The first is a very narrow coastal fringe, varying in width from half a mile to two miles, which extends from the mouth of the Ogmore River to Barry, and from the Wentloog Level to Chepstow. The Monmouth and Trothy basins form the second relatively dry area. Most of the Vale of Glamorgan, the Cardiff area, the Monmouthshire section of the Usk basin, and the Talgarth Gap in Breconshire, have less than 45 inches of rain. The east end of Wentwood, and the hills stretching from it to Trelleck and the Wye, have 40 to 50 inches. South and east of the coalfield, and in the middle Usk basin, totals increase gradually from 40 to 50 inches, but sharper increases from 50 to over 90 inches occur on the middle and higher slopes of the coalfield west of the Taff, and on the Brecon Beacons and Fforest Fawr. In the rain-shadow area of the coalfield, east of the Taff, totals are 60 to 70 inches over the highest parts of north-west Monmouthshire, but areas such as the Gelligaer Basin have less than 50 inches.

On the narrow coastal fringes (with totals of less than 35 inches) rain falls on about 170 days of the year, whilst much of the coalfield and the Black Mountains, which have totals of up to 60 inches, have about 200 rain-days. On the highest

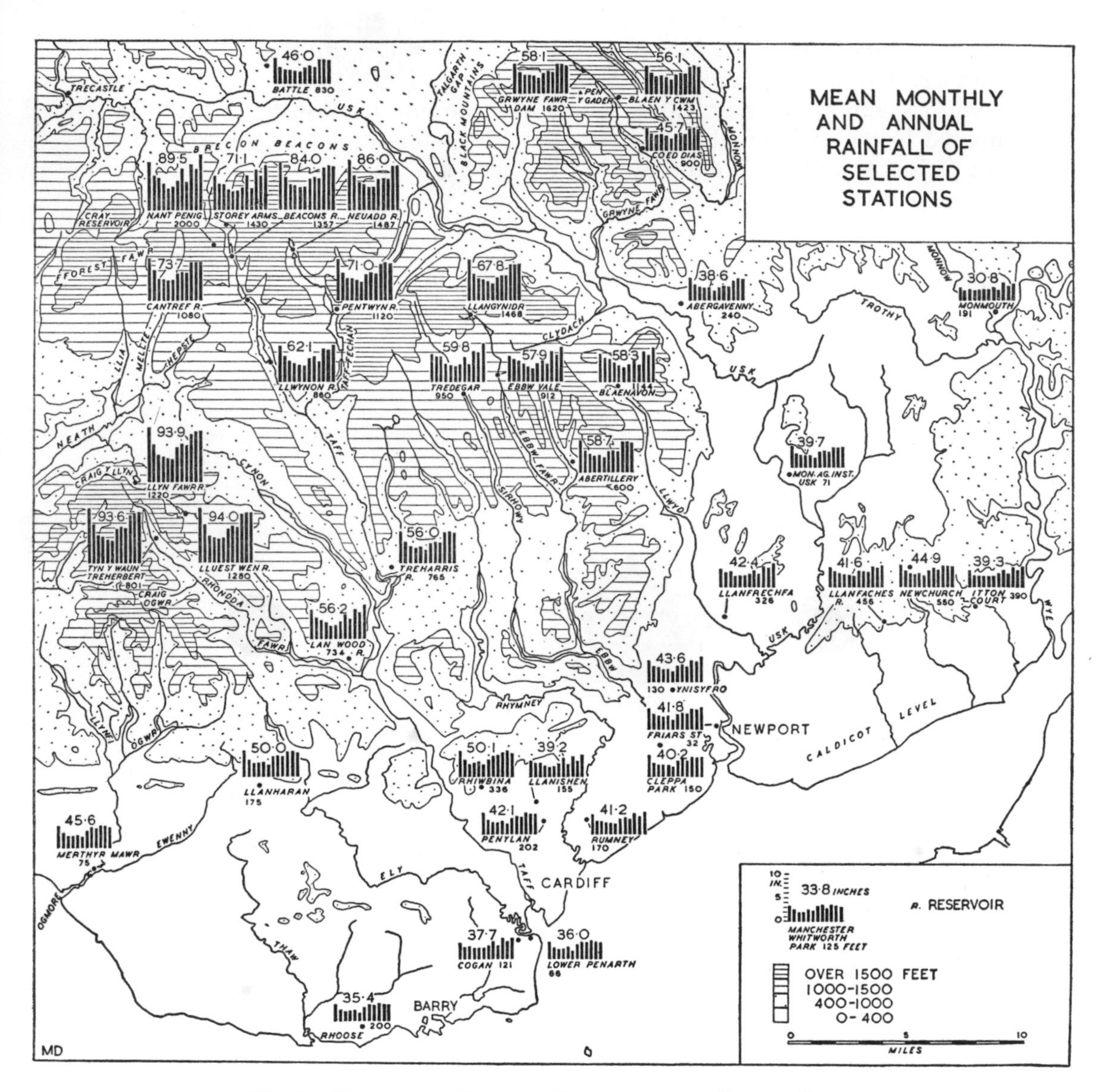

Fig. 5. Rainfall of Selected Stations in the Cardiff Region
Based on records supplied by the Waterworks and Public Health Departments of the City of Cardiff, by Newport Corporation Waterworks Department and by the Meteorological Office

summits of the coalfield plateau and the Brecon Beacons there may be as many as 250 rain-days annually, with much cloud and little drying out of soils. Rain-days are fairly evenly spread throughout the year, varying at Cardiff (Penylan) from 13 days in June and 14 in May and October, to 19 days in January and 21 in December. The average monthly total of hours during which rain falls at Cray reservoir, a station lying at 1,044 feet in the extreme north-west of the area, is compared below with London (Camden Square) lying at 111 feet. Cray's total is about 65 inches and the London station averages 25 inches.

	J	F	M	A	M	J	J	A	S	O	N	D	Year
Cray:													
Monthly duration	154	103	86	90	81	91	89	101	86	132	146	135	1,294
London:													
Monthly duration	43	39	44	31	29	30	27	28	25	45	47	49	437
Cray:													
Daily mean	4·9	3·7	2·8	3·0	2·6	3·0	2·9	3·5	2·9	4·2	4·9	4·3	3·54
London:													
Daily mean	1·4	1·4	1·4	1·0	1·0	1·0	0·9	0·9	0·8	1·5	1·6	1·6	1·20

From E. G. Bilham, *The Climate of the British Isles*, 1938, p. 112

Seasonal Variations

Fig. 5 shows that, as elsewhere in western Britain, most rain falls in the winter half-year over the whole of the area. Relatively low rainfalls in spring and early summer are also characteristic. Of the forty stations, twenty-eight widely distributed stations have their minimum rainfall in June, the month of the main hay harvest in the lowlands. Ten stations have May as their driest month: they are all in rain-shadows and are found in both the driest areas (Cogan and Itton Court) and in the wettest parts of the area (Lluest Wen, Nant Penig, Storey Arms and three adjoining reservoirs). Monmouth and Llanfrechfa have April minima. At all stations April, May, and June are relatively dry months and there is a pronounced secondary minimum in September, the month of the corn, and sometimes of the second hay, harvest in western Britain. During late September the rainfall usually increases again.

The highest monthly totals are recorded in January at nineteen stations and in December at fourteen. These thirty-three stations repeat a pattern found throughout Wales. November also has high totals everywhere, and at two stations behind the Black Mountains scarp the maximum monthly total occurs then. Four stations in the driest parts of the area record maxima in October. They are Merthyr Mawr, Rhoose, Lower Penarth and Monmouth, and Cogan has an October total of 4·45 inches as against 4·49 inches in December. The southern shores of the Bristol Channel, notably in Somerset (e.g. Bath, Long Ashton, Clevedon) and in Devon (e.g. Barnstaple) have October maxima, as has the Hereford Basin which adjoins the Monnow Basin. The months October to January have the highest totals at these stations, as elsewhere in the area. All stations show a July–August

[*Photo:* H. Tempest Ltd.

Plate I.—The Taff gorge from the south. Beech-covered limestone ridges backed by grits and the coalfield plateau. Upper left, Treforest Industrial Estate with Nantgarw colliery to right of it.

Plate II.—Cardiff from the north. Civic centre in foreground with Castle keep to right of it. Beyond these, shopping and commercial centre, the five docks and Penarth on its headland.

[*Photo:* H. Tempest Ltd.

[*Photo:* H. Tempest Ltd.

Plate III.—The Rhondda valleys from the south-east. Porth (with new factories) and Cymmer (confluence) in foreground. Rhondda Fach on right, Rhondda Fawr with Tonypandy and Clydach Vale on left.

Plate IV.—The Taff valley, Merthyr Tydfil and the Brecon Beacons from the south. Troed-y-rhiw village on left, wooded Cwm Bargoed on right. Ridge-top pastures on Mynydd Cilfach-yr-encil in foreground.

[*Photo:* H. Tempest Ltd.

increase in rainfall, after the March–June period of low rainfall. Thunderstorm rain makes a smaller contribution to this summer total than in the Midlands or eastern England. August, the wettest summer month, often sees the end of water shortages in the area. Cardiff, drawing its water from the Beacons, Cantref and Llwynonn reservoirs, and from such valleys as Nant Penig, suffers water shortages less frequently than towns in the Monmouthshire coalfield valleys which are supplied from smaller reservoirs near at hand which lie in the rain-shadow of the high coalfield plateau.

The relatively low February totals at all lowland stations, combined in most years with a dry March, facilitate tillage, especially of heavier soils. Snow seldom lies long on the coastlands or on lower sunward-facing hillsides in these or other winter months. On the average Cardiff has snow lying on four mornings a year, and up to ten mornings have snow lying over most of the south of the coalfield and the eastern hills. The higher coalfield surfaces may have up to twenty mornings with snow lying, and the Brecon Beacons and Fforest Fawr range from sixteen in southerly valleys, as at Cantref (1,080 feet), to as many as sixty mornings on their highest slopes. The Black Mountains of Monmouthshire, which present an unbroken barrier to both north-west and north-east winds, may have snow lying on the Gader Ridge continuously from January to March. Snow lies on surfaces above 2,000 feet in this eastern outpost of highland Wales much longer than on its western mountains.

TEMPERATURE

No inhabited area in south-east Wales has a rigorous climate, though industry attracted people into some areas where conditions are poor in relation to the lowland periphery. In the late eighteenth century, iron works and settlements were built on the high North Crop of the coalfield where winds are often fresh and usually bring 40 inches of precipitation in the winter half-year. Coal mining, particularly in the second half of the nineteenth century, produced ribbons of houses in the bottoms of deep valleys which suffer from high rainfalls and also from temperature inversions and winter fogs.

South-east Wales does not record high average summer temperatures or great ranges of temperature. Fig. 6B shows the mean monthly temperatures of three stations which are typical of the coast (Cardiff, Penylan), the uplands (Cantref) and the interior (Monmouthshire Agricultural Institute, Usk), and Fig. 6A the monthly range of temperature at the same stations. Usk shows the highest maxima and the highest range of temperature, as would be expected from its inland position. Only in lowland Monmouthshire do maximum temperatures and low rainfall produce an approximation to conditions in wheat-growing areas of England. Newport's figures are intermediate between those of Cardiff and Usk and reflect a slight increase in 'continentality' eastwards up the narrowing Bristol Channel.

The curve of mean monthly temperatures at Cantref shows that, in comparison with the two lowland stations, differences are greatest when temperatures are at their highest and at their lowest, and least in spring and autumn, when the influence

of the sea is weakest. The range of temperature at the Cantref station, which adjoins a large reservoir, is very similar to that of Cardiff.

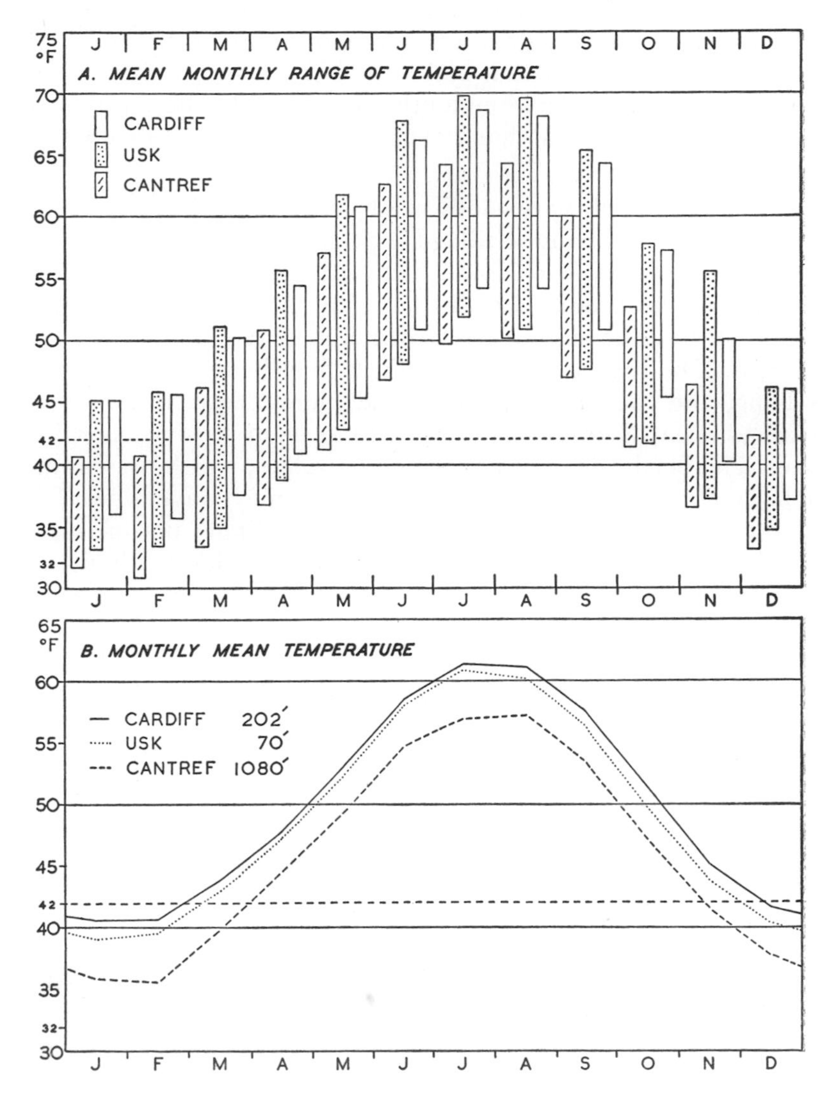

Figs. 6A and 6B. Temperatures at Selected Stations
Fig. 6A. Mean monthly range of temperature
Fig. 6B. Mean monthly temperature
Based on Meteorological Office, M.O.571, 1953

All three stations show the gradual warming-up, from February to July, of a sea-fringed land. Maximum temperatures at Cantref occur in August, mainly because the night minima are higher then. Both days and nights are warmer in autumn than in spring at all three stations; Cardiff has noticeably warmer autumn

nights than the two inland stations. In January, Usk and Cardiff record their lowest average temperatures, and in February the lowest minimum temperatures are recorded at Cardiff and Cantref. Cantref also has its lowest average in February, a feature which, like its August maximum, it shares with many coastal stations in West Wales. Many unrecorded average minima, lower than those shown on Fig. 6A, must occur in the bottoms of high narrow valleys in the coalfield.

The period from May to September is generally frost-free in most of the area, and near the coast the period may be extended by two months. The long growing season, when temperatures average more than 42°F, is seen on Fig. 6B. It usually extends from March to November on the lowlands and from April to October on the hills. Sheep (and formerly cattle) are taken to the upland pastures on the Brecon Beacons and Black Mountains in May to graze the first growth and the young ewes and lambs are brought down late in September or in early October. Minimum winter and early spring temperatures at Usk, and at many points intermediate in height to Usk and Cantref, suggest cold nights and mornings, and cattle must be kept in well after the morning milking at these seasons.

Favoured areas where spring comes earliest stand out on maps of floral isophenes of the British Isles, i.e. lines joining average first dates of flowering of twelve common flowers such as the bluebell, wood anemone and coltsfoot. South Wales is well represented. The scattered patches where first flowering occurs before 27th April are the peninsulas of Co. Kerry, some smaller areas in south-west England between Freshwater in the Isle of Wight and the Lizard, and the lowlands along the Bristol Channel, which all have early springs, in contrast with, for example, the Thames lowlands. On the Somerset shores of Bridgwater Bay, on the meadowlands of the Severn estuary south of Gloucester, on the western half of the Caldicot Levels and on the southern fringes of the Vale of Glamorgan and the Gower peninsula, first flowering occurs before 27th April. The whole of lowland Pembrokeshire, the most maritime part of Wales, has similar early springs.

SUNSHINE

Daily totals of bright sunshine vary tremendously in south-east Wales, especially in its deeply-cut valleys, but even in the better favoured southern coastal regions totals are a good deal lower than in south-east England. Yearly totals of hours of sunshine recorded in the area are: Cardiff 1,566 (daily average 4·29); Newport 1,537 (average 4·21); Usk 1,394 (average 3·82); and Cantref 1,368 (average 3·75). Cardiff and Newport exceed many Midland stations, and Cantref, lying at 1,080 feet in the Brecon Beacons National Park, receives thirty-one hours more sunshine than the Regent's Park headquarters of the National Parks Commission. But coastal stations in similar longitudes in south-west England, e.g. Sidmouth (1,635) and Exmouth (1,616) exceed Cardiff's total. The British average nearest to that of Cardiff is recorded at Douglas in the Isle of Man (1,562 hours).

Averages of bright sunshine naturally decrease as cloudiness increases upslope, and while most of the Vale of Glamorgan probably averages about four-and-a-half hours daily, the mountains in the north of the area have about three-and-a-half

hours. Aspect is all-important for cultivation on all but the gentlest hillsides, and northward-facing slopes are usually left in pasture. Arable land in the coalfield and its border ridges is limited to southward-facing slopes or to high patches which lie in the eye of the sun, above the valley sides where the steep slope flattens out towards the plateau top. The Vale of Glamorgan and the Cardiff area have more summer sunshine than the coastal fringe of Monmouthshire, as typified by Newport, or its interior lowlands. Fig. 7 provides a comparison between the Monmouthshire lowland station of Usk, and Cardiff: Cantref again represents the uplands.

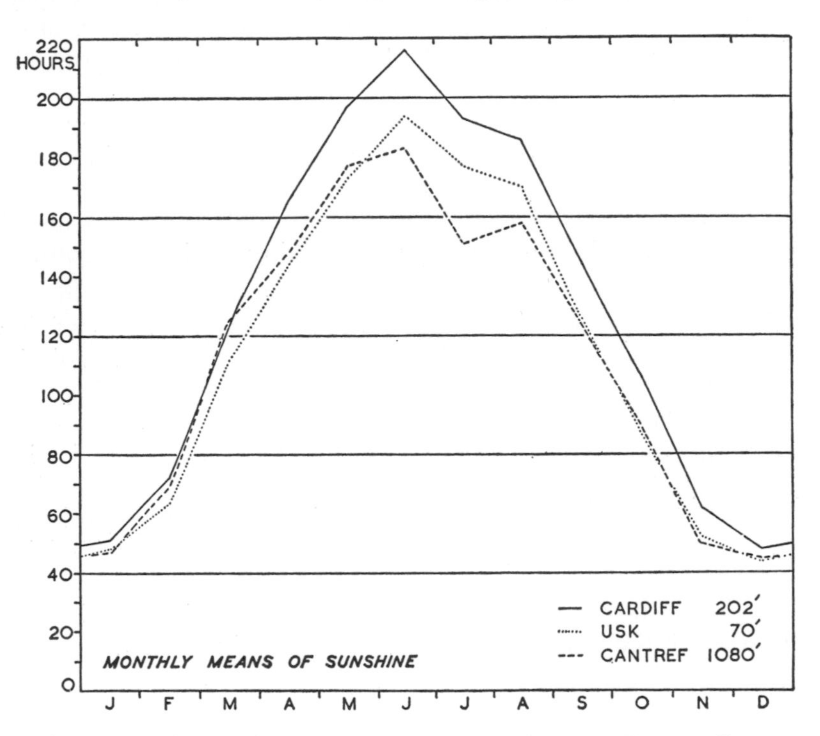

Fig. 7. Monthly Means of Bright Sunshine at Cardiff, Usk and Cantref
Based on Meteorological Office, M.O.572, 1953

All three stations record a sharp decrease of sunshine after the June solstice and a less marked fall between the July and August totals. Secondary sunshine maxima in August, such as that shown for Cantref, are common in the Welsh uplands. From February to May, and to a slighter degree in October and December, totals at Cantref exceed those of Usk. In March, Cantref has 125 hours as against 124 hours in Cardiff. Spring is often a period of excellent visibility and considerable sunshine on the high hills of the region. In February and March radiation fogs develop over the lowlands during anticyclones, but the higher hills often have sunshine and clear skies. Fogs are most frequent in the lowlands of Monmouthshire and in the coalfield valleys, though on the average they do not form on more than thirty days in a year there. Sea fogs may come a short way inland in both winter and early

summer. A large volume of colder fresh water is then carried into the relatively warm sea by rivers such as the Ely, Taff, Rhymney, Ebbw, Usk and Wye, and this increases the risk of fog during anticyclones.

In south-east Wales there is a gradual transition in climate both from west to east and from south to north. The west of the region is drier and has greater ranges of temperature than stations in west Wales at similar altitudes, but the east of the region is drier still, and temperature and rainfall regimes are similar to those of the English Midlands. The coastal strips have a soft climate, but inland there is considerable modification of maritime conditions. Sharp contrasts in rainfall and temperature occur between the Vale of Glamorgan coast and the Brecon Beacons, or between the Caldicot Levels and Blaenavon. From the sixteenth century onwards topographers, like the late eighteenth-century reporters to the Board of Agriculture, stressed the contrast between the coastlands and the high plateaux. John Fox said of the Vale of Glamorgan in 1796: 'The breezes arising from the ocean cool the gleam of summer. The summer is generally genial, not sultry, and the weather is without that inclemency inseparable from less favoured districts'. Cardiff shares this climate, which made the Vale of Glamorgan, in the words of Sir Edward Mansel, a Glamorgan subject of Elizabeth I, 'for corn and good fruits the garden of Wales and for good cattle of all kinds the nursery of the West'. It is a climate which combines the lower rainfalls of the English Midlands with the equable conditions of the Welsh coastlands.

REFERENCES

Bowen, E. G. (ed.), 1957. *Wales, a Physical, Historical and Regional Geography*, London; especially the regional chapters XV, XVI, and XIX.

Cliffe, C. F., 1848. *A Book of South Wales*, London, pp. 122–4.

Davies, Margaret, 1954–5. 'Field patterns in the Vale of Glamorgan', *Transactions of the Cardiff Naturalists' Society*, LXXXIV, pp. 5–14.

——, 1955–6. 'Common lands in south-east Monmouthshire', *Transactions of the Cardiff Naturalists' Society*, LXXXV, pp. 5–15.

Evans, C. J. O., 1938 and later. *Glamorgan, its History and Topography*, Cardiff.

——, 1954. *Monmouthshire, its History and Topography*, Cardiff.

Fox, Cyril, and Hyde, H. A., 1939. 'A second cauldron and iron sword from the Llyn Fawr Hoard, Rhigos, Glamorganshire', *Antiquaries Journal*, XIX, pp. 369–404.

Miller, A. Austin, 1935. 'The entrenched meanders of the Herefordshire Wye', *Geographical Journal*, LXXXV, I, pp. 160–78.

North, F. J., 1949. *The River Scenery at the Head of the Vale of Neath*, Cardiff.

——, 1955. 'The Geological History of Brecknock', *Brycheiniog*, I, pp. 9–77.

Randall, H. J., 1955. *Bridgend, the Story of a Market Town*, Newport.

Steers, J. A., 1946, *The Coastline of England and Wales*, ch. V and VI. Cambridge.

Tattersall, W. M. (ed.), 1936. *Glamorgan County History*, vol. I, *Natural History*, ch. I (General Survey), II (Geological History) and III (Climate), Cardiff.

Thomas, T. M., 1959. 'The geomorphology of Brecknock', *Brycheiniog*, V, pp. 55–156.

II

GEOLOGY

J. G. C. Anderson

INTRODUCTION

THE physical and economic features of South Wales, described in other chapters, stem largely from changes in the earth's crust which took place from 170 to 420 million years ago. The most significant of these geological events, dating back some 300 million years, were the deposition of the Coal Measures and their folding into the great basin of the South Wales Coalfield. Without this basin, industrialization and the consequent large increase in population could hardly have taken place, and Glamorgan and Monmouthshire would have remained mainly agricultural counties.

The Carboniferous strata, however, are only part of a well-exposed succession ranging from Upper Silurian to Lower Jurassic (Table I). These strata are entirely sedimentary; the only igneous rocks in South Wales are in a vent and associated intrusion. No beds representing the long interval between the Lower Jurassic and the glacial epoch are present in South Wales, although it was during this time that the broad geomorphological features were determined. The glacial and post-glacial deposits, however, add an interesting late chapter to the geological history.

The limits chosen for geological description are shown on Fig. 8. Geographically they embrace the whole of Monmouthshire, the whole of Glamorgan east of the Vale of Neath and a small part of Breconshire.

OUTLINE OF STRUCTURE

Although Armorican movements have been the main influence in shaping the geological structure of the region, Alpine and pre-Armorican disturbances also played a part.

The Armorican orogeny was responsible for the formation of the major basin of the coalfield with its marked east—west axis. The southern margin (the South Crop) of this basin is steeper and more complex than the northern and is characterized for much of its length by the Pontypridd anticline and complementary Caerphilly syncline and also by minor folds and thrusts, revealed in the workings.

The Vale of Neath fault, running from north-east to south-west, cuts across the coalfield basin (Fig. 8). This forms the western limit of the part of the basin described, although the basin itself continues through western Glamorgan into Carmarthenshire.

The eastern end of the basin (the East Crop) strikes for some miles in a northerly direction, a trend due to the influence of the Usk Axis (see below).

From beneath the North Crop the Old Red Sandstone rises gently northwards towards the heights of the Brecon Beacons.

TABLE I

STRATIGRAPHICAL SUCCESSION

Formation	Conditions of deposition	Tectonic events
—	—	Considerable movements (Alpine)
Lower Lias Rhaetic	Marine Marine	Subsidence
Keuper	Terrestrial and lagoonal, arid	
(great unconformity)		Major movements (Armorican)
Coal Measures Millstone Grit *(unconformity)*	Delta swamps Deltas	} Minor movements
Carboniferous Limestone	Marine (clear sea)	
Upper Old Red Sandstone *(unconformity)*	Flood plains and lakes	Considerable movements (Caledonian)
Lower Old Red Sandstone	Flood plains and lakes	Uplift
Ludlow } Wenlock }	Marine (shelf seas)	

South of the coalfield the Cardiff—Cowbridge anticline brings up Silurian rocks in the eastern outskirts of Cardiff and Old Red Sandstone throughout much of the Vale of Glamorgan. To the south of this anticline the Carboniferous Limestone occurs in the Wenvoe, Bridgend and Barry districts in Armorican folds which are only partially revealed beneath an unconformable Mesozoic cover (Pl. XIV).

Silurian is brought to the surface east of the coalfield by the complex Usk anticline, of Armorican age. Its north-north-east trend and the similar orientation of the nearby East Crop of the coalfield are evidence of the presence of an older structure perhaps partly Caledonian and partly pre-Cambrian (Malvernian). Both this structure and the Lower Severn—Forest of Dean axis further east were active during Carboniferous times and influenced sedimentation (see below).

No Caledonian folding of Upper Silurian age has been recognized within the region. A marked break between the Lower and Upper Old Red Sandstone is, however, evidence of the occurrence of late Caledonian movements.

The Mesozoic rocks, particularly in the south of the region, have been subjected to marked folding, 'normal' faulting and thrusting (e.g. St. Mary's Well Bay and Trwyn y Witch, Southerndown) probably connected with the Alpine orogeny. Some of these faults penetrate the Carboniferous and may be Armorican fractures along which late Mesozoic or Tertiary movement has subsequently taken place.

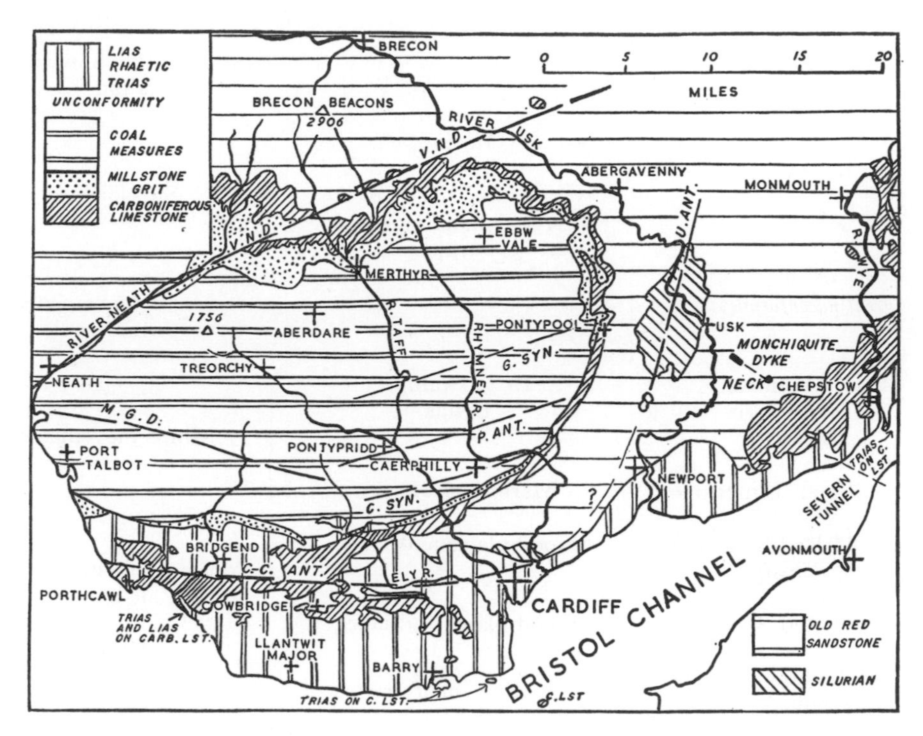

Fig. 8. OUTLINE MAP OF SOLID GEOLOGY OF THE CARDIFF REGION

C.—C.Ant.—Cardiff–Cowbridge Anticline; C.Lst.—Carboniferous Limestone; C.Syn.—Caerphilly Syncline; G.Syn.—Gelligaer Syncline; M.G.D.—Moel Gilau Disturbance; P.Ant.—Pontypridd Anticline; U.Ant.—Usk Anticline; V.N.D.—Vale of Neath Disturbance.

SILURIAN

Silurian rocks are exposed in the Usk anticline and in the Rumney inlier on the Cardiff—Cowbridge anticline (Fig. 8). The relationship between the two upfolds is obscure, although it has been suggested that the axis of the Cardiff anticline curves northwards near Newport to become the axis of the Usk fold. The succession in the two areas is shown in Table II.

The *Usk Inlier*, which has been recently remapped by Walmsley, is a pericline with a north-north-east axis, complicated by sub-parallel folds on its south-eastern flank. These folds are cut by north-westerly faults, all downthrowing to the north-east, which are interpreted by Walmsley as transcurrent faults possibly modified by later normal faulting.

TABLE II

SILURIAN SUCCESSION IN USK AND RUMNEY INLIERS

Series	Usk	Rumney	Common or characteristic fossils
LUDLOW	Local Bone-Bed Shales, siltstones, sandstones and calcareous beds (1,050 to 1,300 feet)	— Shales, siltstones, sandstones and calcareous beds	*Acanthodus* and Thelodont scales *Atrypa reticularis* *Camarotoechia nucula* *Chonetes striatellus* *Dalmanella lunata* *Dayia navicula* *Encrinurus punctatus* *M. leintwardinensis*
WENLOCK	Wenlock Limestone (up to 40 feet) Shales (800 feet)	Sandstones, siltstones, and shales with Rumney Grit near top	*Favosites gothlandicus* *Heliolites megastoma* *Leptaena rhomboidalis* *Atrypa recticularis* *Camarotoechia nucula* *Dalmanites vulgaris*

Wenlock shales, passing upwards into sandy and micaceous beds, form a considerable outcrop in the centre of the pericline. Exposures on the whole are scarce; among localities where these rocks may be examined and fossils collected are the right bank of the River Usk, 1½ miles north-west of Usk railway station, and roadside exposures 3 miles east of Pontypool Road station.

The Wenlock Limestone has been worked in a number of quarries, all now disused. Openings where good exposures can still be seen and a coral-brachiopod-trilobite fauna collected, include old quarries south of the road across Glascoed Common, 2½ miles east-north-east of Pontypool Road station, a quarry at Common Coed-y-paen, 2⅜ miles south-east of the same station, and old openings south of Cilfigan Park, 3¼ miles east of the station.

The Ludlow Series has been subdivided by Walmsley into seven groups based on lithological and faunal differences. The faunas indicate that the full Ludlovian succession (of the shelf facies) is present; rare specimens of graptolites occur among the dominantly shelly fauna. Very fossiliferous beds are exposed in a lane south of Pettingale, 1¾ miles east by south of Pontypool Road station, and along the track which runs westwards from a point 1 mile north of Llangibby on the Newport to Usk road exposures of all divisions of the Ludlow Series can be examined across an anticlinal axis.

On the right bank of the Usk about half-a-mile south of the town opposite Llanbadoc Church there are exposures of calcareous flags, dipping steeply east and rich in the brachiopod *Dayia navicula*.

At the top of the succession there are rare exposures of a thin bone-bed, the fauna of which permits correlation with the Ludlow Bone-Bed.

As a full succession from Ludlovian to Downtonian is present on the south-eastern flank, Walmsley suggests that the fault shown here on the Geological Survey map is not present.

The *Rumney Inlier* forms relatively high ground on the eastern outskirts of Cardiff, including Cyncoed and Penylan Hill. As the inlier is mainly on the northern limb of the Cardiff anticline there is a general northerly dip and the oldest beds, of Wenlock age, form the southern part of the outcrop. Slightly calcareous fine-grained flaggy sandstones, siltstones and shales belonging to this Series, with a rich shelly fauna, are well exposed in a conspicuous disused quarry on the south face of Penylan Hill.

Near the top of the Wenlock Series lies the 'Rumney Grit', a fairly pure, sometimes gritty, quartz-sandstone or siltstone. Current-bedding, ripple-marking and plant debris indicate deposition in shallow water, possibly close to a shore-line. The best exposures are in the Ty-mawr quarry, Rumney, just south of the main Cardiff—Newport road. The same horizon is seen at the base of an almost continuous northwardly dipping succession exposed in the east bank of the Rhymney river upstream from Rumney Bridge.

Above the grit come about 300 feet of fossiliferous flaggy siltstones and shales followed by 4 feet of impure ferruginous limestone with characteristic Wenlock Limestone fossils. This is overlain by a succession of flaggy, fine-grained, calcareous sandstones along with siltstones and mudstones. The fauna appears to indicate the absence of the Upper Ludlow, although further palaeontological research is required on this point. Nevertheless there is a conformable upward succession into red sandstones, siltstones and shales of Downtonian type. The top of the Ludlow has been placed at a poorly exposed grit with fish teeth and scales. Red colouration is not a criterion, as the Ludlow Beds are often locally of this colour, probably owing to percolation from a former Trias cover. The north margin of the inlier is poorly exposed, but recent studies again suggest that the Upper Ludlow is missing. Excavation for housing schemes have recently provided numerous exposures of the western end of the inlier. These have yielded an abundant fauna which seems likely to throw further light on the exact stratigraphical horizons present.

To the south the Silurian disappears under an unconformable Triassic cover. It has been found, however, in bores in the city area at depths of from 290 to 416 feet, under a cover of Keuper marls. On the western outskirts it has been recorded in bores through the Trias at Ely Paper Works at the comparatively shallow depth of 140 feet.

OLD RED SANDSTONE

The major phase of the Caledonian earth movements which took place towards the end of the Silurian times is marked in many parts of Britain by a strong unconformity between the Old Red Sandstone and underlying rocks of varying age. In the present region, however, no angular discordance has been detected below

the basal beds of the Old Red Sandstone, and indeed there appears in general to be a complete succession followed by the Downtonian. This phase of the Caledonian movements, in fact, seems to have been mainly one of uplift resulting in the shelf-sea environment of the Silurian giving way to the deltaic, fluviatile and the lacustrine conditions; the change of environment, and therefore of facies, took place, however, at different times at various localities.

The Old Red Sandstone forms a wide outcrop in the northern part of the region where it rises to 2,906 feet in Pen-y-fan, the summit of the Brecon Beacons. It sweeps round the eastern end of the coalfield, through a large part of Monmouthshire, and continues westwards in the centre of the Cardiff anticline where weathered-down marls in the lower part of the formation underlie the fertile Vale of Glamorgan. In this southerly outcrop, part of the Old Red Sandstone is directly overlain by an unconformable cover of New Red Sandstone (Fig. 8).

The renewal of the Caledonian movements after the deposition of the Lower Old Red Sandstone is marked in some parts of Britain, notably the Midland Valley of Scotland, by strong unconformity beneath the Upper Old Red Sandstone. That this phase was important in the present region is evident from the absence of strata known to be of Middle Old Red age. The junction between the Lower and Upper divisions is, however, not marked by any exposed angular discordance and in some districts is difficult to detect as it appears to lie within the Brownstones, a thick succession of sparsely fossiliferous strata.

Between Chepstow and Monmouth, however, there seems to be distinct westerly overlap of the Quartz Conglomerate at the base of the Upper division on to lower horizons in the Lower Old Red Sandstone.

As might be expected from the conditions of deposition the Old Red Sandstone strata show considerable variation in thickness and facies (Table III).

TABLE III

OLD RED SANDSTONE SUCCESSION

Series	Brecon District	Cardiff District	Chepstow District
UPPER OLD RED SANDSTONE	Red Sandstone, 150 feet Plateau Beds and Grey Grits, 125 feet	Red Sandstone, 150 feet Quartz-Conglomerate, 125 feet	Tintern Sandstone, 250 feet Quartz-Conglomerate 100 feet
DITTONIAN	Brownstones, 1,300 feet Senni Beds, 1,000 feet	Brownstones, 500 feet	Brownstones, 2,200 feet St. Maughan's Group, 1,250 feet
DOWNTONIAN	Red Marls, 3,900 feet* Tilestones, 175 feet	Red Marls, 2,800 feet*	Raglan Marls, 1,600 feet Downton Castle Sandstone, 50 feet

* The top of the Red Marls extends into the Dittonian.

The lower part of the Lower Old Red division consists mainly of a thick succession termed the Red Marls, composed of marls (more accurately slightly calcareous siltstones), thin-bedded sandstones and conglomeratic cornstones. In the Chepstow area the Raglan Marls are equivalent to the lower part of the Red Marls. At the base of the Raglan Marls there is a thin representative of the Downton Castle Sandstone. In the Brecon area thin-bedded, grey, green and yellow micaceous sandstones, known as the Tilestones, with brachiopods, lamellibranchs and gastropods, occur beneath the Red Marls.

In the Red Marls a marine fauna is almost wholly absent. Fish (ostracoderms) have been recorded at a number of horizons; the lower beds, belonging to the Downtonian, yield *Hemicyclaspis* (*Cephalaspis*) *murchisoni*; the establishment of *Pteraspis* in the upper beds show that part of the Dittonian is also represented.

Pteraspid remains from these beds are often fragmentary, but collections made recently by J. W. Baker and R. Allender from a new water-tunnel near Christchurch and other localities north-east of Newport, have yielded comparatively well-preserved specimens which are now being studied.

A distinctive bed, sometimes included within the Downtonian and sometimes taken as the base of the Dittonian, is the so-called *Psammosteus Limestone*. This contains *Traquairaspis* shields formerly called *Psammosteus anglicus*. Above this horizon in the Chepstow area comes the St. Maughan's Group of 'Marls' and sandstones. At the top of the Red Marls in the Cardiff District, the Llanishen Conglomerate is a well-defined horizon.

Above the Red Marls, in the Brecon and Abergavenny areas, a succession of sage-green and dull-red sandstones and micaceous flags are termed the Senni Beds; these have not been recognized further south. The Senni Beds, or the Red Marls in the south, are followed without any recognizable stratigraphical break by the Brownstones, a thick succession of red marly siltstones and brown or dull red flaggy sandstones with some conglomeratic layers, belonging mainly to the upper part of the Dittonian Series (Breconian of some authors). Nevertheless, in one exposure in Breconshire, the uppermost beds have yielded marine fossils, including *Spirifer verneuili*, indicating an Upper Devonian age. Where the Brownstones are most fully developed, therefore, it is possible that they include not only the Upper Devonian but also a small part of the Middle Devonian.

In Carmarthenshire and Breconshire the Brownstones are overlain by pebbly and conglomeratic sandstones known as the Plateau Beds. These form the summits of the Brecon Beacons, overlooking a spectacular northward-facing scarp eroded in the softer Brownstones.

In the southern and eastern parts of the region the base of the Upper Old Red Sandstone is usually drawn at the Quartz Conglomerate. In the Merthyr district it has been claimed that this group overlaps on to the Brownstones and cuts out the Plateau Beds. The relationship is not clear, however, and it is possible that these Beds are simply part of the Quartz Conglomerate group.

The Quartz Conglomerate, particularly on the south side of the coalfield, caps a conspicuous southwardly-facing scarp, the lower part of which consists of the Brownstones.

In addition to the conglomerates, which contain abundant rounded quartzite pebbles up to about 2 inches in diameter, the Group includes grey grits and red sandstones. Current-bedding is common and in the Cardiff district inclines to the south-west suggesting a north-easterly origin; none of the older formations at present exposed in south-east Wales could, however, have served as a source of the quartzite.

The uppermost beds, immediately beneath the Carboniferous, are usually red sandstones; in the Chepstow district these beds are thick enough to be distinguished as the Tintern Sandstone group.

CARBONIFEROUS

Carboniferous Limestone Series

The fluviatile or deltaic conditions of the Upper Old Red Sandstone gave place by fairly rapid subsidence, unaccompanied by folding, to the marine conditions of an early Carboniferous sea, flanked to the north, in what is now central Wales, by the ancient massif of St. George's Land. The transitional, although fairly abrupt, change at the junction between the two systems is seen in several sections, for example that in the railway cutting at Cefn Onn*, north of Cardiff.

The Carboniferous Limestone forms the framework of the South Wales Coalfield, marked, for much of its length, by conspicuous, outwardly-facing scarps. Further east important outcrops occur in the Chepstow district (Pl. XIII). The limestones, etc., of the present region, along with those of the Bristol area and the Mendips, were deposited in a distinctive palaeogeographical unit of Lower Carboniferous times, which is generally referred to as the South-western Province. The South Wales outcrops are noteworthy for the illustrations they afford of lateral stratigraphical variation (Fig. 9), of dolomitization and of the formation of metasomatic haematite ores.

The Series, in South Wales, was lithologically divided at an early date into the Lower Limestone Shales, the Main Limstone and the Upper Limestone Shales. These subdivisions are still useful, but a much fuller understanding of the stratigraphical relations has been reached by the application of the fossil zones worked out by Vaughan in the Avon Gorge near Bristol.

The lowest, or Cleistopora (K), Zone is approximately coterminous with the Lower Limestone Shales; this group would seem to have been deposited in shallow water with a considerable contribution of terrigenous sediment. Its outcrop is often marked by a hollow separating the dip-slope of the top of the Old Red Sandstone from the main limestone scarp. The lowest beds are often shales constituting a *Modiola* phase with lamellibranchs, including *Modiola*, *Ctenodonta* and *Sanguinolites*, annelids and ostracods. In some areas, however, for example north of Cardiff and

* Spelt Cefn On, wrongly, on 1-inch map.

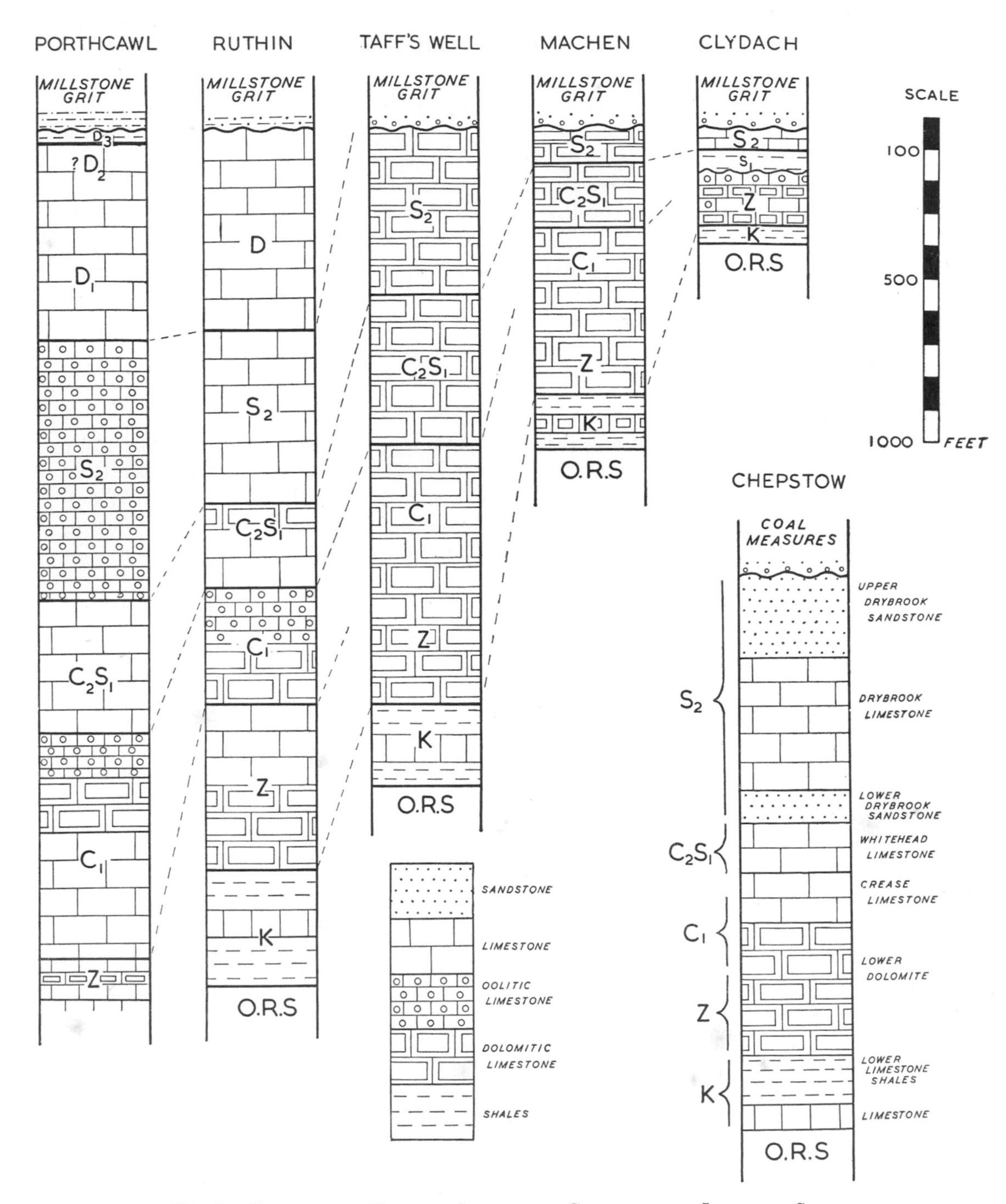

Fig. 9. Comparative Vertical Sections of Carboniferous Limestone Series of Cardiff Region

near Chepstow, there is a well-marked limestone at the base. Higher beds consist of shales with subordinate limestones containing *Vaughania* (*Cleistopora*) *vetus*, occasional zaphrentids and abundant brachiopods. The Lower Limestone Shales diminish in thickness eastwards from about 350 feet near Bridgend to 120 feet in the Ebbw Valley. East of the Usk anticline, in the Chepstow area, the group is about 220 feet thick.

The *Zaphrentis Zone* is characterized by several species of the type genus and by brachiopods including *Spirifer tornacensis*. It shows both progressive dolomitization when traced along the South Crop eastwards, and reduction in thickness from 2,300 feet at Bridgend to 150 feet in the Ebbw Valley.

The *Lower Caninia Zone*, in the south-western part of the region, where it reaches a thickness of about 550 feet, is generally divisible into:

Caninia Oolite	White, fine-grained oolite with few fossils.
Laminosa Dolomite ..	Dark-grey or buff, fine dolomites with beds of crinoidal limestone.
Crinoidal Limestones ..	Thin-bedded crinoidal limestones with calcareous shales, corals including species of *Zaphrentis* and *Caninophyllum* (*Caninia*) *patula*; brachiopods including productids, chonetids and spiriferids.

These beds are well seen in the Bridgend—Porthcawl district, and the lowest subdivision, with plentiful fossils, is exposed in the headlands flanking Whitmore Bay, Barry Island. Eastwards, however, the dolomitic facies encroaches upwards and downwards; near Cardiff and Newport the whole zone is an indivisible succession of dolomites with a few fossiliferous crinoidal limestones; the dolomites have proved of considerable economic importance (pp. 42 and 43).

Along part of the East Crop the Zaphrentis and Lower Caninia Zones are missing. On the North Crop they occur between Llangattwg and the Vale of Neath but their combined thickness does not exceed 80 feet; the *Caninia Oolite*, however, retains its identity. In the Chepstow area the Zaphrentis Zone and much of the Lower Caninia Zone is represented by the Lower Dolomite. The oolitic Crease Limestone is roughly equivalent to the Caninia Oolite.

The *Upper Caninia Zone*. West of the Vale of Neath the Upper Caninia Zone, marking the base of the Upper Avonian or Visean, rests with marked unconformity on the Lower Avonian. Within the present region, although there is generally a clear-cut lithological change, there is usually no break in the succession. In the Miskin district, however, the upper surface of the Caninia Oolite is slightly eroded and is followed by a thin group of shales and calcite mudstones forming a shallow-water lagoon phase at the base of the Visean.

The Upper Caninia Zone generally consists of crinoidal, oolite and porcellaneous limestones. Fossils, which are abundant in the crinoidal limestones, include species of *Caninia* and *Zaphrentis* and, in the upper part, of *Lithostrotion*; brachiopods and gastropods are also plentiful.

Fossiliferous beds of this zone, resting sharply on the underlying Lower Caninia Zone, are well seen on the shore at Sutton, east of the mouth of the Ogmore river;

in this area the zone is some 600 feet but it becomes thinner eastwards. At the same time a lithological change to dolomite takes place, rendering the break between the Upper and Lower Avonian unrecognizable. The Zone is absent in the East Crop, and in the North Crop between Llangattwg and the Vale of Neath it is only about 60 feet thick. In the Chepstow area the Zone is represented by the Whitehead Limestone.

The *Main Seminula Zone*, 1,000 feet thick in the Vale of Glamorgan and 400 feet thick on the North Crop, is also missing in the East Crop. It consists mainly of a massive coarse oolite, the Seminula Oolite. An interesting facies at the base of the Drybrook Limestone, which makes up most of the Zone in the Chepstow area, is a deltaic phase represented by the Lower Drybrook Sandstone.

The *Dibunophyllum Zone*, consisting mainly of crinoidal, coral and brachiopod limestones with some oolites, is well-developed in the western part of the region, although thin on the North Crop. On the South Crop it disappears, owing to Millstone Grit overlap, just west of Taff's Well, and on the North Crop it is not seen east of Dolygaer. The Upper Limestone Shales (D_3 Subzone), important in Gower, occur only in the extreme west of the present region. Near Chepstow the Upper Drybrook Sandstone may be S_2 or may represent the basal part of the Dibunophyllum Zone.

The general stratigraphical picture which emerges is that of a pronounced thinning towards the north, in the direction of St. George's Land. Equally marked is the disappearance of the Upper beds towards the east, accompanied by a thinning of the surviving zones. This is probably related to Lower Carboniferous activity on the Usk Axis.

The formation as a whole records a major marine sedimentary rhythm within which are three minor bathymetric cycles. The first begins with the shallow-water Lower Limestone Shales, continues through relatively deep-water crinoidal and coral limestones and closes with the false-bedded Caninia Oolite. The second begins with the lagoonal deposits of the basal Upper Caninia Zone, continues with the coral limestones of which most of this zone is composed and ends with the shallow-water oolites of the Seminula Zone. The third is marked by the crinoidal limestones of the Dibunophyllum Zone and closes with the Upper Limestone Shales. Besides these vertical cycles, however, are lateral variations within individual zones. Thus in the Upper Caninia Zone, bioclastic limestones south-west of Cardiff pass into calcite mudstones further north. Algal limestones among the calcite mudstone of this and higher zones are held to indicate the presence of widespread, shallow, Visean flats on the south margin of St. George's Land.

Millstone Grit Series

Folding, uplift and erosion preceded the deposition of the Millstone Grit. This rests with marked unconformity on the Avonian, overstepping successively lower beds eastwards until it is separated from the Upper Old Red Sandstone at Blorenge, on the East Crop, by only some 100 feet of Lower Limestone Shales; north of Chepstow Coal Measures directly overlie Carboniferous Limestone.

[*Photo:* A. G. Lyon

Plate V.—Liassic limestone and shale cliffs with calcicole vegetation, salt marsh on raised beach with brackish water pools, storm beach (white). Aberthaw looking east.

Plate VI.—Liassic limestones and shales with limestone pavement in foreground. Looking west at Nash Point.

[*Photo:* J. G. C. Anderson

[*Photo:* J. G. C. Anderson

Plate VII.—River Wye flowing through incised meander with cliff of Carboniferous Limestone and steep slopes with deciduous trees. About 1½ miles upstream from Chepstow.

Plate VIII.—Rhymney river meandering across Puccinellietum alluvial flats to the sea east of Cardiff.

[*Photo:* H. Tempest Ltd.

The Series, in the present region, is not marked by the thick, coarse sandstones which gave it its name in the Pennines, but it remains essentially a deltaic formation. Although showing considerable lateral variation, both in lithology and thickness, it is generally divisible into an upper and lower psammitic group separated by a pelitic group, the Middle Shales. The lower group, or Basal Grit, which often makes a well-marked scarp, consists of quartzites and siliceous sandstones, some of sufficient purity to be of considerable economic importance (p. 43). Beds of quartzite-conglomerate also occur. The Middle Shales, frequently reflected in the relief by a hollow, consist of dark-grey and black shales with sandy beds; the Twelve-foot Sandstone near the base is a well-marked horizon. The Farewell Rock, so-called because in bores or pits it indicates the unlikelihood of workable iron or coal seams being found beneath it, is made up mainly of brown, green and yellow sandstones. Both the sandy groups have been shown to be diachronic.

The Series thin eastwards from about 500 feet on the North Crop in the Vale of Neath to 200 feet on the East Crop between the Clydach Valley and Risca. It then thickens along the South Crop westwards to 1,500 to 2,000 feet in the Vale of Glamorgan. In this Crop, however, further from the old high ground of St. George's Land, the psammitic facies is much more feebly developed and the pelitic correspondingly dominant. On the west side of the Taff Valley north of Cardiff, for example, the Basal Grit is absent and the Farewell Rock is represented by thin-bedded, fine-grained sandstones with shaley partings.

Fossils are rare compared with the Avonian; they include lamellibranchs such as *Posidonia*, *Aviculopecten* and *Sanguinolites*, occasional brachiopods (*Chonetes*, *Productus*, *Spirifer* and *Lingula*), goniatites and plants. The goniatites are of particular importance, and the following major divisions of Bisat's Zonal scheme have been recognized although they are not all present throughout: *Eumorphoceras*, *Homoceras*, *Reticuloceras* and *Gastrioceras*.

Coal Measures

There is no break between the Millstone Grit and the Coal Measures; in fact on faunal and floral evidence the Farewell Rock, which as pointed out above is diachronic, should be included in the east in the Coal Measures rather than the Namurian.

In Coal Measure times, St. George's Land still lay to the north and contributed sediment which was deposited by rivers under freshwater or estuarine conditions; rare incursions of the sea are marked by a few thin beds with marine fossils.

The rocks of the Coal Measures are grits, sandstones, shales, fireclays, coals (less than 2 per cent of the whole) and thin ironstones. These were deposited in a long succession of sedimentary cycles which included delta-swamp phases giving rise to the coal seams. Superimposed on these rhythms, in South Wales, are two dominantly shaley divisions, the Lower and Upper Coal Series, separated by a thick, largely arenaceous, group, the Pennant Series.

Much more precise classification became possible when Trueman and Davies established, in South Wales, the well-known non-marine lamellibranch zones,

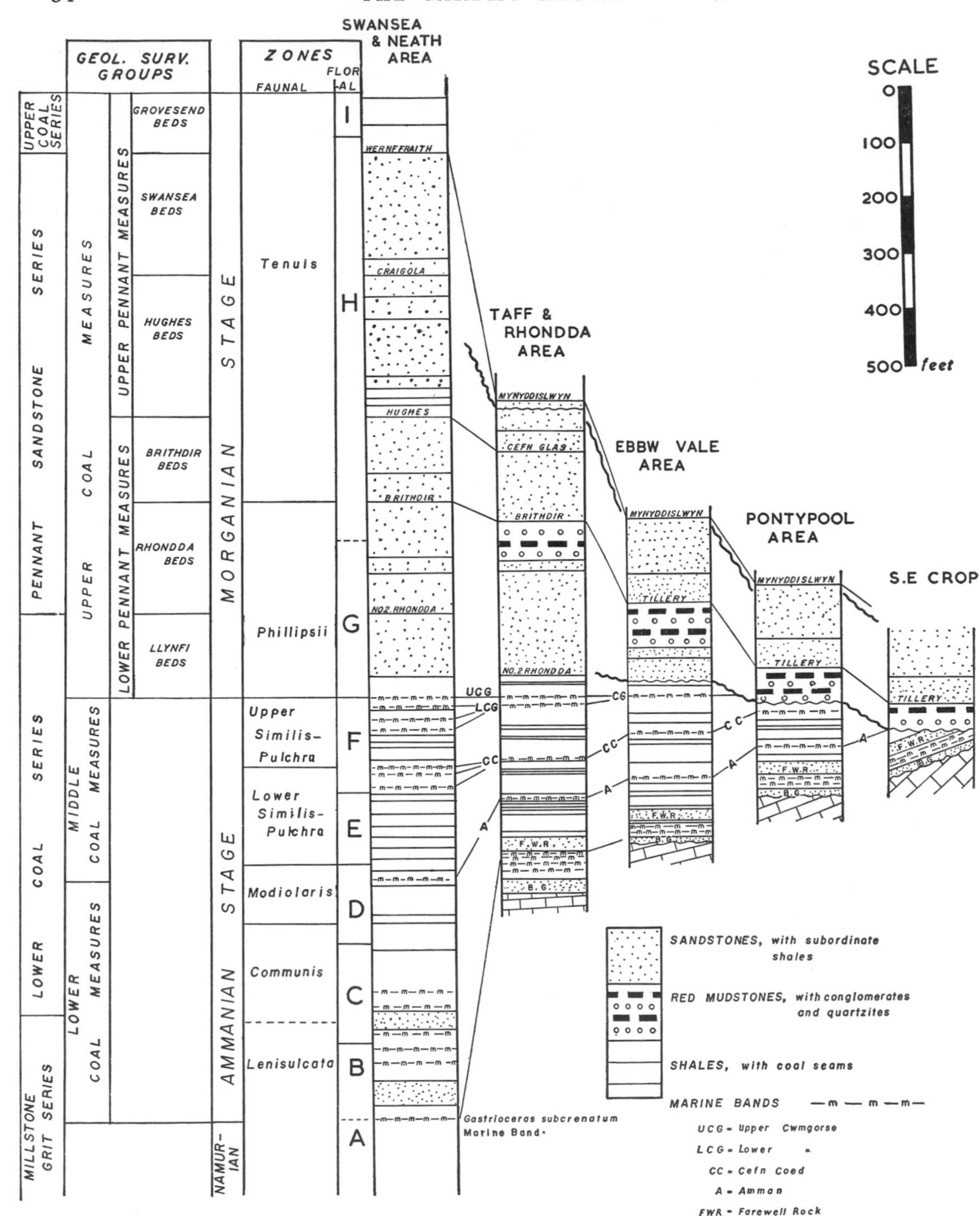

Fig. 10. Comparative Vertical Sections of Coal Measures of Cardiff Region

which have now been applied to all the British coalfields. On this basis the Coal Measures were divided into the Ammanian Series, including all but the topmost beds of the Lower Coal Series, and the Morganian Series, containing the remainder of the succession. Details of the zones and of the scheme of classification adopted by the Geological Survey are given in Fig. 10.

Overall thinning towards the east, due both to unconformity and to reduction in thickness of parts of the succession, persists into the Coal Measures. Thus the Lower Coal Series, about 2,500 feet thick in the west, is only about 800 feet thick in the Pontypool district, and near Risca is absent; the Pennant diminishes from about 3,000 feet in the west to 600 feet in the east. An important unconformity, a result of contemporary uplift along the Usk Axis, occurs at the local base of the Pennant Series throughout most, if not all, of the region; it increases eastwards and reaches a maximum north-east of Risca where the Pennant Series oversteps on to the Millstone Grit.

The Lower Coal Series, consisting mainly of grey-blue and pyritous black shales, often forms strike-hollows at the base of the Pennant scarp. It contains the greatest number of, and the thickest, coal seams in South Wales and also numerous bedded ironstones.

The Pennant Series, besides giving rise to bold scarps surrounding the central part of the coalfield and overlooking the coalfield valleys, forms the 'Mynydd' or flat-topped hills between the rivers. The characteristic rock is a hard, coarse, highly felspathic sandstone which is frequently false-bedded. The direction of the false bedding north of Cardiff suggests currents from the east. Some workable coal seams occur, especially in the west. An interesting development in the Middle Pennant is the occurrence of red and other highly coloured beds; these have been ascribed to post-Carboniferous weathering.

The Upper Coal Series consists of shales and sandy shales with subordinate thin sandstone bands. Only comparatively limited areas have been preserved from erosion, in a few of the synclines, such as those of Gelligaer in the east and Caerphilly in the south.

VOLCANIC VENT AND ASSOCIATED DYKE

A volcanic vent and associated basic dyke, penetrating the Old Red Sandstone south-east of Usk, provide the only examples of igneous rocks in the region (Fig. 8). A quarry just north of Great House, 4 miles south-east of Usk, has been worked partly in volcanic agglomerate and partly in a dyke-like intrusion of fine-grained, dark-grey monchiquite containing crystals of biotite up to an inch long.

Although most of the fragments in the agglomerate consist of monchiquite, there are also large crystals of biotite and pieces of Old Red Sandstone, of dolomite and of crinoidal limestone. Fossils in a block of the last-mentioned rock are compatible with its having been derived from the lower part of the Carboniferous Limestone Series.

Near Glen Court House, about 2½ miles south-east of Usk, similar monchiquite forms a 15-foot dyke, trending south-east, the prolongation of which would pass through the Great House vent.

The monchiquite may, therefore, mark the course of a vertical magma-channel which perhaps acted as a feeder both for fissure eruptions and for a volcanic vent. The discovery of Carboniferous Limestone fragments rules out a previous view that the activity was Devonian. The possibilities remain that vulcanicity was either of Lower Carboniferous or, like that of similar vents in Ayrshire, of Permian age.

NEW RED SANDSTONE AND LIASSIC

The Sub-Mesozoic Unconformity

Following compression at the close of Carboniferous times, the pre-Mesozoic rocks of the region formed the foot-hills of the main Armorican fold mountain-range to the south. Deep erosion, and subsidence, were followed by renewed sedimentation, at first in salt lakes or lagoons and later in the sea. Deposition gradually spread up the slopes of the Palaeozoic landscape, with the hill remnants for a time forming islands.

As a result of this prolonged, intermittent subsidence the basal Mesozoic strata above the unconformity cover a wide time-range, and the South Wales Mesozoic succession is noteworthy for the presence of striking littoral facies of the Triassic, Rhaetic and Liassic.

Triassic

The New Red Sandstone rocks of South Wales are unfossiliferous but on lithological evidence are referred to the Keuper Series. The formation forms much of the southern part of the region and rests on beds ranging from the Silurian (near Cardiff) to Coal Measures (near Llantrisant). In the Cardiff district it reaches a maximum thickness of 500 feet and in the Chepstow area of 150 feet. At or near the base are breccias, dolomitic conglomerates, sandy limestones and sandstones. Above comes a thick succession of red marls, with beds of calcareous, fine sandstone or siltstone. At the top are up to about 30 feet of 'tea-green' marls. Beds of gypsum, often nodular, occur in places, notably south of Penarth.

Coastal exposures provide striking sections of the sub-Triassic unconformity, for example, east of the mouth of the Ogmore, in the headlands of Whitmore Bay, Barry Island, at the south-east corner of Sully Island (Pl. XIV) and at the mouth of the Wye (Fig. 8).

On the east side of the westerly point at Barry Island, the basal Triassic breccia contains blocks of Carboniferous Limestone, up to several feet long, resting on a surface of Carboniferous Limestone descending northwards in a series of small cliffs. The basal breccia is thus strongly diachronic; moreover the breccia at a particular level, when traced horizontally away from the old shore-line, grades through finer breccia and sandstone into marl.

At a number of localities, fissures in the underlying Carboniferous Limestone are infilled with 'Neptunian Dykes' or fissure-breccias of younger sediments. Some of these have yielded remains of Mesozoic vertebrates. Thus reptile remains from a fissure near Bonvilston are of Triassic age; mammal remains from another fissure near Southerndown are of Rhaeto-Liassic age.

The Keuper Beds were deposited in widespread, shallow, salt lakes, subject to periodic desiccation (or perhaps in almost enclosed coastal lagoons) bordered by an arid land. Possibly the conditions were similar to those of the North African 'chotts' of the present day.

Rhaetic

The Rhaetic marks the incursion of the sea over the whole of the southern part of the region, accompanied by the reappearance of fishes, molluscs and echinoderms.

Lithologically the base of the Rhaetic can be drawn, as has been done by the Geological Survey in South Wales, at the base of the black shale group (Avicula contorta Shales) which reaches a maximum thickness of about 25 feet. Above the 'tea-green' marls, however, are grey beds containing *Pteria [Avicula] contorta*, *Ostrea bristovi*, and Rhaetic fishes, which have been named the Sully Beds and are included by some authors in the Rhaetic.

At the base of the black shales, and at several horizons within the group, are thin grits or conglomerates (bone-beds) with worn fish-teeth, fish-scales and reptilian vertebrae. Above the black shale group are about 10 feet of pale-grey calcareous siltstones and fine-grained impure limestones (the White Lias) which on palaeontological grounds are also included in the Rhaetic.

Sandwiched between the Triassic and Liassic beds, the Rhaetic, owing to faulting and gentle folding, appears at several localities (Pl. IX) near the foot of the cliffs between St. Mary's Well Bay and Penarth Head. Further west near Bridgend, the normal Rhaetic is locally replaced by a littoral facies including oolitic limestone and siliceous sandstone (Quarella stone).

Liassic

Liassic limestones and shales (Pls. V and VI) form most of the coast from Penarth Head to Sutton, and in places rise in spectacular cliffs. The succession normally starts with flaggy limestones and dark shales crowded with *Ostrea liassica* and overlain by similar rocks with ammonites. These are succeeded by the Lavernock Shales, followed by nodular limestones. The following zones are represented: Pre-Planorbis, Planorbis, Angulatum, Bucklandi and Semicostatum; some doubt has, however, been cast on the presence of the last zone.

In the Bridgend district a littoral facies appears. West of Sutton this rests with little apparent discordance on the Carboniferous Limestone and falls into two divisions. The lower—the Sutton Stone—is about 20 feet thick; its conglomeratic base passes upwards into a pale-cream, massive limestone yielding lamellibranchs, gastropods and corals. A short distance to the east of Pant-y-slade the terrace of Carboniferous Limestone ends abruptly, and the Sutton Stone, suddenly increased in thickness, is seen to be banked against a Carboniferous Limestone cliff.

The upper division consists of the Southerndown Beds which are only sparingly fossiliferous; the few ammonites which have been found indicate the Angulatum Zone near the base and the Bucklandi Zone in the higher part. These Southerndown

Beds are thicker and less massive than the Sutton Stone, and consist of a brecchia or conglomerate composed of small pebbles of chert and limestone fragments. Towards the east, the Southerndown Beds merge laterally into normal Liassic limestone and shales.

TERTIARY AND QUATERNARY

Tertiary

No rocks of Mesozoic age younger than the Lias, and no Tertiary rocks, occur in the region. During the Tertiary, however, the main geomorphological features were developed. During this period, too, the minor Alpine movements clearly evident in the Mesozoic strata (pp. 24 and 37) took place. The resulting folds are planed by a highly dissected platform at about 400 feet, seen in parts of the Vale of Glamorgan, and by a more clearly defined coastal plateau at about 200 feet evident in the same area. If, as is probable, the folding corresponds to the Miocene phase of the Alpine orogeny, these platforms bear witness to Pliocene erosion followed by uplift. For a time, in fact, the land was considerably higher than at present, and river erosion cut deeper, for the Bristol Channel and its inlets are river valleys submerged in both pre-glacial and post-glacial times (see also below). The drowned nature of the coastal topography would be even more striking but for the burying of the old, deep valleys by glacial and post-glacial drift deposits which have prevented entry of the sea (Figs. 11 and 12).

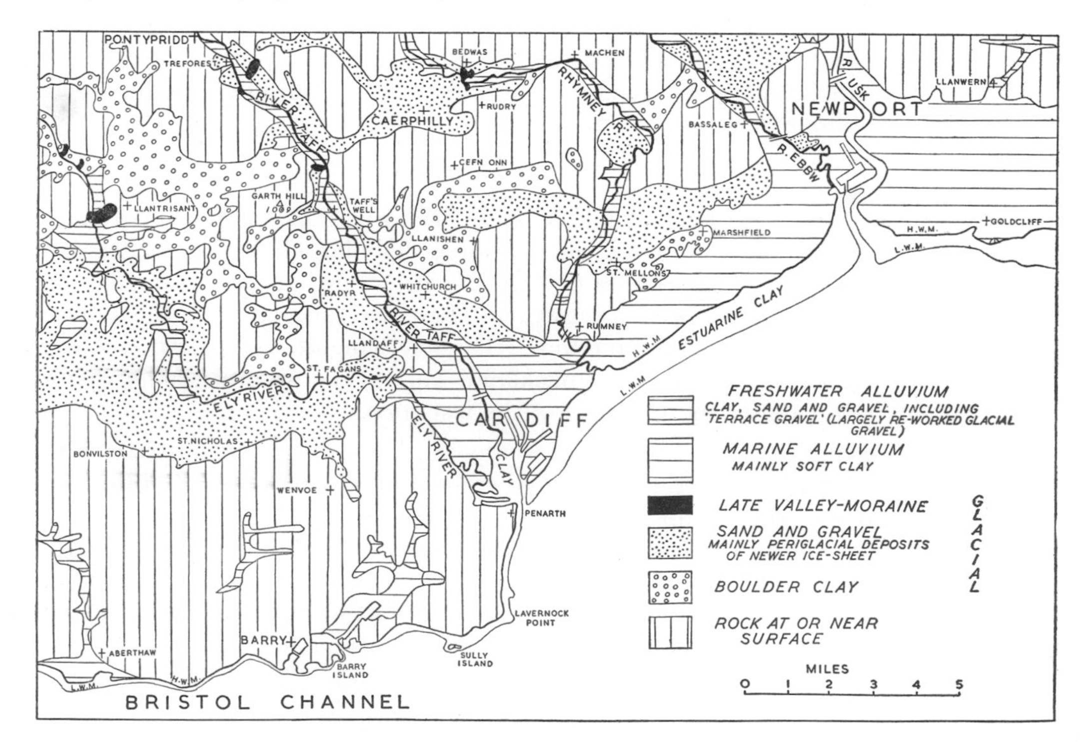

Fig. 11. Map of Drift Deposits in Neighbourhood of Cardiff

Depths to rockhead *below* sea-level recorded near the north coast of the Severn Estuary and the Bristol Channel include the following: River Wye near Chepstow, 56 feet; Severn above Severn Tunnel, 88 feet; Uskmouth, 55 feet; Butetown, Cardiff, 42 feet; Aberavon Moors, 113 feet; near mouth of River Neath, 117 feet.

A pre-glacial raised beach is well-known further west, in Gower, but, even if once developed, has not been preserved in the present region.

Glacial

Although the general morphology of the region was determined in pre-glacial times, the glaciation was responsible for many of the topographical details, both by erosion of rock-surfaces and by the deposition of glacial drifts; the latter are of particular importance on account of their influence on agricultural development and on ground-water conditions.

Erosional features include the U-shaped cross-sections of many valleys, for example that of the Neath and those of the Brecon Beacons, and the corries cut in the Pennant Sandstone at the head-water of the coalfield rivers. Striking corries have also been eroded in the Old Red Sandstone of the steep north face of the Brecon Beacons.

The glacial drifts are broadly classified as boulder clay, interpreted as ground moraine, and sand and gravel, formed as terminal moraine or outwash sediment. The two types of drift are not, however, as clearly distinguishable as in some other British areas; the boulder clay is often of a sandy nature, and the sands and gravels generally contain a considerable proportion of silt and clay. Mapped boundaries are therefore frequently approximate (Fig. 11).

The sequence of events during the glacial epoch was complex, and many details remain to be resolved. The glaciation was, in fact, both composite in space, i.e. there was interaction of ice-sheets from different directions, and multiple in time, i.e. there were alternating phases of advance and retreat.

At least two separate phases of extensive glaciation occurred accompanied respectively by the deposition of the 'Older Drift' and the 'Newer Drift'. During the first glaciation 'local' ice spread southwards from the high ground on to the coastal area. Here it was deflected by a lobe of ice moving up the Bristol Channel from a great mass of ice filling the Irish Sea hollow. The presence of this ice is evident from the occurrence in the Vale of Glamorgan of boulders of igneous and other rocks which could only have come from outcrops in North Wales, Northern Ireland and Western Scotland, and of flints, probably from Cretaceous outcrops under the Irish Sea. Felsite pebbles from North Wales, found in the Cardiff district, afford evidence of the most easterly extension of the Irish Sea drift so far known.

Following a period of retreat, the second glaciation was again marked by a southward advance of the ice, which was less extensive and less powerful than that of the first. Thus 'Newer Drift' of Brecon Beacons origin is mainly confined to the larger valleys and the lower flanks of the Coalfield hills. Moreover, Irish Sea ice, although it again impinged on South-west Wales, did not enter the present area.

The terminal moraine of the second glaciation is marked by a belt of moundy sands and gravels (kettle-hole moraine) extending from north of Newport, through the Vale of Glamorgan, to Swansea Bay. These deposits are particularly well displayed near Radyr, just north of Cardiff.

Valley glaciers characterized the last phase of the glaciation. Their retreat in stages up the main valleys is marked by well-preserved terminal moraines, exemplified by those of the Taff Valley above Taff's Well and those of the Ely Valley above Llantrisant (Fig. 11).

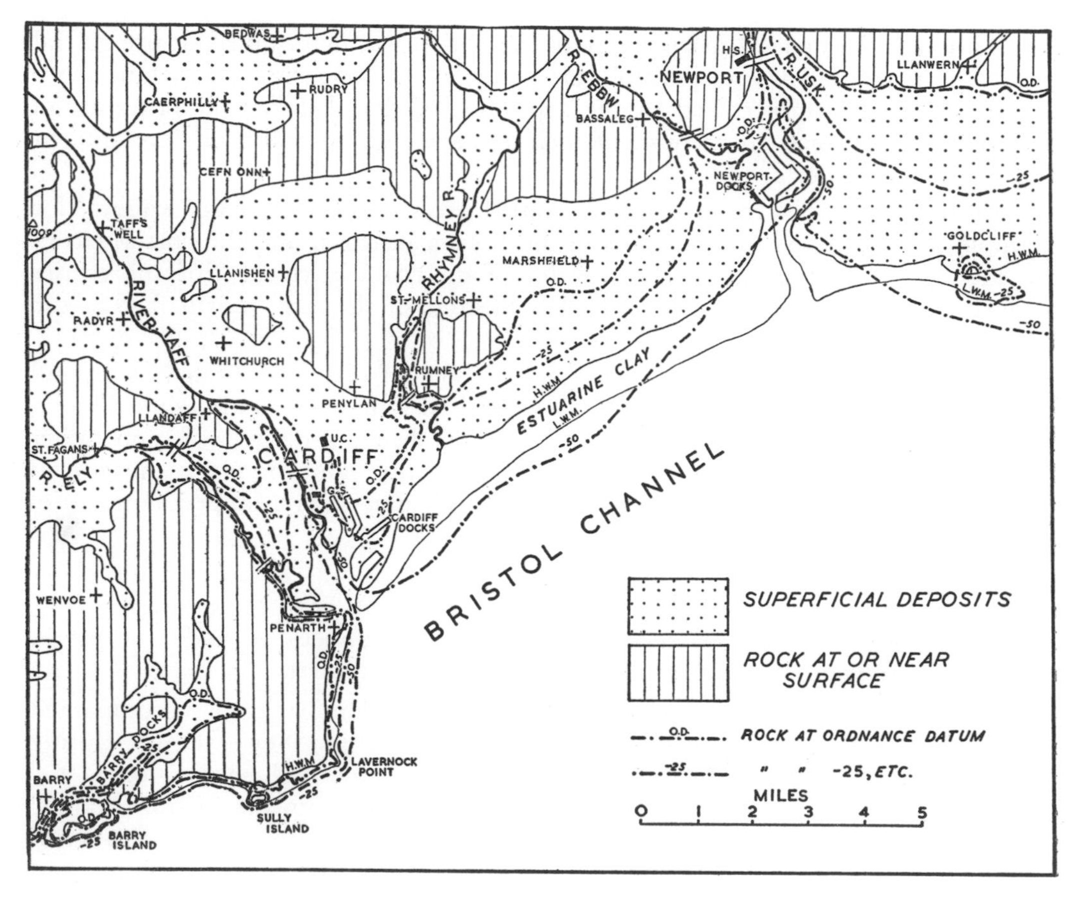

Fig. 12. Map showing Rock-Head Contours in Neighbourhood of Cardiff
(Based on numerous bore-records)

G.S.—General Station, Cardiff; H.S.—High Street Station, Newport; U.C.—University College, Cathays Park, Cardiff

Note siting of docks in areas of deep drift. In the absence of drift deposits the coastline would approximately coincide with the 'ordnance datum' contour

Post-glacial

The coastal flats of the Bristol Channel are often underlain by thick marine alluvium (Pl. VIII). These sediments are very similar to those being deposited in the present channel, as they consist dominantly of mud or clay with subordinate and

often lenticular beds of sand and gravel. Of particular interest are peat beds, intercalated with these marine sediments, which indicate considerable and probably oscillatory changes of the land level in relation to the sea. Depths to the base of the lowest peat bed *below* ordnance datum at various localities are: Portskewett, 10 feet; Llanwern, 14 feet; Newport, 31 feet; Cardiff New South Dock, 17 feet; Barry Dock, 42 feet; Port Talbot Dock, 37 feet.

On the assumption that the peat beds accumulated at least 20 feet above ordnance datum the bed at Barry provides evidence of post-glacial subsidence of at least 62 feet. West of the present area, subsidence of at least 75 feet is suggested by one record.

The coastal deposits also include extensive spreads of blown sand which reach their fullest development in the great dunes of Merthyr Mawr, east of Porthcawl (Pl. X).

Inland, river terraces are a feature of many of the valleys; they are particularly well-developed where rivers, e.g. the Taff near Cardiff, have cut into fluvioglacial deposits flooring their valleys. Another feature of the recent geology is the development of large landslips on the steep sides of many of the coalfield valleys.

Extensive cave systems have been developed in places by solution of the Carboniferous Limestone, especially on the North Crop. Although these are mentioned under the present heading their initiation probably goes back to pre-glacial times. Particularly striking are the solution effects in the upper reaches of the Neath catchment north of Hirwaun, notably Porth yr Ogof (the Gateway of the Cave) on the River Mellte. An underground stream in the Carboniferous Limestone provides a valuable source of water at Schwyll, near Ogmore Castle, Mid-Glamorgan; on the other hand ground water from this formation is a major factor in maintaining the Severn Tunnel. The Liassic limestones are also aquifers at some localities (Pl. IX).

ECONOMIC GEOLOGY

Coal

The coal seams are the most important mineral deposits of the region and indeed more than any other factor have determined its present economic character. The mining industry is discussed in chapter VIII.

Most of the worked seams belong to the Lower Coal Series or the Pennant Series, the Upper Series being confined to limited areas (p. 35); a few thin coals in the shales of the Millstone Grit have also been worked, mainly in association with ironstone. Low dips prevail in the northern and central parts of the field but structurally the southern part is more difficult, with steeper dips, subsidiary folding (e.g. the Caerphilly syncline and the Pontypridd anticline) and thrusting. Low-angled thrusts are fairly common between Llantrisant and Margam, although deep bores near the latter locality revealed that the seams of the Lower Coal Series are not as crushed as had been expected and have encouraged plans for a new pit. A favourable factor in the South Wales field is the complete absence of igneous intrusions.

A problem which has given rise to much controversy is the distribution and development of anthracite. Although the main anthracite seams occur west of the present region a progressive increase in 'rank' accompanied by a decrease in volatiles can be noted from east to west.

Metallic Ores

Bedded ironstones in which the iron occurs as siderite ($FeCO_3$) occur in the shales of the Coal Measures and of the Millstone Grit; they are most abundant in the Lower Coal Series. Although they were formerly worked on a large scale and had an important influence on the industrialization of the region, they are not of present commercial value.

Haematite-ores (Fe_2O_3) occur as replacement deposits in the Carboniferous Limestone of the South Crop, mainly, as far as is known, between the Taff Valley and Llanharry. Some of the bodies are of large size but of very irregular shape and distribution, rendering prospecting difficult. Extensive disused workings occur in Garth Wood, just west of the Taff Valley. Production of iron-ore ceased in 1885, but the mines were temporarily reopened about twenty-five years ago for ochre.

At present there is a considerable output of high-grade ore from the Llanharry Mine. Geophysical prospecting in the Vale of Glamorgan in this vicinity has suggested that other large bodies may be present.

Veins of galena ($Pb S$) occur in the Carboniferous Limestone at a number of localities but have not proved of economic significance; there were formerly workings near Rudry.

Limestones

There is a high output of limestone or lime in the region, for both industrial and agricultural use. The chief source is the Carboniferous Limestone, with the Seminula Zone as the main horizon and the Seminula Oolite generally providing the purest rock. The production of high calcium limestone and lime is mostly from Glamorgan, as much of the succession in Monmouthshire consists of dolomite; in Breconshire, Ystrad Quarry yields large tonnages of high-calcium limestone.

Roadstones

The Carboniferous Limestone is one of the main sources of roadstone in the region, and for this purpose both dolomitization and the presence of siliceous impurities may prove an advantage. In the coalfield the harder, finer, beds of the Pennant Sandstone are quarried at many localities.

Building Stones

The Pennant Sandstone has been extensively used as a building stone throughout South Wales. It is a strong and durable stone but of rather a drab colour. At Abercriban, north of Merthyr, sandstone of the Plateau Beds was worked for construction of the Taf Fechan Reservoir. Conglomeratic or sandy beds in the Trias have been exploited on a considerable scale near Cardiff (Radyr Stone) and in south-east Monmouthshire (Caldicot Sandstone). Limestone from the Carboniferous Limestone Series and the Lias have also been used as building stones.

Building Materials

Old Red Sandstone marls have been extensively exploited for brick-making in Monmouthshire. Limestone nodules, increasing with depth, have led to difficulties and only two works were using this material in 1958. In the South Crop, Coal Measure Shales have been quarried at several localities, for example near Caerphilly and Llantrisant. The red Triassic marls are also worked for brick-making in the Cardiff district. The calcium carbonate content is rather high, but this difficulty is largely overcome by fine grinding.

Cement is manufactured by three concerns which make use of the Lias limestones and shales. Sand and gravel are obtained by dredging in the Bristol Channel; about one million tons were landed in South Wales ports in 1957. Aggregate for concrete is also obtained both from the Carboniferous Limestone and the Pennant Sandstone.

Refractories

The dolomitized portions of the Carboniferous Limestone provide valuable raw material for the manufacture of dolomite bricks and are quarried for this purpose at Taff's Well, Cefn Onn* and Mynydd Machen. For silica bricks, the Millstone Grit quartzites are worked around Penderyn and the head of the Vale of Neath. The Quarella Sandstone of Rhaetic age was formerly exploited for the same purpose near Pyle and Bridgend. Fireclays occur in the Coal Measures and are worked along with some of the coal seams but have not been utilized in South Wales to the same extent as in other coalfields.

ACKNOWLEDGEMENTS

In preparing this work, invaluable assistance has been given to the author by members of the Staff and Research students in the Geology Department of the University College of South Wales, by officers of H.M. Geological Survey and by Dr. V. Walmsley, University College, Swansea.

REFERENCES

Numerous references to the Geology of the Cardiff District are given in J. Pringle and T. N. George, *British Regional Geology: South Wales*, 2nd ed., Mem. Geol. Surv. (1948).

Works published since that date include:

Anderson, J. G. C., 1960. 'Geology around the University Towns: the Cardiff District', *Geol. Assoc. Guides*, No. 16.

Blundell, C. R. K., 1952. 'The succession and structure of the north-eastern area of the South Wales Coalfield'. *Quart. Journ. Geol. Soc.*, 107, pp. 307–33.

——, 1953. 'Magnetometric mapping for Haematite', *Geol. Mag.*, 90, pp. 57–64.

Eyles, V. A., and Blundell, C. R. K., 1957. 'On a volcanic vent and associated Monchiquite intrusions in Monmouthshire', *Geol. Mag.*, 94, pp. 54–7.

* Spelt Cefn On, wrongly, on 1-inch map.

Francis, E. H., 1959. 'The Rhaetic of the Bridgend District, Glamorganshire', *Proc. Geol. Assoc.*, 70, pp. 158–78.

George, T. N., 1954. 'Pre-Seminulan Main Limestone of the Avonian Series in Breconshire', *Quart. Journ. Geol. Soc.*, 110, pp. 283–322.

——, 1958. 'Lower Carboniferous Palaeogeography of the British Isles', *Proc. Yorks. Geol. Soc.*, 31, pp. 227–318.

Moore, L. R., and Blundell, C. R. K., 1952. 'The Malvernian phase of earth movements in South Wales', *C.R. Congr. Carb. Strat.*, pp. 463–73.

North, F. J., 1949. 'The river scenery at the head of the Vale of Neath', 3rd ed., *Nat. Mus. Wales*, Cardiff.

——, 1955. 'The evolution of the Bristol Channel', 2nd. ed., *Nat. Mus. Wales*, Cardiff.

Owen, T. R., 1954. 'The structure of the Neath disturbance between Bryniau Gleision and Glynneath, South Wales', *Quart. Journ. Geol. Soc.*, 109, pp. 333–65.

Robinson, P. L., 1957. 'The Mesozoic fissures of the Bristol Channel area and their vertebrate faunas', *Journ. Linn Soc.*—Zoology, 93, pp. 260–82.

Trueman, A. E. and others, 1954. 'The coalfields of Great Britain', London.

Walmsley, V., 1959. 'The Usk Inlier', *Quart. Journ. Geol. Soc.*, 114, pp. 483–521.

Woodland, A. W., and others, 1957. 'Classification of the Coal Measures of South Wales with special reference to the Upper Coal Measures', *Bull. Geol. Surv.*, 13, pp. 6–13.

III

BOTANY

MARY S. PERCIVAL

THIS account is partly ecological and partly floristic. It has been impossible to describe all the types of vegetation in the area, and preference has been given to those which are the subjects of current research and also to those whose floras are peculiar or especially rich. The visitor will probably be astonished at the lush growth of the vegetation as a whole. No bare soil is left uncovered for long in this mild moist climate. Though the valley bottoms may be filled with pits, one has only to walk to the end of a drab line of colliery town houses and on to the hillside beyond to find *Wahlenbergia hederacea* at one's feet.

The coal-black rivers are fringed with magnificent stands of *Impatiens glandulifera* and many a tip is silver with Moonshine (*Anaphalis margaritacea*). Glamorgan can also claim a true endemic plant *Aconitum anglicum*, which fringes the River Ely with blue in May.

The writer wishes to thank all those who have so generously permitted her to incorporate in this account data which are as yet unpublished. These are Mr. H. A. Hyde for data from his *Welsh Timber Trees*, 3rd edition, and his *Plant Life in and around the Glamorgan Forests*; Mr. A. E. Wade for notes from his *Flora of Monmouthshire* (in preparation) and his *Mosses of Monmouthshire*; and Mr. F. Palmer for information on the ecology of coal tips, the subject of his Ph.D. thesis. She also wishes to acknowledge gratefully the information obtained from the work of Miss K. Benson-Evans and Mrs. M. A. Williams's *Ecology of Limestone Caves*; Mr. A. Rosser's and Mr. F. Palmer's *Ecology of the Coastal Algae*; and Dr. R. B. Ivimey-Cook's *Ecology of a Limestone Heath*. Mr. R. O. Drummond and Mr. R. E. Stumbles of the Forestry Commission have been very helpful with information on forest management and the location of woodlands. Without Mr. Wade's guidance on field excursions, this account could not have been written.

THE VEGETATION OF THE COAST

The Coastal Algae

The area of the Severn estuary falls naturally into three regions—Chepstow to Cardiff, Penarth to Cold Knap Point and Aberthaw to the Ogmore River.

Chepstow to Cardiff. Beyond the narrow interrupted fringe of salt marsh, this area is mainly tidal mud flats with a few rocky outcrops. There are no rock pools and, indeed, no suitable substratum for algal growth over the greater part of the area. Furthermore, there are deep deposits of silt and a lot of fresh water.

At Goldcliff (ST. 373817), Peterstone Wentloog (ST. 260793) and St. Brides (ST. 290810) *Pelvetia* and *Fucus spiralis* grow on the sea-wall and rocks at high-water mark. The middle shore is sparsely colonized by *Fucus vesiculosus* and *Ascophyllum*

nodosum where any anchorage offers itself, and at Goldcliff both species reach gigantic proportions, the latter measuring up to 10 feet. The habitat here is rather unusual as there is an old eroded peat bed at the bottom. The water is quiet and polluted with a phosphate-rich effluent from a sugar beet factory. One or all of these factors may contribute to the eutrophy of the environment. Another point of interest, *Polysiphonia fastigiata* is almost absent from the *Ascophyllum* fronds.

There is a long rocky lower shore at Goldcliff where well separated plants of *F. serratus* are plentiful. Five other red seaweeds have been recorded here: *Gigartina stellata*, *Lithothamnion membranacea*, *Ceramium rubrum*, *Chondrus crispus* and *Corallina officinalis*. The last three live only at extreme low water mark.

Penarth to Cold Knap Point. Here, particularly at Sully Island and Sully Bay (ST. 160675) are extensive rocky flats and many rock pools. The brown seaweeds are extremely abundant, covering almost the whole region between the tide marks. The zonation follows the usual sequence of upper shore *Pelvetia* and *F. spiralis*, midshore *Ascophyllum* and *F. vesiculosus* and lower shore *F. serratus*, but the two latter are not well defined. The rock pools are fairly rich in species, the reds predominating.

Between *Aberthaw and the Ogmore River* there are extensive limestone pavements with shallow rock pools, and also stretches of sand and pebbles. The upper and middle shores of these rather exposed, wave-beaten beaches are almost bare of fucoids, but in sheltered spots the normal succession occurs. *F. serratus* is plentiful, but stunted, on the lower shore, and at low watermark there are carpets of *Laurencia pinnatifida* and *Corallina officinalis*.

There is no Laminaria zone along all this part of the coast although *Laminaria digitata* does grow in a few deep rock pools at Southerndown (SS. 884725).

The number of species in all classes increases from Goldcliff to Ogmore. The salinity increases while silting greatly diminishes. The red algae which do live up-channel (those listed above) have been found by experiment to survive several months in fresh water, although with some loss of red pigment. Others, species of *Dumontia*, *Rhodymenia*, *Porphyra* and *Lawrencia* died after two to three weeks and were absent from Goldcliff.

Salt Marsh

Small areas of salt marsh occur at the mouth of the Ogmore and Thaw rivers. The latter is now largely occluded by a new dam, but the remaining fragment at East Aberthaw (ST. 040658) is well developed showing the usual *Obione* zone fringing the channels and with *Puccinellietum* on the flats. Salt pans are rare as there are no grazing animals except rabbits. The lowest marsh, which is nearest the raised beach under the cliffs, bears only very short *Armeria*, *Salicornia* and *Triglochin*. A ridge of big Lias pebbles runs between the marsh and the sea, bearing on its crest a line of samphire backed by an open association of *Eryngium*, *Glaucium*, *Senecio Jacobaea*, *Vicia tetrasperma* and *Carex arenaria*. Descending landwards, the stable shingle is colonized by *Festuca rubra*, *Beta maritima*, *Agropyron repens* and a long strip of *Limonium binervosum* (Pl. V).

Further up the channel from the mouth of the Rumney River towards Newport are the Wharflands. These are covered only at high spring tide and are somewhat curiously situated between the sea-wall and an earth cliff. The latter separates them from the lower level muddy marsh with its *Salicornietum* of *S. stricta* and *S. dolicostachya* and its rapidly increasing colonies of *Spartina Townsendii*. They bear a close textured sward which in some parts is mostly Puccinellia and in others mostly Armeria. The ground is heavily grazed by sheep and cattle, whose trampling leads to the blockage of drainage channels and the formation of many shallow salt pans. The Puccinellia turf has also been pared off in many places and here *Alopecurus bulbosus* and *Puccinellia rupestris* are conspicuous as recolonizers of the bare patches. *Aster tripolium* and its variety *discoideus Rchb.* and *Cochlearia anglica* grow thickly along the muddy sides of the creeks (Pl. VIII).

A variant of the normal coastal saltings may be seen at Barry Docks. There is a basin behind the east breakwater which was constructed in 1889. It has never been used, has no outlet, and is fed by seepage through the breakwater at high tide and by a shoot carrying surface water from the railway sidings above. There has been some dumping of vegetable refuse and hard core.

On the sloping bottom, between the litter of timber and cork, the vegetation is zoned as on a salting. There is first a wide band of *Salicornia*, and then successive zones of *Triglochin maritima* and *Juncus maritimus*, and lastly a patch of *Scirpus maritimus* with a few plants of *Typha latifolia*. The vigour of all the plants—especially the *Triglochin*—is remarkable.

On the drier seaward margin the zonation is straight from *Salicornia* and *Glaux maritima* to *Sonchus arvensis*, *Atriplex* and *Hypericum perforatum*. Then comes a close, rabbit-cropped zone which is mostly *Lotus corniculatus* with abundant *Viola hirta*, and higher still some *Limonium vulgare var. pyramidalis C. E. Salmon*. Grasses are almost absent.

The Cliff Vegetation

The soft Lias cliffs fringing the coast from Porthkerry to Southerndown are richly clad, where they are not vertical, with a wind-moulded scrub of hawthorn (*Crataegus monogyna*), gorse, sloe and elder overgrown with ivy, bramble and clematis. This may be succeeded in places by a climax vegetation of trees. On the gentler slopes of rubble piled against the cliff a younger association, a turf with *Arrhenatherum elatius* and *Festuca rubra*, is found, sometimes with carrot or with large patches of *Lithospermum purpuro caeruleum*. The latter is also found inland in a mixed wood of oak and lime. Calcicoles are the chief pioneer plants; these include *Anthyllis vulneraria*, *Blackstonia perfoliata*, *Kentranthus ruber* and *Lotus corniculatus*, and also *Calamogrostis epigejos* and *Festuca arundinacea*. Where rubbish has been tipped over the edge, *Sinapis arvensis* and *Raphanus maritimus* come in and grow to a very large size. Two other notable crucifers, *Brassica oleracea* and *Matthiola incana*, are found at Nash Point. The maidenhair fern still grows hidden in moist crevices of the Lias, but on the harder Carboniferous Limestone which forms the cliffs at Southerndown it is replaced by *Asplenium marinum*.

Sand Dunes

The Kenfig Burrows (SS. 790820). This area is not, strictly speaking, within the area of east Glamorgan. It is the most extensive area of dunes in the county and exceedingly rich in plants. Botanists are urged to visit it soon, as the next decade will probably see its destruction by human agencies. Two years ago the burrows were untouched and the vegetation had improved, thickened and deepened, since the death of the rabbits. Now a big marshalling yard is nibbling into the back of the dunes. The Steel Company of Wales has been permitted to run a pipeline into Kenfig Pool from which they can pump water into the Ogmore River and thence to the works in times of drought. A motorway of limestone chips has been laid down to the edge of the pool, a channel cut in the reeds, and barrel mooring buoys dotted about the water by those who bring sailing boats by car. The eastern shore is now a litter-strewn bathing beach for the inhabitants of the rapidly growing house estates around the nearby villages.

The sand here, as at Merthyr Mawr, is highly calcareous and the flora incredibly rich, not only in the number of species but also in the numbers of individuals. It would seem that this area, which boasts thousands of plants of Epipactis and Orchis, where *Liparis loeselii var. ovata* is 'locally common' and where *Pyrola rotundifolia subspecies maritima* and *Monotropa hypopithys* flourish, deserves a better fate.

The pool itself is about half a mile long and is separated from the road by a fixed turf of *Holcus lanatus*, *Cynosurus cristatus*, *Festuca rubra*, *Briza media* and *Anthoxanthum odoratum*, with bracken invading from the east. The marginal vegetation is zoned, first by a band of *Iris pseudacorus* and *Lysimachia vulgaris* and then by *Scirpus tabernaemontani* and *Equisetum fluviatile*, with a line of *Alisma plantago-aquatica* roughly marking the boundary between the two. There are also large patches of *Eleocharis palustris* amongst the Equisetum. In places, wedges of *Phalaris arundinacea* run out to the edge of clear water between 'meadows' of *Equisetum palustre*. There is one group of *Nymphaea alba* and abundant *Myriophyllum* below water. Willows fringe the west and south shores.

Westward of the pool is a large flat 'meadow' area of *Equisetum palustre* with *Lotus uliginosus*, *Pulicaria dysenterica*, *Holcus lanatus*, *Carex nigra*, *Cirsium pratense*, *Epipactis palustris* and *Orchis*. It is studded with clumps of *Juncus acutus*, and the damp sandy humus below is swarded with *Hypnum*. This meadow-like association varies greatly in the depth of its vegetation, from knee height in the one just described to a short brittle 'turf' of *Equisetum*, *Eriophorum*, *Hydrocotyle vulgaris*, *Salix repens* and *Carex nigra* which is only 6 inches high at most. This also has a close sward of mosses in its bottom. As there may be a considerable seasonal variation in the water table, this thick insulating felt of moss is an important factor in conserving the surface of the land. It is rejuvenated in the winter and spring when the water rises again.

There are two fairly well-defined kinds of dune slack. There are those which support *Salix repens* and *Rubus caesius* and have a black friable sandy humus in which *Botrychium lunaria* grows to perfection, and there are those with a thick sward of

[*Photo:* J. G. C. Anderson

Plate IX.—Frozen springs from Liassic limestone overlying Rhaetic shales. Coast 1 mile south of Penarth.

Plate X.—Fixed and mobile sand dunes, Merthyr Mawr.

[*Photo:* J. G. C. Anderson

[*Photo:* A. G. Lyon

Plate XI.—Zonal vegetation, Pysgodlyn Mawr.

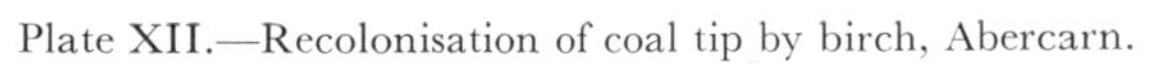

Plate XII.—Recolonisation of coal tip by birch, Abercarn.

[*Photo:* F. Ryan

moss and *Hydrocotyle vulgaris* pierced by *Eleocharis palustris, Juncus articulatus* and *Chara* above sand. The former appear to be more mature, the latter are probably shallow sheets of water in a normal season. Deeper, marshy slacks also occur and fine swarms of Orchids grown about their margin.

The dunes themselves are of various sizes and ages. The crested shore dunes are colonized solely by *Ammophila* with *Agropyron junceiforme* on the seaward side and measure about 22 yards from the edge of the beach to the crest. Some 40 yards beyond this *Rubus* comes in as a sand binder. Within this zone are some partially fixed low dunes with some marram, but chiefly bound by *Carex arenaria* with *Calystegia soldanella, Viola curtisii, Hypochaeris radicata, Sedum acre, Phleum arenarium, Thymus drucei* and also *Tortula ruraliformis, Camptothecium sericeum, Peltigera, Cladonia* and *Parmelia.*

Larger dunes, originally mounded and bound over with marram, *Rubus* and *Festuca rubra,* appear to have had their tops blown off and are now hollow sandy craters with new rhizomes of *Carex arenaria* and marram marching down from the lips. Further east, big dunes, knife-edged and steeply sandy on their southern faces, and closely swarded with *Rubus caesius* and *Festuca rubra* on their sheltered northern sides, lie at an angle to the prevailing south-westerly wind. Some of these, however, have been eroded on both sides.

At *Merthyr Mawr Warren* (SS. 860770) sand has piled up over the out-cropping limestone to form dunes which exceed 200 feet in height. These are the tallest in Europe, excepting only those in East Prussia. This invading wall of sand threatened to engulf the village and in 1834 Scots and maritime pine was planted in an endeavour to halt it. More recently conifers have been widely planted up the valley (Pl. X).

The dunes are still partly mobile and a broad tongue of yellow sand is still encroaching east of the ruins of Candleston Castle. The trunks of half-buried trees, already dead, stick up from it. Generally speaking the dunes form a series of ridges with scoured channels of loose sand running roughly from west to east. The southern faces may be bare or partly bound by *Carex arenaria* or marram with depauperate *Ononis repens. Reseda lutea* may form large patches and *Rosa spinosissima* is also an important stabilizer. The northern faces are usually densely covered with *Rubus caesius* and *Holcus lanatus. Hippophae rhamnoides* has stabilized certain ridges, with creeping stolors reaching out into bare sand at the base, changing to low scrub, and finally reaching the size of tall shrubs on the crest. The innermost dune grades into a bracken-covered slope with dense foliaged, flat topped spindle bushes (*Euonymus europaeus*) looking like tea trees and also with wayfaring tree (*Viburnum lantana*) with the same curious form. This leads up to woodland which is a mixture of *Populus canadensis, Populus alba, Betula verrucosa, Quercus ilex, Acer pseudoplatanus* and *Ulmus glabra.* The last is regenerating abundantly.

THE VEGETATION OF LIMESTONE HEATH

The Ewenny Downs (SS. 885760). Carboniferous Limestone outcrops on the slopes (10°–20°) of the 300-foot summits of the Downs. Here limestone heath has

developed and is maintained as such by the constant grazing by sheep which prevents the establishment of tree seedlings. The soil on the top and on the gentle slopes is a mildly acid deep brown earth which is top-dressed with blown sand from the dunes of Merthyr Mawr on the other side of the Ogmore river. This sand is calcareous and maintains the base supply in the soil and probably prevents podsolization.

The vegetation is of two kinds. Firstly, occupying 400 acres of Ogmore Down, is a grass heath, dominated by tussocked *Agrostis setacea* and Molinia, and Pteridium (which are all relatively distasteful to sheep), and flat grazed hummocks of *Ulex gallii*. Secondly, on 200 acres of Old Castle Down, is a limestone heath, which is a closed association of patches of heath plants (*A. setacea*, *Erica cinerea*, Calluna and Ulex) curiously pierced through with deep-rooting calcicoles (*Helianthemum chamaecistus*, *Poterium sanguisorba*, *Thymus drucei* and *Lotus corniculatus*) and separated by channels of close-cropped grassland. At the northern end of Ogmore Down, where the soil is thin and limestone outcrops, there is thick turf of *Festuca ovina* with *Poterium sanguisorba* and other calcicoles. *Cirsium acaule var. caulescens* fringes the road between the downs.

WOODLANDS

'Managed' Woods. If one looks at the Ordnance Survey map it would appear that there are considerable stretches of woodland in east Glamorgan and Monmouthshire, but nearly all these have been felled and replanted by the Forestry Commission. Although conifers now occupy most of the ground, in St. Pierre Great Woods near Chepstow (ST. 500920) the final crop will be beech with some 'shade bearing' conifers such as *Tsuga*, *Abies grandis* and *A. procera*. This wood lies at 250 feet on Old Red Sandstone. After the felling in the middle thirties, coppice was allowed to develop from the old top canopy of *Quercus robur*, *Tilia cordata*, ash and aspen. This was thinned to a single shoot on each bole and the 'cultivated' crop planted in between. The regeneration of hazel and bramble has been very luxuriant and this has been trashed to permit the crop to survive. So at present there is an open wood, some 25 feet or more in height above the young beeches, with a rich field flora which includes *Holcus mollis*, *Orchis fuchsii*, *Listera ovata*, *Euphorbia amygdaloides*, *Hypericum hirsutum*, *Galium odoratum*, *Vicia sylvatica*, *Anemone nemorosa* and *Fragaria vesca*. There are also considerable stands of *Milium effusum* whose culms measure up to 5 foot 6 inches.

Oakwoods formerly clothed most of the coal-mining valleys up to about 1,000 feet. This old tree line is probably roughly traced by the bracken line today, for in surviving fragments of woodland it is very often co-dominant with bluebell in the field flora.

Lowland Pedunculate Oakwood on Old Red Sandstone and Marl (Mascoed Mawr, ST. 270900). The southern part of this wood has already been felled and replanted with a border of Douglas Fir and beech. Within is a zone from which the mature oaks have been removed, leaving straggling birches, oaks, rowan and moribund hollies. Lime and ash are absent and bracken has strongly invaded the ground since the top canopy was removed. Sloping to the south-east in planted glades,

bracken and bramble are being trashed to free the young firs, but northwards, towards the crest of the hill, the wood is still virtually intact and will remain so for a few years. As one descends the northern slopes on to the Red Marl, ash and sycamore largely replace the oak and the acidic elements disappear from the field flora. Instead *Dryopteris borreri*, *D. filix-mas* and *D. dilatata* become plentiful. The bracken stops on the crest, where lie the remains of a fine beech. The bole is about 20 feet in circumference at 3 feet, and the gap left in the surrounding vegetation is some 28 yards across. It was probably the seed parent of the young beeches which occur sporadically throughout the wood.

Lowland Lime Wood on Limestone

There is an example of this near Carrow Hill (ST. 435900) on a rendzina soil. The lower part of the wood is dense hazel and ash coppice, with an occasional standard of apple or cherry. This changes quite abruptly to pure *Tilia cordata* coppice, with some admixture of larger beech trees on the steeper slopes towards the top of the limestone ridge. Here a few fine old limes, now moribund, have been spared the axe. The burred bole of the largest is 15 feet 10 inches at 3 feet; two others measure 8 feet 11 inches and 8 feet 6 inches. They are multi-stemmed above a short trunk, and may be very old coppice.

The Tilia coppice is remarkably strict in its growth and the boles so bare that one might mistake it for ash. Defoliation by caterpillars was very severe in 1959, and patches of bare ground were grey with the mycelia of *Chaetomium elatum* radiating from the pinheads of the larval excreta.

Beechwoods. Beech charcoal has been found in a prehistoric hearth at Radyr (ST. 136804). This proves the tree to be truly native in Glamorgan. There are many relict beech woods from Pant-tawel eastwards and northwards which link up with the magnificent natural woods at Tintern. They are usually on the Carboniferous Limestone, the largest westerly one being the Garth Wood (ST. 120820) just north of Cardiff. Formerly, this was a fine wood but the big timber was felled in the thirties and now a huge quarry is eating into the dolomite of the southern side.

A good example of natural beechwood is to be found on the limestone escarpment on the slopes of the Blorenge at about 1,200 feet (SO. 277105). The extreme nature of the terrain, and its distance from the mountain road, have been the chief reasons for its preservation. It straggles along and below the cliffs of the main escarpment, but above this there is another skyline cliff where a few stunted beeches, rowans and ashes cling. A strip of talus lies between and is remarkable for its large pure stands of Beech Polypody. *Circaea intermedia*, which was recorded here by Burton in 1813, is also abundant between the boulders, together with *Geranium robertianum*, *G. lucidum*, *Fragaria vesca* and *Veronica chamaedrys*. The stones themselves are well colonized by mosses such as *Hypnum cupressiforme*, *Ditrichum flexicaule*, *Dicranum scoparium*, *Pseudoscleropodium purum* and abundant *Camptothecium sericeum*.

On the steepest part of the lower escarpment, the beech forms a nearly closed canopy, together with some ash, wych elm and, near the springs, alder. On the

gentler slopes below, the trees are well separated and together with sessile oak, ash, rowan and crataegus produce 'park' trees, branched, in the case of the oak, to the ground. There are some well-formed hollies, too. Hazel is present but not plentiful. *Circaea intermedia* is again plentiful in the shade of the beeches!

The limestone is not the only formation to support natural beech wood in this area. On the eastern side of Mynydd y Lan (ST. 210920), there is a stream marked on the Ordnance Survey map running from the summit to the Ebbw River. This is now a dry gully with an old beech wood on both sides and also curving in an arc northwards. The trees are rooted in the Pennant Grit. The boles of two of them measured respectively 11 feet 3 inches and 8 feet 8 inches at a height of 3 feet. The outermost trees are separate and short-trunked, but in the gully they are taller and in close canopy over the dry, bare ground. There are also a few rowans, ashes and birches (both *Betula verrucosa* and *B. tomentosa*) and one or two sessile oaks. The beech is regenerating on the southern side. The saplings were judged to be about three years old, and it is an open question whether their presence is a consequence of the heavy mast year of 1956 or a result of the disappearance of the rabbit, or of the disturbance of the soil when the Japanese larch, which now flanks the wood, was planted. *Boletus scaber*, *Scleroderma vulgare* and *Russula emetica* were found below the fringe trees.

The finest beechwood in Monmouthshire borders the Wye Valley. At Black Cliff (ST. 533985) the trees are below a high cliff. Those nearest it have been drawn up and have tall slim trunks with small crowns. *Tilia cordata*, *Sorbus anglica* and *Fraxinus excelsior* are all present and are replaced by beech and yew, in close canopy, as one moves away from the cliff. Very large boulders lie tumbled below the cliff and form shady dells which resemble a little the Killarney Woods. The boulders are covered in luxuriant mosses, and between them the ground is yellow with *Chrysosplenium alternifolium* interspersed with *Athyrium filix-femina* and *Polystichum setiferum*.

Below the mixed wood is a carpet of lily of the valley with particularly fine *Paris quadrifolia*, many plants of the latter having five leaves. During the past three years this association has become seriously invaded by *Mercurialis perennis* and copious ash saplings. This is perhaps a consequence of myxomatosis. *Cardamine impatiens* is plentiful at the edge of the paths and on the top of the stone walls, and *Carex digitata* is not infrequent. Below the beeches there is little of note except *Neottia nidus-avis* and, rarely, *Pyrola secunda* and *Euphorbia stricta*.

A part of this wood is to remain untouched, but elsewhere, particularly where the trees are moribund, the foresters are removing them. They have cleared 2-acre plots and are permitting natural regeneration to take place. Ash has grown thickly and they are hoping for oak and beech which they will retain as the crop. If these do not appear, they will be planted.

Lady Park Wood (SO. 546145) is the finest of our natural beechwoods. It crowns a limestone ridge and descends the precipitous escarpment to the River Wye below. On the ridge the standard beeches are in close canopy together with yew and some large limes (*Tilia cordata* and *Tilia platyphyllos*). The escarpment is

also well wooded and great ivies climb and flatten against the vertical faces of the cliff. One, of five twisted strands, measures 2 feet 11 inches at a height of 3 feet. The rock face itself bears, in places, tufa-encrusted *Seligeria*. Four species in all have been recorded in this wood: *Seligeria Doniana*, *S. acutifolia*, *S. pusilla* and *S. recurvata*.

On the gentler slopes below the escarpment, the woodland is more open and richer in species. It is chiefly old coppice of the limes mentioned above, hazel and *Ulmus glabra*, with some standards of beech, *Quercus petraea*, and an occasional ash and some large yews. The field flora varies in density. *Carex pendula* grows up to 8 feet in height, *Deschampsia caespitosa*, *Mercurialis perennis*, ivy and woodruff are common, while *Mnium undulatum* is particularly abundant in the ground layer. *Lathraea squamaria* is frequent on the hazel. *Luzula Forsteri* is also common.

Where the road runs along the bottom of the wood there are other uncommon plants including *Dipsacus pilosus*, *Brachypodium pinnatum*, *Campanula trachelium*, *Festuca altissima* and, curiously enough, *Rubia peregrina*. The welted thistle, *Carduus acanthoides*, is plentiful along the disused railway track below the road.

Amanita phalloides, *Russula emetica*, *Psalliota silvatica* and *Sparassis crispa* the size of a dinner plate, are found under the beeches on the crest of the ridge.

Happily the scourge of woodlands in Glamorgan, the honey fungus (*Armillaria mellea*), is not prevalent in these old Crown woodlands. In Redding's Enclosure (SO. 540135), which adjoins Lady Park Wood, there has been a considerable amount of clearing and replanting with conifers amongst the natural regeneration of ash and hazel. In the old mature wood, the attacks of defoliating caterpillars in the high canopy of beech and lime may be severe, as in the spring of 1959. An audible patter of excreta rains down on the undergrowth and leads one to speculate as to what degree its luxuriance may be attributed to a thinning of the leaf pattern above and the partial prolongation of the vernal conditions on the forest floor.

THE MOUNTAIN GRASSLANDS

These are quite varied and interesting. On the hills above some of the colliery workings the land has dried out, dangerous cracks have appeared, and only very poor thin *Nardus* grassland remains, or it is replaced by a bilberry moor.

As one climbs the mountain pass over Craig Ogwr (SN. 930947) one sees a clear zonation of grasslands. The *Molinia* turf on the gentle slopes (1,000 feet) changes to *Deschampsia flexuosa* as the gradient steepens, and then is abruptly replaced by *Festuca rubra* turf at and above the road (1,200 feet). The first two zones are now planted with conifers. As the summit (1,700 feet) is reached the *Festuca* turf deepens and thickens and a little *Molinia*, *Anthoxanthum*, *Carex binervis* and *Juncus squarrosus* appear in it. As the land dips gently to the west, patches of *Eriophorum* and *Molinia* appear and there is some peat.

The New Zealand adventive, *Epilobium pedunculare*, is now growing in abundance in the roadside streamlets and damp stone walls of the mountain pass, and has even penetrated up the mountain steams where it appears completely naturalized amongst *Anagallis tenella* and *Wahlenbergia hederacea*. Some colonies are heavily 'infected' with *Trichothecium roseum*.

Further east, in north Monmouthshire, as one approaches Trefil (1,340 feet) there is some moist grassland bearing the rich flora associated with basic soil. This is exploited for hay, and somewhat resembles the alpine meadows of the Central Pyrenees.

Above Trefil (SO. 117133) a knife-sharp contrast is seen of limestone pasture with *Cirsium acaule*, *Festuca rubra*, *Briza media*, *Thymus drucei*, *Aira caryophyllea*, *Carex flacca*, *Carlina vulgaris* and *Linum catharticum* on one side of the road, and Calluna-Vaccinium-Empetrum moor on the other. Beside Nant Trefil, below the road embankment, the two floras meet. *Pinguicula vulgaris and Anagallis tenella* grow among *Carex flacca* and *Juncus inflexus*, while in the water is lime-encrusted *Chara vulgaris*. A strip of Molinia turf separates the stream and the moorland on whose boulders of Millstone Grit *Andraea Rothii* grows.

Any limestone pasture is apt to be severely grazed by sheep, but in some parts, such as the land bordering Rhastas Pond (1,300 feet, SO. 094070), and along the A.465 at 1,200 feet between Merthyr and Bryn Mawr, where there are luxuriant swards of Molinia with *Agrostis tenuis*, *Deschampsia flexuosa*, Anthoxanthum and *Juncus conglomeratus*, the Molinia is apparently kept in this turf form by cattle and pony grazing.

On disturbed ground in this area, however, the recolonization may be by *Nardus stricta* alone. The Welsh sheep tear it out by the roots and discard it, as do the Spanish sheep in the Pyrenees—but catastrophic erosion does not follow in this mild damp climate.

BOG VEGETATION

Trelleck Bog (SO. 510038) is, as the layer of sand in the soil profile above the conglomerate proves, on the site of a glacial lake. The vegetation is an almost pure *Molinietum* with the tussocks reaching 3 feet, and many of them also supporting *Deschampsia flexuosa*. The Molinia is of two kinds, the one with rather strict, deep-green leaves, the other with lax, yellow-green leaves. Both forms are abundant, but young plants, recolonizing the bare soil beside the forestry road, all have strict foliage, highly coloured with violet. There are a number of mountain ash and Scots pine saplings, rooted, apparently, in the sphagnum above the peat. The former look yellow and unhealthy, the latter vigorous, one of 5 feet being in cone. The presence of these trees and the dry conditions of the bog are a consequence of the draining away of its water to feed an emergency water tank. No less than fourteen species and nine varieties of Sphagna have been recorded, *Sphagnum papillosum* being abundant. *Eriophorum angustifolium*, *E. vaginatum* and *E. latifolium* are all present, and a little *Oxycoccus palustris*.

Bracken and gorse have invaded the eastern part of the bog, and the peat of the northern fringe, abutting on the conifer plantations, has been ploughed as a fire-break. It is not intended to plant the bog itself but the flora is doomed unless the water supply is restored. *Rhynchospora alba* seems to have disappeared already.

LOWLAND AQUATIC VEGETATION

Behind the wharf land of Rumney and Peterston Wentloog lie water meadows separated by reens. These latter contain a rich aquatic and fringe flora. Before the

last war, the farmers used to pile the farmyard manure on the verges of the roads, whence it drained into the reens and enriched the water. This is no longer done, but the vegetation is still very vigorous and the reens have to be cleared regularly to prevent them choking. Among the floating aquatics are the *Lemnas* (*L. trisulca*, *L. minor* and *L. gibba*), *Hydrocharis morsus-ranae*, *Ranunculus Baudotii* and *R. trichophyllus*. The last two are in the reens just behind the sea-wall. The most striking free-floating plant is *Azolla filiculoides* which transforms the surface of the water into a thick red carpet. This is the westernmost limit for this exotic. Rooted aquatics include *Elodea canadensis*, *Callitriche obtusangula*, *Potamogeton* spp., *Sparganium*, *Alisma plantago-aquatica*, *Butomus umbellatus* and *Phragmites communis*. *Carex riparia*, *Glyceria maxima*, *Iris pseudacorus*, *Ranunculus sceleratus* and *Oenanthe crocata* are abundant in the fringe vegetation.

Moorland Lake. Pysgodlyn Mawr (ST. 043760) on Mynydd y Glew has a gravelly bottom and the east end has been dammed to conserve water for foresters' cottages. The original setting of the lake was rough moorland, but in the early 'thirties conifers were planted round it. A narrow margin of rather wet heathland remains with *Molinia* tussocks, *Calluna* and *Erica tetralix*, *Agrostis setacea*, *Drosera rotundifolia* and *Sphagnum*. The accumulated silt at the western end of the lake is zoned first with *Salix atrocinerea*, then with *Eriophorum angustifolium* and *Potentilla palustris* together with *Carex buxbaumii*, then with *Carex rostrata* and finally *Equisetum fluviatile* stretches into the open water (Pl. XI).

The southern arm is a willow swamp with *Caltha palustris*, *Menyanthes trifoliata* and *Carex vesicaria* where a pair of swans always build. The eastern shore in 1959 had a veritable turf of *Pilularia globulifera*. This is the only place where it occurs in Glamorgan.

MOUNTAIN TARNS

Below the precipitous escarpment of Craig y Llyn (SN. 910038) there are two small mountain lakes, Llyn Fach and Llyn Fawr. The latter has been converted into a reservoir but the former is a good example of shallow oligotrophic water containing *Isoetes lacustris* and *I. echinospora*, *Littorella uniflora*, *Lobelia dortmanna* and *Fontinalis antipyretica*. On the crumbling face of Craig y Llyn itself there are many uncommon plants such as *Hymenophyllum wilsonii*, *Lycopodium selago*, *Thalictrum minus*, *Sedum forsterianum*, *Pyrola secunda* and *Rubus saxatilis*.

THE VEGETATION OF WASTE LANDS

The Cardiff and Barry docks are very rich floristically. No less than 500 adventives have been recorded at Cardiff alone. Although this number has decreased since the change to water ballast, the vegetation on the flats between the railway sidings is still composed of a great variety of species of open ground, both native and exotic, growing with the customary luxuriance engendered by the mild climate of South Wales. Among the adventives at Barry, *Melilotus officinalis*, *Reseda alba* and *Peucedanum graveolens* are all abundant and *Lactuca virosa*, *Cochlearia Armoracia* and *Erigeron canadense* are quite plentiful. At Cardiff Docks, *Lathyrus tuberosus* and *Scrophularia scorodonia* are thoroughly naturalized. *Orobanche minor* grows at both sites.

THE VEGETATION OF COAL TIPS

Mr. F. Palmer is investigating the ecology of coal tips in this area. He has found that the colonization proceeds to two different climaces depending on whether or not grazing animals have access to the site.

At Merthyr Common (SO. 070059) there are acres of old level-topped tips among which 'oases' of the original mountain pastures occur around stone-built cottages. The cottagers keep pigs and poultry, and these, with the sheep, range free. The tips are at least fifty years old.

The primary sere, which persists on the steepest (30°) southern slopes, is of *Festuca ovina* in small individual tufts, with *Hieracium pilosella* as a later colonizer. (*Arenaria serpyllifolia* is one of the first colonizers of *new* tips.) *Calluna* sometimes replaces *Festuca* on *northern* slopes. On the less severe slopes and on the flat tops, there is a preclimax sere of *F. ovina* and *Agrostis tenuis*. The plants are still in separate tufts and the intervening spaces are clothed with *Rhacomitrium lanuginosum*, *Polytrichum*, *Cladonia impexa*, *Cladonia uncialis*, *Cetraria aculeata* and abundant *Aira praecox*. There are signs of preferential grazing even here—the *Festuca* and *C. uncialis* and any stray plants of *Calluna* or *Ulex gallii* are severely cropped. The biotic climax is a stable grassland of *Agrostis tenuis* and *Festuca ovina* with a little *Nardus stricta*. Wild white clover, which is abundant in the surviving patches of mountain pasture, follows the sheep tracks across the tips. Below the grassland is an inch of humus and 2 inches of humus mixed with pit material and roots and then the unchanged pit heap. Water is plentiful 9 inches down. Where there are no grazing animals, the story is different. At Abercarn (ST. 215964) a 500-yard tip occupies an ellipse of land between the old Monmouthshire Canal and the Ebbw River. Here colonization is far advanced towards a woodland. The primary colonizer, even on the steepest (60°) north-west slopes, is *Betula verrucosa* and a few Scots pines. On the flat 'valleyed' top, and on the south-east slopes, is a well-developed scrub of birch and willow with scattered beech, sycamore, oak and alder. The sycamores and alders are 25–40 feet tall, the oak 5–15 feet and the beech 3 feet. The ground between the trees is sparsely colonized by *Polytrichum formosum*, *P. piliferum*, *Agrostis tenuis* and *Carlina vulgaris*, except in the oldest parts where dog rose, bramble, raspberry, bracken and bluebell give a virtually closed association. The source of the beech is a hanger to the south-east which overtops the tip (Pl. XII).

Perhaps the prettiest tip is on the side of Mynydd y Lan—a cone pink with *Calluna*.

THE VEGETATION OF LIMESTONE CAVES

Grid Refs.: Llangattock scarp (SO. 187159) near Brynmawr, the Wye Valley between Monmouth and Symonds Yat (SO. 550147) and the region around Pont Nedd Fechan (SN. 901077). Miss K. Benson-Evans and Mrs. A. Mason-Williams are investigating this little-known field.

At the cave thresholds, the bryophyta show a remarkably strict zonation both in species and growth form, which can be attributed directly to variation in light intensity, as the temperature and relative humidity are virtually constant in this

unique environment. All growth forms are present at 24 lux, but, as the light intensity falls, cushion and tall turf forms lose their dominance, and at 5 lux virtually only weft and thalloid forms are present. Alka tolerant mosses such as *Barbula recurvirostre*, *Fissidens bryoides*, *F. taxifolius*, *Ctenidium molluscum*, are the most frequent at all thresholds, together with the hepatics, *Pellia epiphylla* and *Plagiochila asplenoides*.

In the dark zone of the caves where the relative humidity and temperature are steady at 80 per cent and 8°C, respectively, the sole macroscopic plants are fungi which grow on any organic debris, but the potential flora in the form of spores and resting stages in the cave soil, is abundant and varied. Soil cultures need only to be exposed to light to reveal the viability and range of this 'reserve' which include: *Chlorococcum humiculum*, *Synechococcus aeruginosus*, *Navicula* spp., *Fragilaria* spp., *Synedra* spp., *Nostoc muscorum*, *Lyngbya* spp., *Chroococcus turgidus*.

The bacterial population of caves is also large and varied. Autotrophic and heterotrophic species are present in the soil, water and air. Isolations from the cave soil include *Pseudomonas fluorescens*, *Pseudomonas pyocyanea*, *Bacterium* spp., *Bacillus* spp., *Clostridium pasterianum*, *Nitrococcus europea* and *Nitrobacter winowgradski*, and from the cave water, *Azotobacter* sp., *Nitrosococcus* sp., *Nitrobacter winogradski*. It will be noted that the last five species are autotrophic, and may have a special significance in the ecological succession.

IV

ZOOLOGY

J. Brough, C. Matheson and G. T. Jefferson

INTRODUCTION

IN writing this section of the volume it is not possible or even desirable to give a full account of the animal life of the region. Not possible, because of the limitations of space, and not desirable because by far the greater part of the matter would be much the same as that for any other region of similar size in Britain. Furthermore, an account of the Zoology of part of this region has already appeared in the *Glamorgan County History*, volume I, which contains extensive faunal lists, and to which readers are referred for more detailed information. There are, however, certain aspects of the fauna which may be uncommon or of special interest, and the whole of this essay will be devoted to these.

The region is very varied physiographically and falls into a number of fairly distinct areas. This has a marked effect on the distribution of organisms. These areas can best be described by proceeding from the sea-shore in a northerly direction. The shore itself is of interest, since it forms part of the northern border of the Bristol Channel and the Severn Estuary. The water at the western end, towards Porthcawl, is almost fully marine, and carries a large and varied marine fauna. As we move eastward there is a steady impoverishment and dying out of the more typical marine forms, until at the eastern extremity, near Chepstow, there is a restricted estuarine fauna. The inter-tidal region may be sandy, but only substantially so in the west, as at Ogmore, and in a few restricted bays further east. From Ogmore almost to Cardiff the foreshore is mainly rocky. Around and east of Cardiff the inter-tidal region is almost solely of a glutinous dark-coloured mud.

The coast between Ogmore and Cardiff is characterized by a series of fairly high cliffs, but to west and east of these there are two quite different types of habitat. To the west there is an extensive sand-dune area at Merthyr Mawr and Kenfig, which carries a typical sand-dune fauna, with one or two rarities which will be referred to later. Between Cardiff and Newport, and Newport and Chepstow, there are two extensive areas of land which are not above sea-level at the highest tides, but which are protected by a series of sea walls that have been maintained apparently from Roman times. This low-lying, but fertile, area must be drained, and there is in fact an extensive network of drainage channels which carry an interesting fresh-water fauna. From these coastal regions the land rises northward, and in the Glamorgan part of the area does so in two distinct stages. The country between Cardiff and Bridgend consists of a somewhat irregular tableland of about 300–400 feet high, dissected by valleys. This is the Vale of Glamorgan, and is a well-wooded and fairly rich agricultural area, heavily intersected by hedgerows, giving good cover for an abundant and varied animal life. North of this the land rises fairly

sharply. This high hilly country, intersected by numerous fairly deep valleys, running roughly north and south, forms the greater part of the area under consideration. It consists very largely of open grassy moorland with a somewhat restricted and characteristic fauna. This region culminates in the inhospitable 3,000-foot peaks of the Brecon Beacons. This hilly country has been the scene of much activity by the Forestry Commission, and large schemes of reafforestation are in progress. Many thousands of acres are, or will be, covered by coniferous forests and this is undoubtedly having, and will have, an increasing effect on the nature of the fauna.

The natural fresh waters in the area, with its abundant rainfall, consist mainly of large numbers of streams, many of them fast-flowing, and a few sizeable rivers. Natural lakes, and even ponds, are relatively rare. Llangorse Lake is the only relatively large stretch of natural freshwater in the region. In the hills, however, water is impounded as reservoirs to give a large number of artificial lakes, some of them of considerable size.

A curious habitat, actually within the boundaries of the city of Cardiff, is provided by the small pond fed by St. Dennis's Well. It obviously has a deep source, the temperature being 11° to 12°C, and varying less than 1° throughout the year. This level is maintained even in the hardest winters, and during many years of observation the pool has never been frozen over. These conditions have an effect on reproduction both in the plants and animals of the pond. The reproductive rhythm of certain invertebrates in near-by normal fresh waters is not seen here, and larval forms are liable to occur at almost any time during the year.

The fauna of the region has, as in any highly industrialized area, suffered much at the hands of man. The many building activities, industrial and domestic, have, especially in the valleys, modified and impoverished these areas from the faunal point of view. The interesting and varied coastal area is disappearing under a cover of steel works, power stations, etc., with a consequent faunal and floral impoverishment.

Not the least far-reaching interference with animal life has been effected by the pollution of the rivers. This, originally by coal dust from washeries and by sewage, has been added to by industrial effluents of various kinds. All of this has produced extensive, and in some cases total, pollution. The trend of past decades has now been reversed, and the River Boards, armed by new legislation, are making a vigorous attack on this problem. A study of depollution in the Usk system is now being made jointly by the Usk River Board and members of the Biology Departments of University College, Cardiff, and data are being collected of the recolonization of certain streams as the purity of the water is gradually being restored. In the Afon Lwyd, above Abersychan, pollution abatement has been considerable, with the result that a varied fauna is making its appearance, including pollution-intolerant forms. In view of this, and of the good quality of the water, trout fry have now been introduced. Only one major polluting effluent remains to be dealt with, and then one would expect to see a good fauna throughout the length of this river.

THE FAUNA OF THE BRISTOL CHANNEL

Any division between the Bristol Channel and the Severn Estuary is clearly arbitrary, and no such distinction need be made for present purposes. Estuarine conditions in varying degree are met with throughout the whole of the upper part of the channel east of Swansea, and the main interest of its fauna lies in the extent to which it reflects these conditions.

Physical Conditions

To the west of Swansea the water is virtually full sea-water, with a salinity approaching 34 grams per litre, but this falls as one passes up channel to an average value of about 25 g.p.l. for Cardiff Roads, and 17 g.p.l. at Beachley near Chepstow. Perhaps even more important than the mean salinity at any point, however, is the extent to which it varies with time. Differences in the amount of fresh water being discharged by the rivers would be expected to affect salinities, and indeed these are generally lower in winter than in summer. C. B. Rees (1939), for example, found extreme values in Cardiff Roads of 19·8 g.p.l. on 25th January and 28·0 g.p.l. on 25th August, 1937. Such conditions are due partly to greater rainfall in winter and partly to reduced evaporation throughout the catchment areas. The tides also affect the salinity in the estuary, since on the flood a body of water moves up-channel and then returns with the ebb. The extent of these tidal effects on salinity may vary greatly between spring and neap tides, but the variation is rather small at places like Weston and Cardiff, where high-water salinity is rarely more than 1 g.p.l. above that at low water. Further up the estuary, however, these effects are often greater.

In many estuaries there is a vertical salinity gradient, salt water which enters with the tide passing below the lighter fresh water, and so giving an increase of salinity with depth. In the Bristol Channel, however, this does not happen; the tidal sea-water passes up the estuary as a more coherent mass pushing the progressively more brackish water before it. At any one time and place, therefore, there is very little variation in salinity with depth.

The tides of the Bristol Channel are said to be the second greatest in the world; certainly tides which, on equinoctial springs, can produce a vertical range of 45 feet are big by any standards, and they undoubtedly have far-reaching indirect effects on the fauna. Vast masses of water surging up and down the channel twice in little more than a day and producing tidal currents which sometimes exceed six knots, tend to keep in suspension much of the silt and mud brought down by the various rivers. The notorious turbidity of Bristol Channel water is largely due to suspended silt, but other forms of pollution play a part. Considerable quantities of fine coal dust are brought down from colliery washeries, particularly by the South Wales rivers, and there is a heavy discharge of untreated sewage from the large centres of population on both sides of the estuary. In the lower part of the channel the water turbidity varies to some extent with tidal and climatic conditions. It tends to be greater at low water, especially on springs when banks of mud which are just sub-littoral may become disturbed. Higher up, the effects of tides are greater

owing to the constriction and shallowing of the channel, and although the amount of suspended matter may vary with the tides, the water is always very dirty. The general picture, then, in the part of the Bristol Channel which concerns us here, is one of silt-laden water with a progressive increase in turbidity as one passes up-channel.

The large tidal range also accounts in part for the extensiveness of the mudflats exposed at low tide in the upper part of the Bristol Channel; in places these are nearly 3 miles wide. They are often flanked on the shoreward side by extensive saltings which are only covered by a few of the highest tides each year, and in the pools of which conditions of temperature and salinity fluctuate widely.

It has been shown by Purchon (1937), Rees (1939) and others that in spite of turbidity and pollution the oxygen content of Bristol Channel water is generally quite high and not likely to be a limiting factor for animals. Similarly the pH, ranging from 7·8 to 8·1, is not very different from that of full sea water, nor is the range of temperature excessive. Phosphates and other salts also seem to be present in adequate amounts.

The Fauna

Extensive studies of the fauna of the southern side of the Bristol Channel have been made by Bassindale and others from the Department of Zoology of the University of Bristol. Their results have been published in a series of papers the more relevant of which are referred to below. On the northern side Rees (1939) studied the plankton and also the ecology of a mudflat (1940), while Purchon, who had earlier worked on the southern side, published in 1948 an account of the littoral and sub-littoral faunas of shores near Cardiff. In addition to this published material a considerable number of records and other data have been accumulated in the Zoology Department at University College, Cardiff, and altogether a fair body of information is available. It would be neither desirable nor possible, in the space available, to give fauna lists, which would make tedious reading in a general survey of this nature. Instead, the faunas of the various habitats will be discussed in relation to the physical factors already outlined.

It is convenient to start with the plankton, since this constitutes the early links in the major food chain of the community. The detailed study of the plankton of Cardiff Roads, carried out by Rees (1939) showed a marked poverty of both phyto- and zoo-plankton. Twenty-four species of diatoms were identified and it is interesting to note that all except one estuarine species were typically marine forms, including the four species *Biddulphia sinensis*, *B. regia*, *Rhizosolenia setigera* and *Bacillaria paradoxa*, which made up the bulk of the tow-net catches. The numbers involved, however, were very low; the maximum number of diatom chains observed in a 20 cc. sample of water was seventy-two, while counts of over 10,000 are not infrequent elsewhere. Other phyto-planktonic organisms were also very sparsely represented.

The main reason for the paucity of phyto-plankton is undoubtedly the opacity of the water which restricts photo-synthetic activity to a very thin surface layer.

Were it not for this, the presence of sewage pollution with the associated levels of phosphate and other salts might be expected to give rise to a very rich phyto-plankton. The reduced salinity might, of course, play a part, but, as Rees points out, this is more likely to restrict the number of species present than the density reached.

The poverty of the phyto-plankton is reflected in the zoo-plankton which depends upon it for its food supply. Rees found only five species of pelagic copepods in significant numbers and not one of these was really numerous. He did, however, record a fair number of animals which appeared in his tow-nets in smaller numbers from time to time. Some of these were essentially bottom forms which often appear with the plankton in shallow turbulent waters, but the others included several species of mysid, the small ctenophore *Pleurobrachia pilosa*, the arrow-worm *Sagitta setosa*, and, fairly commonly during the summer, *Oikopleura dioica*. Larval forms were moderately numerous and were mainly crustacean, molluscan, and annelid, but on one occasion echinoplutei and post-larval asteroids were present. This is interesting in connection with the distribution of echinoderms which will be discussed later.

Again, reduced salinity may play a part in restricting the number of species present in the zoo-plankton and the feeding of some forms may be directly affected by the large amounts of suspended silt. The all-round poverty of the plankton, however, is no doubt due to the indirect effect of silt in making the water opaque and thus restricting the all-important photo-synthetic activity of the phyto-plankton.

Bassindale (1943 and 1955) showed that on the southern side the inter-tidal fauna, which is extensive at Ilfracombe, becomes progressively depleted as one passes upstream. The same is true on the northern shores; the littoral fauna of the Gower is rich and varied, but eastwards from Swansea the number of species becomes progressively reduced. In spite of this, some groups are still moderately well represented on the stretch of coast, which can be taken as representative of the middle reaches of the channel, between Nash and Lavernock Points. Some forty-three species of Crustacea have been recorded here, including the common crab, prawns, hoppers and slaters, but only one species of squat-lobster (*Galathea squamifera*). All the usual inter-tidal acorn barnacles are present including *Elminius modestus* which is thought to have been introduced into British waters from New Zealand. Not all the crustacean records, however, are of common species; in 1951 a single specimen of *Axius stirhynchus* Leach, one of the rarer British decapods, was found near Lavernock.

The polychaetes, although relatively numerous with thirty-eight species recorded, call for little special comment except in the case of *Sabellaria alveolata* which is very common here. In many places reef-like masses of the sandy tubes of this worm are exposed by low tides and it is also widely distributed in the sub-littoral. Perhaps mention might also be made of the particularly handsome specimens of *Nereis virens* which are to be found in mud among the boulders of the Lavernock area. Two species of the gephyrean *Golfingia* (= *Phascolosoma*), *G. elongata* and *G. minuta* have been found and seem to be not uncommon.

Gastropods predominate among the thirty-one recorded species of molluscs and include the four periwinkles, limpets, whelks, dog whelks and the usual top shells; a number of nudibranchs are also present, but these are less common. Among the lamellibranchs there are several rock-borers and mud-dwellers as well as the familiar cockles, mussels and oysters. There used to be commercial oyster beds in Swansea Bay, and very occasionally single specimens are found as far up-channel as Barry.

The inter-tidal fauna in this area also includes a fair number of polyzoans, a few of the commoner shore fishes, several nemertine worms and the turbellarian *Leptoplana tremellaris*. The coelenterates are represented by several hydroids, including *Tubularia indivisa*, and a small number of sea anemones, *Actinia equina* being much the commonest. Sponges are not numerous and ascidians almost absent, but the distribution of echinoderms is particularly interesting. Holothurians and crinoids seem to be very sensitive to estuarine conditions and none have been recorded east of Swansea. Echinoids may be slightly less sensitive; sand urchins are common on the Gower, but the only recorded sea urchins east of Swansea are a single *Psammechinus miliaris* from the sub-littoral off Breaksea Point and the echinoplutei found by Rees in the plankton (see earlier). The ophiuroids are also represented here by a single species, *Amphipholis squamata*, which occurs very sparsely as far up-channel as Breaksea Point, but has not been found further east. Asteroids fare a little better, two colourful species, *Solaster papposus* and *Henricia sanguinolenta*, being not uncommon at Llantwit Major and occasionally found as far up-channel as Barry.

Although the shore fauna falls off progressively all the way up-channel, there seems to be a particularly big drop as one passes east of Cardiff. Purchon (1948) has pointed out that lack of suitable substrates may, in addition to the more estuarine conditions, play a part in this. Certainly the inter-tidal fauna is very poor; the total number of species recorded from the mud-flats at Peterstone Wentloog, for instance, is only just over forty (compared with over 160 in the middle reaches), although this does not include some incompletely identified elements of the micro-fauna which Rees (1940) found to be quite abundant in the mud there. The dominant macrofaunal species of these upper estuary mud-flats seem to be the polychaete *Nereis diversicolor*, the amphipod *Corophium volutator*, the gastropod *Hydrobia ulvae* and the bivalve *Macoma balthica*. Shore crabs and common shrimps are also quite numerous.

The saltings on the landward side of the mud-flats consist of level areas several feet higher than the top of the mud beaches and covered with short grass. Numerous shallow pools are present, and these are replenished with salt water by a few of the very highest tides each year. Conditions of salinity, temperature and oxygen tension undergo very great fluctuations in these tide pools, but even so they are not devoid of animals. Many contain *Nereis diversicolor*, sphaeromids, and the prawn *Palaemonetes varians*, a species which also occurs on the other side of the sea wall in fresh water drainage reens (Lofts, 1956). The brackish water nudibranch *Limapontia depressa* has also been found in one tide pool.

Purchon (1948) made a number of dredge and trawl hauls in that part of the Bristol Channel from Stout Point to Newport and found the sub-littoral fauna to be an impoverished one. *Sabellaria* reef is present over considerable areas of the bottom, but the most widely distributed animals are common shrimps, the prawn *Pandalus montagui*, and the strange 'glass shrimp' *Pasiphae sivado*. This is laterally compressed and remarkably transparent; elsewhere it is usually confined to deep water, but is very numerous in the Bristol Channel and is taken in considerable numbers in the shrimp 'putts' and 'hose' nets of the southern shores. Squids (*Sepia*), although not often seen, must be quite numerous in the channel to judge by the number of 'cuttle fish' shells washed up; viable eggs have been found at low-water mark at Llantwit Major and Barry.

The list of marine fishes recorded in the Bristol Channel is surprisingly long (see Lloyd, 1941), but commercial fishing has practically ceased apart from some winter netting of sprats at Weston. A number of migratory fish pass up and down the estuary; the Severn, Wye and Usk are famous salmon rivers, and these fish are caught during the summer in special wicker traps or 'putchers' as they move up towards the rivers. In the spring fantastic numbers of elvers pass up the estuary and provide a considerable fishery in the Severn; some are sold for food and others exported alive for restocking rivers on the continent and elsewhere. Although not now of any commercial significance, a few Allis and Twait shad still run up the Severn, and in most years two or three sturgeon are taken in the upper reaches of the estuary.

There is a surprising number of records of marine mammals, especially cetaceans, from the Bristol Channel, but these have been reviewed by Harrison Matthews (1941) and only a few need be mentioned here. The common porpoise is fairly often seen in the channel and the remains of these animals are washed up from time to time; occasionally they penetrate right into the Severn. The bottle-nosed dolphin has been found on a number of occasions in the upper part of the channel, including the Cardiff area, but the common dolphin has not been recorded nearer than the Gower. Several species of rorqual have been stranded well up the estuary, including a lesser rorqual at Cardiff and Rudolphi's rorqual beyond Newport.

The seals of the Bristol Channel are extremely interesting; in addition to some very infrequent visitors, both the grey and common seals are present. The former is the usual seal of the west coasts and although it does not breed in the estuary, individuals often enter it. Most of those formerly recorded from the Bristol Channel as 'common seals' were undoubtedly grey seals (see Salmon, 1935), but there now seems to be no doubt that a small breeding colony of true common seals has, within the last forty years, become established in the estuary near Chepstow.

The Bristol Channel, being funnel-shaped, facing south-west and having strong tidal currents, tends to act as a trap for drifting forms which may be brought to the south-western approaches by the Gulf Stream and the prevailing wind. In this way a number of quite exotic forms are brought into the channel, particularly to its Welsh shores. The portuguese man-of-war has appeared in several years, and *Velella*

[*Photo:* J. G. C. Anderson

Plate XIII.—Anticline in Carboniferous Limestone, roadside ¼ mile east of Chepstow.

Plate XIV.—Triassic conglomerate, sandstone and marl unconformable on steeply dipping Carboniferous Limestone. South-east corner of Sully Island.

[*Photo:* J. G. C. Anderson

[*Photo:* D. Hunt

Plate XV.—A Breconshire cave (Ogof Ffynnon Ddu) showing flowstone column and pool.

is sometimes cast up in considerable numbers. The buoy barnacle, *Lepas fascicularis*, has appeared in great numbers twice since the war (Jefferson, 1955), and although such forms are more frequently stranded in the lower channel, the three mentioned have all been seen in the middle reaches. Exotic fishes also occasionally make their way into the channel, an interesting example being the occurrence in 1946 of a trigger-fish (*Balistes capriscus*) of which probably not more than a dozen authentic specimens are known from British waters. It was caught at the Splott tidefields, Cardiff, and is now in the National Museum of Wales.

Conclusions

The occasional influx of exotic or migrating forms and the presence of unusual animals like the glass shrimp should not be allowed to obscure the essential poverty of the estuarine fauna as a whole. Reduced and varying salinities are no doubt the main agents restricting the number of species present, but the large amount of silt kept in suspension by the fierce tides is also an important factor. Purchon (1937) found that a number of species, including the jelly fish *Aurelia aurita* and some ciliary feeding forms such as bivalves and even ascidians, could live in the dock at Portishead, but not in the estuary outside it. The physical conditions of the dock water, including its rather low and variable salinity, were very similar to those of the estuary except for the absence of suspended silt in the much calmer water. Experiments with bivalves from the dock confirmed that they could not survive in water heavily charged with silt.

Perhaps even more important than the direct effect of silt in restricting the number of species is its indirect effect on the 'ecological productivity' of the estuary. This results from the extreme turbidity of the water which drastically cuts down light penetration and restricts photo-synthetic activity to a thin surface layer. The resulting poverty of the phyto-plankton is reflected throughout the complex food nexus of the whole estuarine community.

LAND VERTEBRATES

The mammalian fauna of the district is of interest as including three species absent or uncommon elsewhere in the country. The polecat, *Mustela putorius*, was once abundant in most parts of Great Britain. The first specimen ever exhibited in the London 'Zoo' was caught in Regent's Park in a trap in 1828, and in Scotland it was so abundant that in the early 1830's from five to six hundreds pelts annually were offered for sale at the Dumfries fur fair. So far as can be ascertained, the animal has been extinct in Scotland for about the past forty years, and there are very few reliable records in England in recent times. But over a considerable area of central Wales, including Breconshire, there is a well-established polecat population, with smaller numbers in some of the adjoining counties. It has been found in Glamorgan, for example at Ynys-y-bwl, north of Pontypridd, near a reservoir on the outskirts of Cardiff and elsewhere. Polecats appear to have increased in numbers during the past half century, an important factor in this being probably the decrease in game-preserving dating from the first world war.

Many polecats carry numerous specimens of the parasitic tick *Ixodes hexagonus*, and among internal parasites may be mentioned the nematode *Molineus patens* (Dujardin, 1845), several of which were identified from the intestine of a polecat from Monmouthshire in 1951. This species had not previously been recorded from polecats in Britain, though it was known from stoat and weasel.

The pine marten is, and has long been, much rarer in Wales than the polecat, and it is an unexplained fact that it still occurs in parts of Scotland while the polecat appears to be quite extinct there. Although found in Wales principally in the north, it has reappeared in south Breconshire in recent years, and there is some reason for thinking that the pine marten has been seen recently in Glamorgan, where the last previously-known specimen was killed in 1910. The extensive coniferous plantations established by the Forestry Commission may be a factor aiding the spread of this very rare and beautiful mammal in the type of habitat from which it derives its name.

On account of its considerable coastline with important seaports, the area includes in its mammalian fauna another species rare in most parts of Britain, the so-called black or ship rat, *Rattus rattus*. In Cardiff, at least, the species apparently persists and breeds in small numbers with little or no recruitment from ships. A survey made between 1928 and 1938 (Matheson, 1939) showed that the black rat was established in premises of various types up to one-half or three-quarters of a mile from the docks. Over 560 were killed in 1940, including a considerable proportion of young ones. The melanic form *Rattus rattus rattus* was the commonest, but the two forms *R .r. frugivorus* and *R. r. alexandrinus* also occurred. A more recent survey by Hill (see Matheson, 1958) indicated that, almost two decades later, the geographical distribution of the species within the city was, except for its disappearance from two small locations, practically the same. During and since the last war some black rats have been discovered in warehouses in several towns far inland, from which they had long been absent, particularly towns linked to the ports by inland waterways, although road-carriage of goods may also have played a part. In Glamorgan a few black rats were reported from the Treforest Trading Estate, some miles inland from Cardiff, in 1945. The intensive measures now being adopted against both species of rats make it unlikely that the black rat will ever become re-established to any great extent.

The otter is still widely distributed, particularly perhaps in Breconshire, and until fairly recently was even found occasionally near the lake in Roath Park, Cardiff, and in the grounds of Cardiff Castle. An otter caught in 1952 near the feeder in the Castle grounds had its bile duct infested with *Pseudomphistomum truncatum* (Rud. 1819), a trematode which had been recorded from a wide variety of carnivores, but only once before from the otter (in France) and apparently never previously in this country. Badgers and foxes are common throughout the area and have even been seen in urban districts.

Although the American or grey squirrel had spread into Monmouthshire by 1937, and by the end of that year had got as far west as Llanover on the Usk, it was not until towards the end of the last war that it began to establish itself in Glamorgan

or Breconshire. It is true that a few were turned down in the public park at Aberdare in Glamorgan as far back as 1922, but this colony was never very flourishing, and the establishment of the animal in South Wales appears to have been due mainly to its natural spread westward from the English border counties. By the end of the 1940's it was widely distributed in both Glamorgan and Breconshire. The indigenous red squirrel still occurs in both counties, for example near Bridgend in Glamorgan and Ystradfellte in Breconshire, but in decreasing numbers. Most of the small field rodents occur in their usual numbers, but there is no record within the area of the yellow-necked mouse, *Apodemus flavicollis wintoni*, although it occurs just beyond it in limited parts of Breconshire and Herefordshire. Nor is there any record of the harvest mouse.

Deer were once numerous, as is shown by fine red deer skulls excavated from the docks at Cardiff, Newport and elsewhere. At the present day, however, only a few fallow deer occur in limited areas of Monmouthshire and Glamorgan, all of them being recent park escapes or their descendants.

The bird fauna of the area is rich and varied and has been extensively studied by local ornithologists, particularly H. Morrey Salmon and G. C. S. Ingram (see *County History*, vol. I). On the diverse habitats of the coastal region may be seen on occasion, in the autumn and winter, large or small flocks of dunlin, knot, snipe, curlew and other waders, as well as white-fronted geese and several species of duck, although industrial developments are gradually reducing their numbers. The freshwater pool at Kenfig, with its surrounding sand-dunes, is a well-known bird haunt. Among the winter visitors here are Bewick's and whooper swans. Inland in the Vale of Glamorgan a wide variety of bird life is present. In the woods at Dinas Powis, near Cardiff, the visitor may see a range of species from the kestrel and the buzzard, among the birds of prey, to the nuthatch (a recent colonist of the Vale and spreading as a breeding species in the area), the green and the lesser spotted woodpeckers, lesser whitethroat, and various tits and finches; while on an adjacent pool may be swimming the mute swan and a party of moorhens. The crossbill may be seen occasionally and here, too, on a summer evening may be heard the nightingale, which in east Glamorgan is at the extremity of its western range.

Glamorgan and Breconshire also mark the approximate western limit of the breeding range of one or two other species, such as the reed warbler and the lesser whitethroat. The reed warbler as a breeding bird is well distributed over south-east and central England, but in northern and western England and in Wales it breeds only in a few isolated localities. Llangorse Lake is noted as one of the most westerly breeding places, Breconshire being one of four Welsh counties where it breeds regularly. This lake is also notable as having the oldest established breeding colony in Wales of the great crested grebe, dating back for eighty years or more. The breeding density of the species is greatest across central England and thins out towards the west and north. The extensive reed beds are among the features of the lake which make it an admirable habitat for both these species. The pied flycatcher, a bird of scattered distribution, although found breeding regularly over much of Wales, was until recently only a bird of passage in Glamorgan, and had not been

recorded as a breeding species until within the past ten years. There are only two heronries surviving in Glamorgan (one of them at Hensol near Cardiff), but the species is rather more numerous in Monmouthshire where in 1954 there were three, and in Breconshire where there were five, heronries. The total number of breeding pairs in Breconshire was estimated at approximately sixty-one, higher than for any other county in South Wales except Carmarthenshire (Burton, 1956). The little owl appeared in Monmouthshire and Glamorgan considerably earlier than in other parts of Wales, having bred for the first time in Monmouthshire in 1914 and in Glamorgan in 1916.

Typical of the highland region in the north of the area are the raven (which has also nested in trees near Cardiff), the ring ouzel and the red grouse, which here probably occupies its most southern natural habitat in Great Britain, although not many remain. At the western end of this highland region, in south-west Breconshire, lie the cliffs of Craig Cerrig Gleisiad, haunt of buzzard, raven and peregrine and recently declared a National Nature Reserve.

The reptiles found in the area are the grass-snake, the adder, the common lizard and the slow-worm, all common enough in suitable localities. It is perhaps to be expected that the largest British examples of these poikilothermic vertebrates should occur in the south, and it may not be without significance that some of the largest recorded in Britain have been from Glamorgan. They include a grass-snake of 5 feet 9 inches in length, a male adder of 23 inches, and a male common lizard of almost 7 inches.

The three species of newts found in this country—the warty (*Triturus cristatus*), the smooth (*T. vulgaris*) and the palmate (*T. helveticus*)—have all been recorded from Glamorgan; and the last two (but not yet the warty newt) from the counties of Brecon and Monmouth also.

FRESHWATER FISHES

The distribution of freshwater fishes in the British Isles is curious and significant. It is an impoverished fauna in comparison with that of the fresh waters immediately across the English Channel and the North Sea. This impoverishment is more marked in some areas than in others, although the decrease is not altogether sporadic. The maximum number of species of true freshwater fishes in Britain is found in the south-eastern counties of England, and from there there is a more or less steady decrease to west and north. This is linked up with the relatively brief and irregular land connection between Britain and the Continent since the retreat of the glaciers at the close of the great Pleistocene glaciation. Less than a dozen indigenous and truly freshwater species are listed for the County in the *Glamorgan County History* (excluding migratory and partially marine species). This compares with the maximum number in eastern England of twenty-two species.

As we pass eastward from Glamorgan there is a not unexpected increase. Chub and dace which are absent from Glamorgan are very numerous in the Wye, and dace also occur in the Usk. In the Severn the freshwater fish fauna is again more numerous and varied and includes the bream, barbel, bleak and ruffe, which do

not occur further west. Perhaps the most remarkable record with regard to freshwater fishes is that of the occurrence of the burbot in the upper reaches of the Severn estuary, where three were taken in kypes in 1938 (Lloyd, 1938). This is, to say the least, unexpected, since this fish, the only freshwater member of the cod family, is otherwise restricted to a few river systems in the east of England.

In dealing with these freshwater fishes there is always the chance that man has interfered with the natural distribution, and it is sometimes not easy to be sure how far certain species are indigenous. For example, the grayling, which apparently is an indigenous species in Monmouthshire, seems to have been introduced into Glamorgan fairly recently.

LAND AND FRESHWATER INVERTEBRATES

Some thousands of species of land and freshwater invertebrates occur in the region and detailed lists are available in the works given in the Bibliography, and particularly in the *Glamorgan County History*. We shall concern ourselves here with accounts of a few notable occurrences and features of special local interest.

Entomologically, the sand dunes along parts of the Glamorgan coast are of great interest. They have long attracted collectors, notably in recent times the late H. M. Hallett, whose work has yielded many rare species. A number of our scarcer bees and wasps are characteristically inhabitants of sand dunes, and from the Glamorgan dunes have been recorded, for example, *Coelioxys mandibularis* (noted also from similar habitats in Cheshire and Lancashire) and *Stelis ornatula*. *Mimesa bruxellensis*, *M. celtica* and *Oxybelus argentatus* are others that may be mentioned out of many interesting species. The Diptera are also well represented, including rare species of the genera *Trypeta* and *Pamponerus*, and many of the scarcer Coleoptera also occur on the dunes. At the seaward edge of the dunes, almost on the beach itself, a striking beetle, *Eurynebria complanata* (L.) occurs fairly commonly. This carabid is interesting not only because it seems to be virtually confined to the coasts of the Bristol Channel, but because most of its cuticle is of an unusual creamy-white colour.

Other interesting insects, apart from the sand dune fauna, include the conformist moth, *Graptolitha furcifera*, which was first recorded as British on the basis of specimens taken in 1859 at Llantrisant, near Cardiff. Later the species was taken also at Port Talbot by H W. Vivian (whose extensive collection of British Lepidoptera is in the National Museum of Wales), and it has subsequently been found from time to time in Glamorgan and Monmouthshire. Stray specimens (some of them apparently casual immigrants from the Continent) have been noted in counties as far apart as Yorkshire and Kent, yet South Wales, in the words of Richard South, 'appears to be the home of this species in the British Isles'. This anomalous isolated distribution in south-west Britain, and the fact that the continental representatives are slightly different and classified as a distinct subspecies, lend support to the suggestion that it is a relic of considerable antiquity. Somewhat similar may be the case of the wood white butterfly, *Leptidea sinapis*, distributed rather locally over southern England westward to Devon and the

South Wales border area and represented by a separate subspecies in southern Ireland. Species like the white-letter hairstreak, *Strymonidea w-album*, which has a fairly continuous distribution over south-eastern England and the Midlands westward to Glamorgan, and is apparently still spreading in Wales, have been interpreted as more recent arrivals.

The comma butterfly, *Polygonia c-album*, once apparently common over much of England and Wales, was by the early years of this century practically unknown except in one area of the south-west, including the counties of Monmouth, Hereford and Gloucester. Within the past forty years, however, besides becoming much more numerous in these counties, it has extended its range so far across South Wales and elsewhere that in 1951 it was described as 'quite common' in Carmarthenshire, where in 1905 Barker could only say that he had seen one 'some years ago', and had heard of others. The *Glamorgan County History* (1936) states that the lime hawk-moth, *Dilina tiliae*, had been looked for in vain and that the only record for the county was of larvae at Merthyr Mawr. The imago has been found several times since then in the Cardiff district and elsewhere.

The scarabaeid beetle, *Trichius fasciatus*, has a curious distribution in Britain, being apparently absent from England, but present in both Scotland and Wales. This handsome beetle is quite rare even where it does occur, but several have been recorded in the area, even within the city boundary of Cardiff.

Of the many species of leeches occurring in the area, one is worthy of special mention. This is the terrestrial form *Trocheta subviridis* which lives in clay soil and can frequently be seen on the pavements in Cardiff and Penarth after heavy rain. The occurrence of the freshwater nemertine *Stichostoma graecense* is also noteworthy, its occurrence being rare and sporadic in Britain. An introduced, probably South American, form which is very rare in natural conditions in this country is the freshwater medusa *Craspedacusta sowerbii*. In 1933 it was found in large numbers in a pit feeder near Tredegar, Monmouthshire, and it has since appeared (1959) in a small lake at Ferndale in the Rhondda Fach.

The parasites of freshwater and terrestrial organisms have formed a subject of study for local zoologists for many years, and some interesting observations have been made. The tapeworm *Diphyllobothrium* has been noted from time to time, and has attracted attention because of its troublesome plerocercoid stage, which is found in the trout. There was a major outbreak in 1943–4 in the Cardiff district (Duguid and Sheppard, 1944) and it has been reported since, particularly in 1959, from the same source.

The freshwater fauna of Glamorgan is abundant and varied and in association with this there have been described a large number of trematode larval stages (Cercariae, Tetracotyle and Diplostomulum) parasitic in the snails, leeches and fish of the region.

The first record of cercariae from snails in Glamorgan was by Matheson (1930) who discovered *Cercaria pseudocellata* in the artificial lake at Roath Park, Cardiff, after reports from bathers of cercarial dermatitis. In 1932, F. G. Rees, in a general survey of Glamorgan, recorded ten cercarial species (four of them new) of which

three were again present in Roath Park Lake. A notable addition was made by Llewelyn (1957) who described a further twenty-two species from Glamorgan. These included twelve new species and six new records for Great Britain. Twelve of these twenty-two species occurred in Roath Park Lake, Cardiff. Erasmus (1959) described another new cercaria from this lake. Thus, of the fifty-six cercarial species which have been recorded from British freshwaters, twenty-nine occur in Glamorgan and sixteen of these are present in Roath Park Lake. Two of these Roath Park species have persisted over a period of thirty years (Erasmus, 1954).

As a result of this abundant cercarial fauna the fish in Roath Park Lake are heavily infected with *Diplostomulum* and *Holostephanus* metacercariae (Erasmus, 1958, 1959) and with *Phyllodistomum folium* which has not been previously recorded from Glamorgan. Life-history studies on this Roath Park material (Llewelyn, 1957; Griggs, 1959; Erasmus, 1958, 1959) have resulted in the collection of three adult trematode genera (*Apatemon*, *Cyathocotyle* and *Holostephanus*) previously not recorded from Great Britain.

Recent work on the parasitic fauna of earthworms in the Cardiff district has resulted in the description of sixteen new species of gregarines and two new species of ciliates, and also the recording of the occurrence of *Albertia vermicularis*, a very rare parasitic rotifer (B. Rees, 1959). Among investigations on parasitic insects may be mentioned a survey made over the period 1926–38 of the fleas found on black and brown rats on dock premises in Cardiff (Matheson, 1942). This indicated that in the earlier years a considerable proportion (about one-fifth) were plague fleas, *Xenopsylla cheopis*, but that by 1938 the numbers had been greatly reduced, this being possibly associated with increased anti-rodent measures on shipping.

THE FAUNA OF CAVES AND MINES

South Wales has, during the past fifteen years, been the scene of very active cave exploration, in the course of which the biological aspects have not been neglected. Although British caves cannot boast of blind fish and salamanders, many do contain animals which, if not very impressive in appearance, are nevertheless of considerable interest; this is particularly true of caves in South Wales.

The majority of animals found in local caves, as in those of other regions, are not confined to an underground habitat. Such animals are of relatively little interest in the present context, and the only ones that will be mentioned are the greater and lesser horseshoe bats which roost in the caves, and the very occasional white fish, probably blanched trout, seen in subterranean streams. True underground animals, specially adapted to the habitat, do, however, occur in the area, the most interesting being the blind white cave crustacea. *Asellus cavaticus*, a small aquatic isopod, and a well shrimp, *Niphargus fontanus* (Amphipoda), are to be found, usually in rimstone pools, in several of the caves, while the extremely rare *Crangonyx subterraneus* has been found (Hazelton and Glennie, 1953) in a cave in the upper Tawe valley. This amphipod had previously been recorded only twice in Britain, over a century ago, from deep wells.

Little is known of the ecology of cavernicolous crustaceans. *Niphargus* seems to be largely carnivorous and has been seen to eat *Asellus* which in its turn can feed

upon a curious 'water fungus' which occurs in underground pools. Whether these are the main sources of food of the respective animals, and whether this represents part of a regular food chain is, however, not certain. In fact the initial source of energy available to the whole cave community is not fully understood. Animals in general are dependent ultimately on the sun's energy absorbed by green plants, and the cave community is presumably based on organic matter carried in by streams or floods, or as bat droppings. There is, however, a slight element of doubt as to whether this is a complete explanation. *Asellus* is sometimes found, apparently feeding on 'water fungus', in small pools well above flood level and containing only percolating water. Organic matter may, nevertheless, reach such pools in the form of spores and pollen grains carried into the cave by air currents, but there is also the possibility that chemoautotrophic bacteria, which are present in caves (see Mason-Williams and Benson-Evans, 1958) may make a separate contribution of energy. A further possibility, suggested by recent discoveries in other fields, is that percolating water may itself carry traces of dissolved organic matter into the cave.

Whatever may be the position in caves, there can be no doubt about the initial source of energy for those animals which have colonized the deep coal mines of the area; large quantities of organic matter are taken underground particularly as pit timber and as food, both for ponies and men. Fungi grow on pit props, and in many parts of most mines there is an abundance of decomposing organic matter such as rotting wood, spilt chaff and faecal material; the earthy debris on the floors of disused headings and roadways is often particularly rich.

In addition to the inevitable rodents, a surprising number of invertebrates are to be found in most pits. Some of these are wood-borers or stored-products pests associated with the pony fodder, but quite a number are forms which, although introduced fortuitously, sometimes on foreign timber, have taken advantage of the warm damp conditions and colonized the pit. The rich soil-like material usually contains vast numbers of small springtails, including a blind species, *Sinella coeca*, and several species of annelid worms. Woodlice, particularly *Androniscus dentiger*, are often present, and in one pit a small thysanuran insect is quite numerous. This belongs to the genus *Nicoletia*, hitherto unrecorded in Britain, and is particularly interesting in that only parthenogenetically reproducing females are present.

A larger scavenger, very common in many mines, is the 'American' cockroach *Periplaneta americana*, and in one pit a white-eyed mutant form of this is present (Jefferson, 1958) forming about 5 per cent of the population. Where cockroaches are absent, their scavenging duties are often undertaken by beetles such as *Blaps* or *Harpalus*.

The numerous small scavenging and fungus-eating forms are preyed upon by a variety of predators. These are mostly centipedes and spiders; the ordinary house spider is the commonest, but others are present and the very rare species *Zelotes rusticus* has been found in two pits. Occasionally fungus gnats appear in the workings in sufficient numbers to be a nuisance, but, on the whole, the presence of a rich invertebrate fauna in a pit seems to cause little trouble and its scavenging activities may even be useful.

REFERENCES

Bassindale, R., 1941. 'Studies on the biology of the Bristol Channel, IV. The invertebrate fauna of the southern shores of the Bristol Channel and Severn Estuary', *Proc. Bristol Nat. Soc.* (4), IX, pp. 143–201.

——, 1943. 'Studies on the biology of the Bristol Channel, XI. The physical environment and intertidal fauna of the southern shores of the Bristol Channel and Severn Estuary', *J. Ecol.*, XXXI, pp. 1–29.

——, 1955. 'Fauna', in *Bristol and its adjoining Counties* (British Association, Bristol).

Burton, J. F., 1956. 'Report on the national census of heronries, 1954', *Bird Study*, vol. 3, pp. 42–73.

Duguid, J. B., and Sheppard, Edith M., 1944. '*Diphylobothrium* epidemic in trout', *J. Path. and Bact.*, vol. 56, p. 73.

Erasmus, D. A., 1954. Ph.D. Thesis in University College, Cardiff. 'Studies on the morphology, physiology and life histories of certain parasitic Platyhelminthes.'

——, 1958. 'Studies on the morphology, biology and development of a Strigeid Cercaria (*Cercaria X* Baylis 1930)', *Parasitology*, vol. 48, pp. 312–35.

——, 1959. 'The migration of *Cercaria X* Baylis (Strigeida) within the fish intermediate host', *Parasitology*, vol. 49, pp. 173–90.

Glamorgan County History, vol. 1. *Natural History* 1936 (ed. W. M. Tattersall, Cardiff).

Griggs, Ann E., 1959. (Unpublished.)

Hazelton, M., and Glennie, E. A., 1953. 'Cave fauna and flora' in *British Caving* (ed. Cullingford, London).

Jefferson, G. T., 1955. 'A note on some tropical or subtropical barnacles and other animals from the Bristol Channel', *Trans. Cardiff Nat. Soc.*, LXXXII, pp. 32–5.

——, 1958. 'A white-eyed mutant form of the American cockroach *Periplaneta americana* (L.)', *Nature*, 182, p. 892.

Llewelyn, C., 1957. Ph.D. Thesis in University College, Cardiff.

Lloyd, A. J., 1938. 'Occurrence of burbot in the estuary of the River Severn', *Nature*, 142, p. 1118.

——, 1941. 'Studies on the biology of the Bristol Channel, V. The marine fish fauna of the southern shores of the Bristol Channel', *Proc. Bristol Nat. Soc.* (4), IX, pp. 202–30.

Lofts, B., 1956. 'Notes on the distribution of the prawn *Palaemonetes varians* (Leach) in a typical area of salt marsh', *Ann. Mag. Nat. Hist.* (12), IX, pp. 521–5.

Mason-Williams, A., and Benson-Evans, K., 1958. 'A preliminary investigation into the bacterial and botanical flora of caves in South Wales.' Publication no. 8, Cave Research Group of Great Britain.

Matheson, C., 1930. 'Notes on *Cercaria elvae* Miller as the probable cause of an outbreak of dermatitis in Cardiff', *Trans. Roy. Soc. Trop. Med. and Hygiene*, vol. 23, pp. 421–4.

——, 1939. 'A survey of the status of *Rattus rattus* and its subspecies in the seaports of Great Britain and Ireland', *J. Animal Ecol.*, vol. 8, pp. 76–93.

——, 1942. 'Some animals and public health', *J. Royal Sanitary Institute*, vol. 62, pp. 128–35.

——, 1958. 'The black rat at British seaports', *Pest Technology*, vol. 1, pp. 4–7.

Matthews, L. H., 1941. 'Studies on the biology of the Bristol Channel, VI. The marine mammals of the Bristol Channel', *Proc. Bristol Nat. Soc.* (4), IX, pp. 231–50.

Purchon, R. D., 1937. 'Studies on the biology of the Bristol Channel, II. An ecological study of the beach and the dock at Portishead', *Proc. Bristol Nat. Soc.* (4), VIII, pp. 311–29.

——, 1948. 'Studies on the biology of the Bristol Channel, XVII. The littoral and sublittoral fauna of the northern shores, near Cardiff', *Proc. Bristol Nat. Soc.*, XXVII, pp. 285–310.

Rees, B., 1959. Ph.D. Thesis in University College, Cardiff.

Rees, C. B., 1939. 'The plankton in the upper reaches of the Bristol Channel', *J. Mar. Biol. Ass.*, XXIII, pp. 397–425.

——, 1940. 'A preliminary study of the ecology of a mud-flat', *J. Mar. Biol. Ass.*, XXIV, pp. 185–99.

Rees, Gwendolen, 1932. 'An investigation into the occurrence, structure and life-histories of the trematode parasites of four species of *Lymnaea* and *Hydrobia jenkinsi* (Smith) in Glamorgan and Monmouth', *Proc. Zool. Soc. Lond.*, pp. 1–32.

Salmon, H. M., 1935. 'Seals on the west coast', *Trans. Cardiff Nat. Soc.*, LXVIII, pp. 13–36.

The more important papers and faunal lists which have appeared in the *Transactions* of the Cardiff Naturalists' Society and which supplement the bibliography published in the British Association Handbook for the Cardiff meeting in 1920 will be found on pp. 213–14.

V

ARCHAEOLOGY

PREHISTORY

R. J. C. Atkinson

THE distribution of prehistoric finds in the region (Figs. 13–15)[1] is clearly related to the topography. Physiographically the area lies athwart the boundary of the highland and lowland zones of Britain. In the north and west the high ground, rising in most parts well above the 1,000-foot contour, forms the south-eastern margin of the highland massif of central Wales. It is sharply dissected by river valleys draining south-eastwards, which provide easy routes for the penetration of settlement and trade from the coast, but restrict movement in an east—west direction. By contrast, the coastal plain forms a westward extension of the lowland zone of England, and presents few barriers to movement, either along the coast or across the Bristol Channel to the opposite shores of Gloucestershire and Somerset.

Evidence for pre-neolithic settlement in the region is scanty. The industries of the Lower Palaeolithic are represented by the solitary find of an Acheulean hand-axe of quartzite from Penylan, an eastern suburb of Cardiff; and those of the Upper Palaeolithic are restricted to King Arthur's Cave, near Ross-on-Wye. The same site has yielded, at a higher level, a microlithic assemblage assignable to the Mesolithic; but elsewhere this period is represented only by numerous microliths from the sand dunes of Merthyr Mawr Warren, south-west of Bridgend. It is probable, however, that many other sites have been lost through the extensive coastal submergence which is known to have occurred during and since Boreal times.

The first evidence of large-scale human penetration of the area is provided by the megalithic tombs (Fig. 13), which form two distinct groups, one inland, to the east and south-east of Brecon, and the other less compactly distributed in the Vale of Glamorgan. An isolated site at Heston Brake, south-west of Chepstow, contains a chamber in the form of a long narrow gallery, and may perhaps represent a direct link with the West French type of gallery grave (*allée couverte*). The remaining tombs in both groups are of the Severn–Cotswold type. In spite of their westerly position in relation to the main concentration of these tombs in England, it seems improbable that they represent direct colonization by sea from southern Brittany, where the prototypes of the transepted form of gallery grave have long been recognized. Neither group in the region contains an axial transepted gallery, of the type of West Kennet or Stoney Littleton, a feature generally regarded as early in the tomb sequence; while the cairns, like their Cotswold neighbours, are markedly

[1] The authors are much indebted to the Department of Archaeology, National Museum of Wales, for compiling the data shown on figs. 13–15.

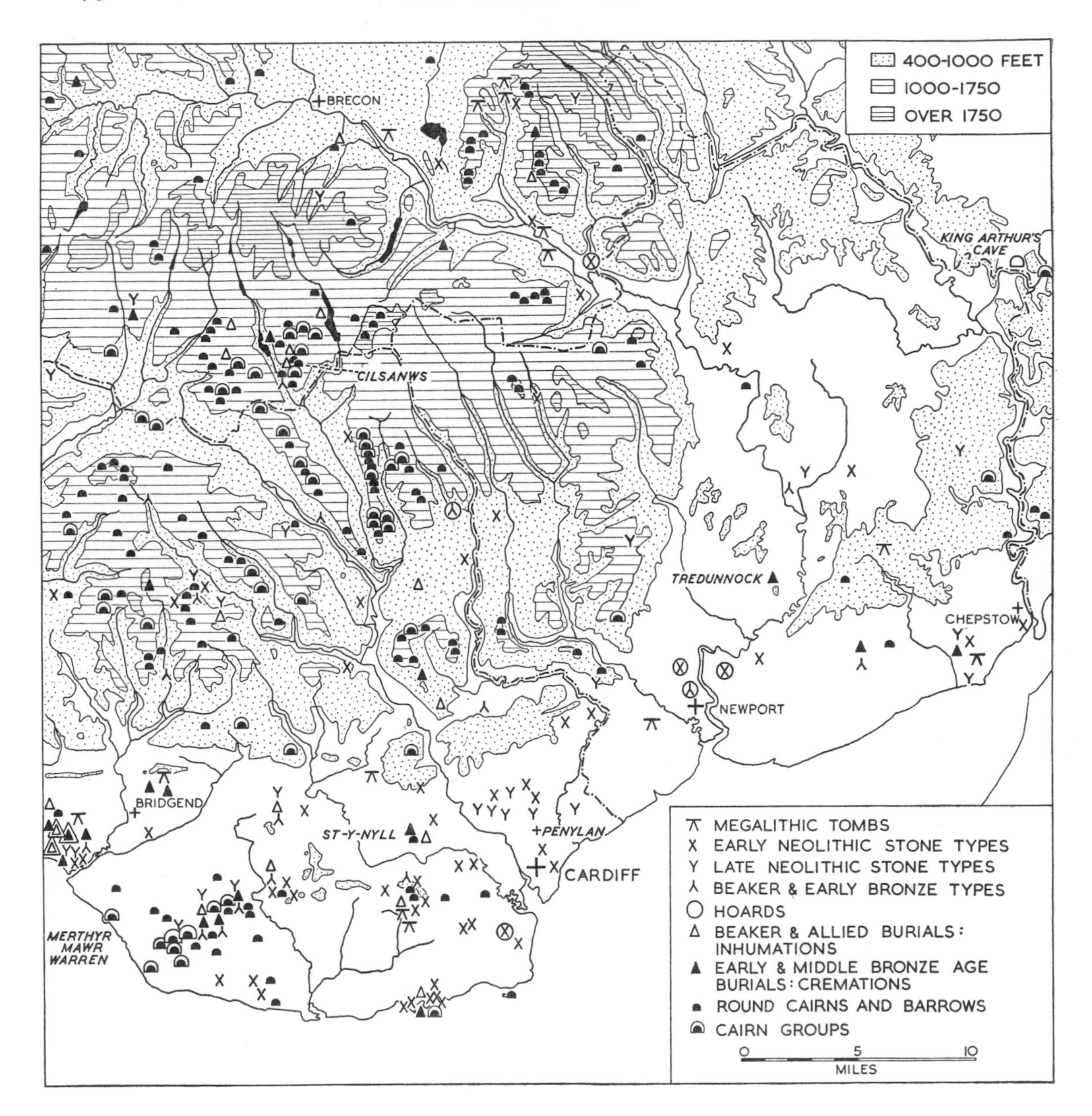

Fig. 13. Earlier Finds to 1000 B.C.

rectangular or trapezoid in plan, and cannot be paralleled in France. It is thus probable that both groups are the result of secondary colonizations of tomb-builders from across the Bristol Channel; and this is in some degree confirmed by the fragmentary pottery from two sites (Tinkinswood, west of Cardiff, and Ty Isaf in Brecknockshire), which suggests origins in the Windmill Hill culture of Wessex rather than further to the west and south.

Other evidence of Primary Neolithic activity is restricted to stray finds of stone axes and leaf-shaped flint arrowheads, the great majority coming from the coastal plain, though there are some signs of penetration up the valleys, particularly that of the Usk. The occurrence of small hoards of axes near Cardiff and Newport points, perhaps, to the existence of 'ports' there even at this early date. No settlement sites have yet been found, and it is thus not possible, in the present state of knowledge, to distinguish in the region any Primary Neolithic culture other than that of the chambered tombs.

Secondary Neolithic settlement has so far been recognized only at two sites, Cefn Cilsanws in southern Brecknockshire and Saint-y-Nyll near Cardiff. At both, small timber structures have been found, associated at the former with a sherd of Peterborough ware and at the latter, beneath a cairn covering a cremation, with pottery resembling the Fengate type. Otherwise the Secondary Neolithic cultures are represented only by a few stray finds of stone mace-heads and petit-tranchet-derivative arrowheads. This paucity of material may perhaps reflect the poor representation in the area of the Mesolithic cultures from which the Secondary Neolithic springs; though it must be remembered that many of the numerous stone axes in the district are likely to be the products of the Secondary Neolithic axe-factories located further to the west and north.

With the arrival of Beaker people, probably during the seventeenth century B.C., south-east Wales takes on a new importance. Over forty per cent of all beakers hitherto recorded from Wales have been found within the comparatively small area covered by Fig. 13. The main concentration lies in the Vale of Glamorgan and its immediate hinterland, especially on the sand dunes of Merthyr Mawr Warren. The isolated group on the southern foothills of the Brecon Beacons is presumably the result of a movement inland up the valley of the Taff.

All three of the principal varieties of beaker (Abercromby's types A, B and C) are represented, and in each case there can be little doubt that a secondary colonization from southern England is involved. In the absence of any beaker burials from Monmouthshire, such colonization is more likely to have been by sea, across the Bristol Channel; and it should be noted that the best parallels for the distinctive 'bar-chevron' ornament of many of the A beakers are to be found in Somerset.

This concentration of Beaker material must surely be related to the introduction of metal-working into Britain at this time, and the establishment along the south coast of Wales of a trade route between Ireland and the principal areas of Beaker settlement in southern England. It is against this background of economic

links between Wessex and the West that we must see the transport of the Stonehenge bluestones from Pembrokeshire.

The succeeding Early Bronze Age, of the sixteenth and fifteenth centuries B.C., is characterized in southern England by the burials of the rich Wessex Culture; and in view of the known dependence of this culture upon Irish metal resources (and for gold in particular), one might expect settlement and trade along the south Welsh coast to be intensive at this time. In fact, however, evidence for the penetration of the Wessex Culture into the region is surprisingly slight. Burials are confined to a single bell-barrow, at Crick in Monmouthshire, and to the well-known Breach Farm site near Cowbridge in the Vale of Glamorgan; otherwise the culture is represented by no more than three or four stray finds of bronzes, all from the southern part of the region.

The scarcity of this material must reflect some radical shift in the route connecting Ireland with southern England in the middle of the second millennium B.C.; and this is confirmed by the otherwise northerly distribution of objects and burials of Wessex type in Wales, a pattern apparently related to the use of the Severn valley route.

There is, however, no lack of evidence for a numerous population in the region in the latter half of the second millenium, as is shown by the dense concentration of barrows and cairns. Their distribution, whether of groups or of single monuments, shows a very marked preference for high ground, apart from a compact group in the western part of the Vale of Glamorgan, which includes the well-known turf barrows with internal stake circles excavated by Sir Cyril Fox.

The majority of these sites are still unexplored; but the excavated examples have yielded only cremated burials, and it appears that in this region the inhumation rite does not outlast the Beaker cultures, and was obsolete soon after 1500 B.C. The associated grave-goods include enlarged food-vessels, cinerary urns and pygmy cups, but there is at present insufficient evidence to allow any distinction to be made between these types in date or distribution. It may be noted, however, that barrows and cairns are rare in Monmouthshire, especially in the lowland area of the county; and that so far pottery of the Early and Middle Bronze Age is confined to a single cinerary urn. The marked paucity of finds of the second millennium B.C. in this eastern part of the region suggests that the Forest of Dean formed a natural barrier to communication with the Cotswold area by land through Gloucestershire; so that as in the Neolithic period the easiest communications with the east lay across the Bristol Channel.

There is some evidence, however, that in the latter part of the Middle Bronze Age contact between South Wales and Somerset was broken. As Fig. 14 shows, implements of Middle Bronze Age type (rapiers and broad-bladed palstaves, with and without loops) are relatively scarce, and occur chiefly in the coastal plain, with only slight penetration of the valleys to the north. There is a notable absence of any of the exotic objects of North European origin (ridge-button sickles, bronze torcs, ribbed armlets and loop-headed pins) which are the most striking features of the Somerset hoards of this period; and even the south Welsh palstaves, though

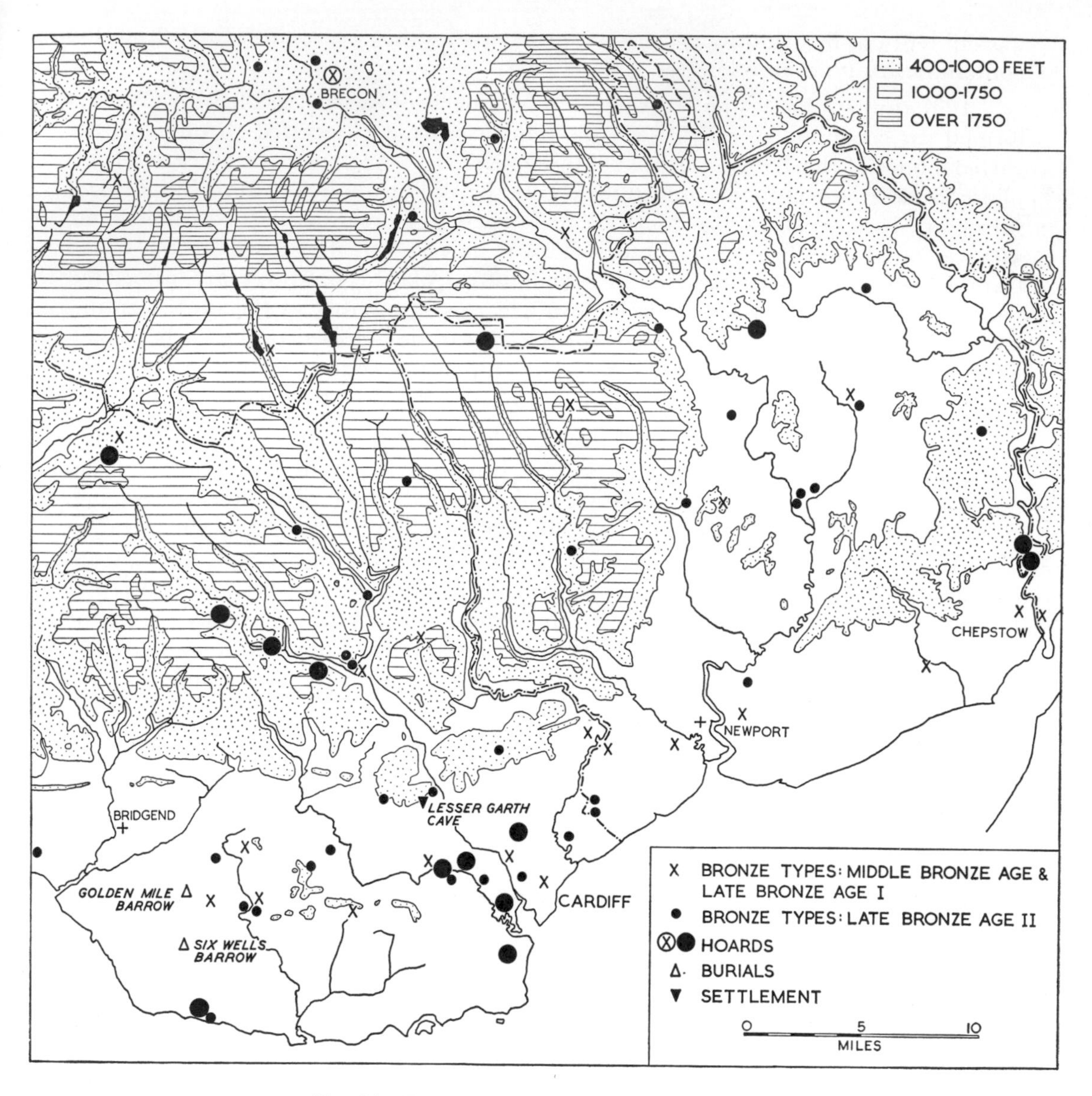

Fig. 14. Later Prehistoric Finds, 1400–400 B.C.

undoubtedly of British origin, exhibit characteristics that distinguish them from the contemporary types in Somerset.

It is thus probable that in the later Middle Bronze Age the Bristol Channel formed an economic frontier; and this appears to have persisted throughout the earlier phase of the Late Bronze Age, to about 750 B.C. Types characteristic of this phase in more easterly areas of Britain (e.g. in the Wilburton hoard from Cambridgeshire) are rare or absent in South Wales, where it is reasonable to assume some survival of Middle Bronze Age types. This is indeed well illustrated by the hoard from Ffynhonnau, near Brecon, in which broad-bladed palstaves are associated with an exotic single-edged knife of Urnfield type, probably of the ninth century B.C. This is the only hoard in the region which can be ascribed to the earlier phase of the Late Bronze Age, and its isolation emphasises that the beginnings of the 'industrial revolution' were retarded in this part of the British Isles.

It is only in the latter phase of the Late Bronze Age, from about 750 B.C., that we can discern signs of a distinctively local bronze industry in the region, characterized by the 'South Wales' type of socketed axe with three ribs, often converging, cast on the faces of the blade. This type is widely distributed in the area, in a pattern closely tied to the river valleys; and examples also occur, though less frequently, on the southern side of the Bristol Channel. These axes are well represented in a number of small hoards grouped around Cardiff, which may reflect the use of the estuaries of the Taff and Ely rivers by importers of scrap metal.

The importance of Cardiff as a landing-place is still further underlined by the two important hoards, from Cardiff itself and from Llyn Fawr at the head of the Rhondda Valley, which contain Hallstatt C types and provide clear evidence for the penetration of western Britain by sea from the Continent, and most probably from the Lower Rhineland, during the sixth century B.C. That the character of this penetration was war-like, rather than merely commercial, is suggested both by the iron sword from Llyn Fawr and the bronze cap for the draught-pole of a chieftain's wagon (or less probably a chariot) in the Cardiff hoard.

Apart from hoards and stray finds of bronze objects, evidence for Late Bronze Age settlement and burial in the region is slight. Two barrows in the western part of the Vale of Glamorgan have yielded pottery related, though distantly, to Deverel-Rimbury types; and similar material has been found in an inhabited cave in the Taff valley, north-west of Cardiff.

The history of the Iron Age occupation of the region, in the last half of the first millenium B.C., is archaeologically still obscure. The main evidence in the field consists of the numerous hill-forts and related earthworks, whose distribution is shown in Fig. 15; but until much more excavation has been carried out these sites can be interpreted only in morphological terms.

It is noticeable, first of all, that the earthworks exhibit a marked division into two groups; the first in the coastal plain and the second in the upper basin of the Usk around Brecon. The intervening area of ridge-and-valley, in northern Glamorgan, though providing many natural sites admirably adapted for defence,

[*Photo:* H. Tempest Ltd.

Plate XVI.—Lias limestone coast, Vale of Glamorgan. Looking east past the wooded Tresilian cove to the Colhugh river mouth and Stout, Summerhouse and Breaksea Points.

Plate XVII.—St. Hilary from the south. In this typical Vale of Glamorgan village, farmsteads built of local limestone cluster around the medieval church.

[*Photo:* H. Tempest Ltd.

[*Photo:* H. Tempest Ltd.

Plate XVIII.—Tintern Abbey from the south-west. The abbey, rebuilt by the Cistercians in the thirteenth century, includes a church which is unusually wide for its length and cloisters and conventual buildings on the north side of the church.

Plate XIX.—Chepstow from the south-west. The tidal Wye cutting through Carboniferous Limestone and the unique medieval castle set on a narrow ridge. The Norman church (right margin), was the church of the Benedictine Priory of St. Mary.

[*Photo:* H. Tempest Ltd.

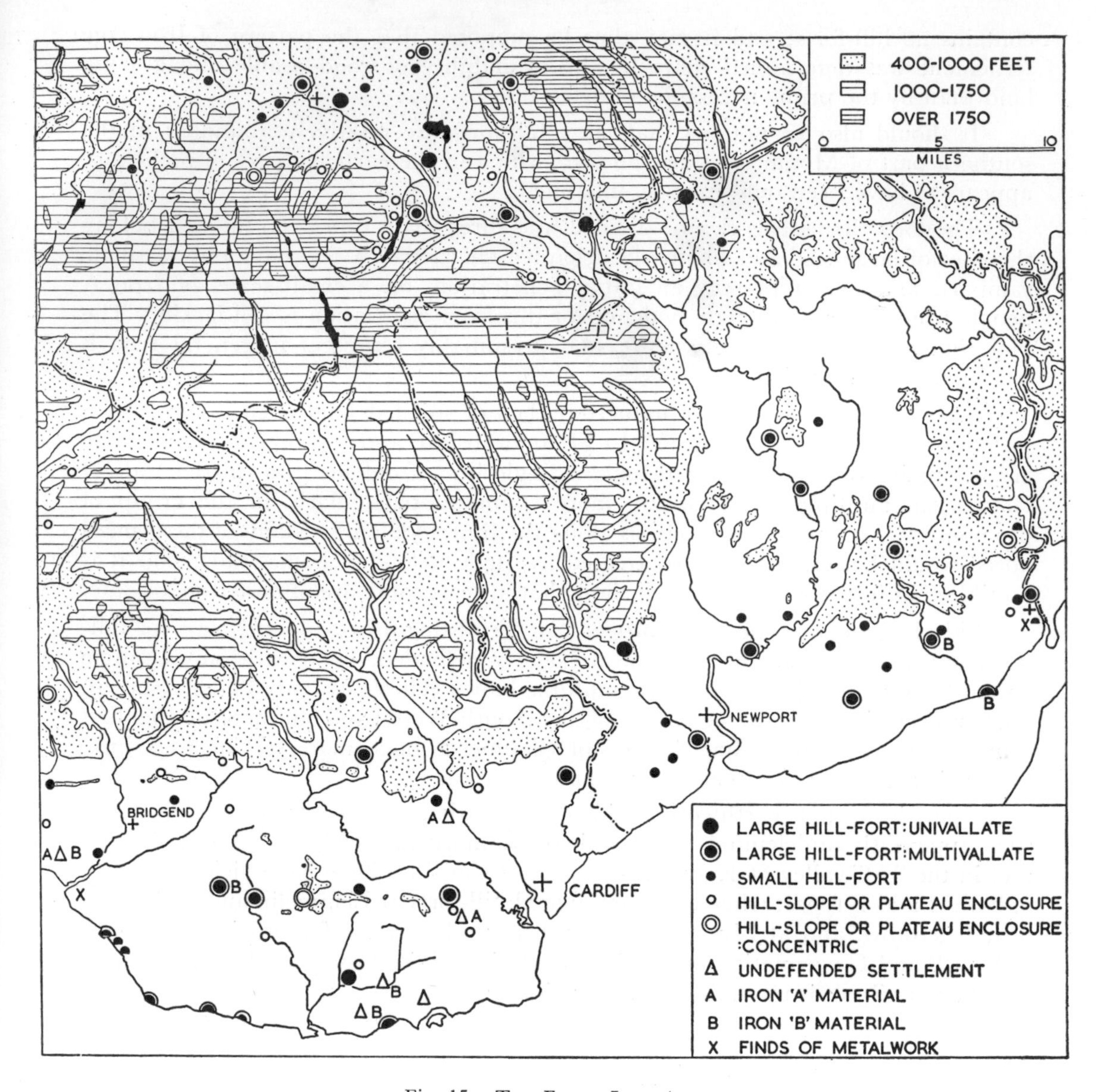

Fig. 15. The Early Iron Age

contains no hill-forts; and it may thus be supposed that the pattern of Iron Age settlement was determined more by the availability of good arable and grazing land than by the prime necessities of defence.

It should also be noticed that large hill-forts are relatively abundant in the southern part of Monmouthshire, an area which in the earlier phases of prehistory appears to have been only sparsely inhabited.

The forts themselves can be divided into three main types. To the first belong the sites of large size and obviously defensive character. A few have only a single rampart, and may represent an initial penetration, on a small scale, of Iron A people from the east; though evidence for this from excavation is still lacking. The majority, however, are multivallate, and presumably represent in general Iron B traditions of fortification.

Secondly, there is a more numerous class of small defended enclosures, often little more than an acre in extent. In Monmouthshire and the Brecon region these are normally contour works with only a single line of defence; but in the Vale of Glamorgan multiple ramparts are more common, particularly in the group of promontory forts spaced at intervals along the limestone cliffs. Many of these small 'forts' would better, perhaps, be treated as single defended homesteads; and it is possible that future excavation will show that at least some are of post-Roman date.

Side by side with the forts proper can be distinguished a third class, of hill-slope and plateau enclosures which are poorly defended, often with only a single bank, though a few have concentric multiple banks. These, as Lady Fox has shown, must reflect the pastoral economy of the South-Western B cultures of the first century B.C., and show that the Bristol Channel is once more serving as a link, rather than as a barrier, between its opposite shores.

Apart from these earthworks, evidence for settlement is confined to a few house sites, apparently undefended, in the Vale of Glamorgan, on Merthyr Mawr Warren and in the Taff valley at Radyr, north-west of Cardiff. These have yielded pottery of both A and B types; whereas the excavated hill-forts at Llanmelin and Sudbrook, near Chepstow, and at Llysworney, near Bridgend, have so far provided evidence of Iron B and C occupation only. The elucidation of the history of the Silures must thus necessarily wait upon further excavation.

ROMAN AND EARLY MEDIEVAL PERIODS

Leslie Alcock

The first contacts between the Roman invaders and the native tribe of the Silures lay in a period of warfare protracted from about A.D. 47 to A.D. 75. The hilly, broken and densely-wooded topography of south-east Wales, together with the loose political organization of the Silures, were well-suited to guerilla campaigns, and the writings of the historian Tacitus make it clear that the Romans suffered a number of reverses. Archaeologically speaking, this phase is reflected in the discovery of Roman pottery and other objects, the fruits of trade or plunder, in

native hillforts and settlements; and in the remodelling of the entrance—always the weakest point of the defences—at the Llanmelin hillfort to meet the tactical needs of defence against the Romans. The Roman base camp was at Gloucester, which has yielded a well-known tombstone depicting a cavalryman riding down a Siluran warrior.

In the field, the Roman forces doubtless halted for the night within the earthen bank of a temporary marching camp. Considering the long duration of the campaign, surprisingly few of these marching camps have been discovered on the ground. Two are known, however, from the borderlands between the Silures and their western neighbours the Demetae, upon the watershed between the Usk and Towy valleys. Others are now known in Glamorgan too, but their defences were always so slight that they have suffered heavily from subsequent agriculture.

The conquest of the Silures was finally effected about A.D. 75, partly by the penetration of the middle Wye valley, but principally by a sea-borne out-flanking movement along the South Wales coast, where frequent river valleys offered both harbours for the landing of troops and supplies and also lines of penetration into the hinterland. The area was then brought under military control by the establishment of auxiliary forts at convenient river mouths, with others along the valleys and ridgeways inland. The forts were then linked by well-engineered roads, so that the tribal area was split up into a number of small, easily-policed blocks. The forts themselves were at first temporary structures, with defences of earth and timber enclosing wooden buildings. In the second century A.D. they were given more permanent form, the defences being strengthened with a mortared stone wall and some at least of the more important internal buildings also being rebuilt in stone.

A typical example is The Gaer near Brecon, where a rectangular area nearly 8 acres in extent was defended by an earthen bank about 20 feet wide and 5 feet high, with two external ditches. This was a construction of about A.D. 75. In the first half of the second century, a stone revetment wall was added to the front of the bank, which was now increased in height to some 10 feet. Each side of the fort had a stone gateway, in the form of a double-arched roadway flanked by look-out towers with a bridge over the gate to carry the sentry-walk continuously round the fort. The headquarters building, commandant's house and fort granary were also rebuilt in stone at this time, but the barracks, stores and other buildings were still of timber. Outside the fort sprang up a civil settlement with shops, baths and other buildings housing camp followers and travellers.

Such forts would house a garrison of either 1,000 or 500 troops. These were principally infantry, though many units might have a quarter of their strength made up of cavalry. Some forts, indeed, especially in forward areas, had a garrison entirely of cavalry, and this was the case at the Brecon Gaer. The auxiliary troops themselves were recruited from the conquered provinces of the Empire. Brecon, for instance, was manned during part of its history by a cavalry unit recruited from a Spanish tribe, the Vettones.

The history of the forts after about A.D. 150 is obscure, but it has generally been held that the pacification of Wales, together with more urgent military needs in northern Britain, led to the removal of the greater part of the troops, some forts, however, retaining cadre garrisons. Recent excavations in Radnorshire have suggested that this generalization may need modifying, in that parts of Wales were still so unruly in the second half of the second century as to need substantial garrisons. At Brecon, on the other hand, the construction within the fort of a bath-house—a luxury building usually erected extra-murally—implies that part at least of the interior was no longer occupied by barracks, while the minute size of the bath-building itself confirms that the garrison had been drastically reduced.

The main base for all this military activity had been moved about A.D. 75 from Gloucester to Caerleon, a site with many natural advantages; set on a low ridge, surrounded by water on three sides, readily supplied by sea, and controlling the main land route in south-east Wales up the Usk valley. Here was established a legionary fortress covering nearly 50 acres. Like the auxiliary forts this was initially an earth and timber structure, but an inscription of the year A.D. 100 records the construction of one of the main internal buildings in stone, and implies that the site was given permanent form, with stone defences and stone barracks and administrative buildings, about that time. The subsequent history of Caerleon, though obscure in detail, suggests an occupation fluctuating in intensity according to military needs, and continuing until late in the fourth century. Immediately outside the south gate of the fortress are the well-preserved remains of an amphitheatre, used doubtless for military exercises as well as for the entertainment of the troops. On the same side of the fortress, beyond the parade ground and its boundary wall, excavation has revealed an important civil settlement, with sizeable private houses and rows of shops. Inscriptions suggest that a number of pagan temples are also to be sought in this area.

Obscure though the military history of the middle period of Roman rule may be, there are clear signs of renewed activity in the late third and the fourth centuries. Along the South Wales coast road the erection of milestones inscribed with the names of emperors of that period attests the refurbishing of the road system. At the same time a new type of fort was erected at Cardiff. This, with its high, narrow walls enfiladed by projecting bastions, and with entry restricted to two gateways, implies a defensive rather than offensive strategy. Similar forts are known along the coast of south-east England where they are believed to have operated in conjunction with mobile land forces and naval patrols to resist the attacks of Saxon raiders. At Cardiff a similar function may be assigned, though the attackers here were Irish. Presumably the Cardiff fort formed merely one unit in a chain of defence round the western coasts.

Turning now to the civilian aspect of Roman rule, the most striking evidence comes from behind the military zone, from the town of Caerwent. Here, in a fertile plain between the hills and the sea, conveniently accessible by ferry from south-western England, was created an urban settlement of some 44 acres. The town was the main instrument used by the Romans to diffuse the Mediterranean form

of civilization. Their success may be judged at Caerwent, despite its small size, by the regular lay-out of the streets; the construction of important public buildings such as market place, town hall, temples and bathing establishments; and the enclosure of these, together with private residences and shops, by a defensive wall which still stands to a height of 17 feet. One inscription shows that Caerwent was the tribal capital of the Silures who thus enjoyed a degree of political autonomy, while others demonstrate the degree of assimilation between Celtic and Roman paganism which the Roman themselves encouraged.

The history of Caerwent is at present subject to revision, but it seems likely that it was founded immediately after the conquest of the Silures as an instrument of pacification. The original bank and ditch defences may have been walled in stone at the end of the second century. Projecting bastions intended to serve as artillery platforms were added to the walls in the mid-fourth century in response to that same Irish threat which had led to the refortification of Cardiff. Perhaps at the same time the north and south gates were blocked up. About A.D. 400 Caerwent was flourishing as a place of refuge in the troubled times which accompanied the collapse of the Empire, but there is at present no evidence to prove that it continued long into the fifth century.

The second main aspect of civil life is reflected by the villas, or Romanized farmsteads, of which important examples have been excavated at Ely and at Llantwit Major. The latter was a fine country-house, covering 2 acres and with architectural refinements such as mosaic floors, heated rooms, and a bath-suite. Recent fieldwork has shown, indeed, that such villas were far more common in the rich farming lands of the Glamorgan and Monmouthshire sea-plain than had formerly been suspected. They doubtless reflect the wealth and security of tribal magnates under the *Pax Romana*. Less is known of the ordinary tribesmen who dwelt probably in timber houses. It may be suspected that some of them continued to live within the partially demolished ramparts of the pre-Roman hill-forts. Their main activity would be farming, perhaps with a heavier emphasis on arable than in earlier periods. Some of them were probably recruited under strict Roman supervision to exploit the mineral resources of South Wales. There is at least clear evidence that the Romans were working lead deposits in Monmouthshire and iron in the Vale of Glamorgan.

With the departure of the Roman armies in the late fourth century, Caerleon and Caerwent, the forts and the villas, were all more or less rapidly abandoned. The idea that there followed a Dark Age of decay and stagnation is, however, no more than a reflection of the historian's ignorance. Newly-won evidence from Dinas Powis makes it clear that there was a reorientation of trade and cultural connections towards the Irish Sea, the Atlantic sea-routes, the west coast of France and Spain, and ultimately the Mediterranean, for Mediterranean amphorae and fine table wares appear in some quantity at Dinas Powis. A Celtic artistic revival also took place, manifesting itself particularly in the production of bronze brooches with ornamental settings of enamel and glass. In the economic sphere, the emphasis swung back to pastoralism at the expense of arable farming.

The fifth to seventh centuries were also a period of intensive missionary activity, when Christianity was introduced to Wales from Gaul and the Mediterranean. Important monasteries were founded at Llantwit and Llancarfan in the Vale of Glamorgan, but no archaeological remains of the period have so far been located on these sites. Indeed the only material remains which demonstrate the introduction of Christianity are a series of rough stone pillars and slabs bearing contemporary inscriptions. The idea behind the erection of such stones appears to be pagan, Celtic and perhaps specifically Irish in origin. Very frequently in south-west Wales, commonly in Brecknockshire, and rarely in Glamorgan, they bear an inscription in the Irish script known as Ogham, and in the Goidelic language; such stones are a testimony to actual Irish settlement in the late Roman period. The Ogham inscriptions themselves usually record the name of a person, presumably deceased, and sometimes his or her parentage. This formula (*The stone*) *of A son of B*, reflecting as it does Celtic tribal organization, is also found on stones with Latin inscriptions executed in Roman script of progressively debased form. Epigraphic and linguistic details suggest that Latin and the appropriate script had not been taken over from Roman Britain, but had been introduced afresh from Gaul or the Mediterranean by Christian missionaries. In consequence, there appear on the Latin-inscribed stones not only the Celtic 'A son of B' formula, but also specifically Christian forms. Chief among these is the formula HIC IACIT, *Here he lies.* The Christian monogram Chi-Rho, and various forms of cross, may also appear; and occasionally the presumably pagan Ogham stones were Christianized by being inscribed with a cross, sometimes after the stone itself had been inverted. Despite the words HIC IACIT, archaeology has so far failed to reveal burials in association with the stones, and it seems most likely that they are to be thought of as memorials rather than as actual grave-stones. Not infrequently they were set up along the ridgeways whose use went back into prehistoric times and whose line had been followed by Roman roads. Excavation shows that these roads were largely abandoned and overgrown by the time the stones were set up in the late fifth to seventh centuries.

In the succeeding centuries, the archaeological picture grows faint, for the accidents of discovery have not yet revealed any sites of the period to compare in richness with Dinas Powis. Finds of metalwork and coins from limestone caves in Glamorgan suggest that these were in use either as places of refuge or as regular habitations. Perhaps in the seventh to ninth centuries the ridgeways of north Glamorgan were barred against raiders from Brecknockshire by cross-ridge dykes—earthen banks and ditches designed to impede cattle rustlers. There is no direct evidence for their date, but on analogy with similar dykes erected along the frontier between Mercia and Wales they may plausibly be assigned to this period. Of Viking activities in the ninth to eleventh centuries, the only relic is to be found in place-names: a handful of Norse names in and around the ports of Cardiff and Swansea, and others among the islands of the Bristol Channel.

This dearth of secular evidence is made good to some extent by an abundance of Early Christian stones. From the seventh century on, inscriptions become less

important and the cross itself gains in significance. At first this was merely incised on the surface of a roughly-dressed slab or pillar of stone; but by the ninth century the cross was sculptured in more or less high relief, and sometimes emerged from the slab form as a three-dimensional free-standing high cross. Both sculptured cross slabs and high crosses may bear the name of the man who erected them, but they are to be thought of primarily as witnesses to the faith, or as praying-stations, rather than as memorials. The surface of the stone is enriched with Celtic (and in one case, Viking) knotwork and interlace, and occasionally bears figure representations, especially crucifixion scenes, which are a pale reflection of contemporary Irish sculpture. One of the finest of these later monuments is at Llanynys in Brecknockshire, but their greatest development within the region of the present study was in Glamorgan, where distinctive local styles and cross-forms flourished. The richest area was around Llantwit Major, where, as inscriptions show, a royal burial ground was located When compared with the achievements of Ireland, Scotland or Northumbria, the Early Christian monuments of Wales seem lifeless in conception and rude in execution; but in south-east Wales they represent at least an independent school of Celtic art and a symbol of native devotion which was abruptly suppressed by the Norman conquest and the consequent ecclesiastical re-organization.

VI

HISTORY

FROM THE END OF THE ROMAN OCCUPATION TO THE NORMAN CONQUEST

H. R. LOYN

THE term 'Dark Ages' has passed out of fashion, but might profitably be revived for the benefit of the region to describe the centuries that run from the end of Roman military occupation to the coming of the Normans. So much happened, yet so little is recorded. The period opens with a presumably loosely organized tribal society, speaking a Brythonic tongue, capable of writing Latin, left to its own devices by its former Romanized masters and facing with intermittent success raids from the Goidelic-speaking peoples of Ireland. It ends with the long-established, though somewhat elastic, kingdoms of Morgannwg facing invasion from the Normans newly settled in England. The political development of the kingdoms of Morgannwg and the growth of the church are the only major historical themes upon which the fragmentary sources throw positive light.

Yet there remain other themes, fundamental to an appraisal of the nature of South Welsh society, that defy complete treatment for lack of evidence. Two problems are outstanding. What happened to the fertile lowlands, potentially good corn-growing land, above all, what happened to the Vale of Glamorgan? And, secondly, what happened to the Roman settlements of the lowlands, to Caerwent, Caerleon, Cardiff and Neath, above all, what happened to the harbours and ports of the coastal strip? On balance it seems unlikely that there was much extension of arable farming in the area. Indeed, where Roman villas decayed—though a villa is not, of course, automatically a centre of arable farming—there may have been positive diminution of the acreage under the plough. As late as the sixteenth century, Morgannwg was still regarded as the home of the stock-breeder rather than the corn-grower. It may well be that the long thin cantrefs of Morgannwg, running from highland to the sea, were the homes of relatively mobile groups, accustomed to seasonal migration from lowland to upland pasture, with the rivers as ranch boundaries rather than political borders. The Welsh laws, inasmuch as they may be used for this period and for this area, do not give the impression of a society where arable farming was the paramount element in economic life. The territorialisation of political power, an almost automatic companion of arable predominance in north-west Europe, had little advanced in pre-Norman Morgannwg. It seems likely that Norman feudal lord and Saxon peasant were the first to make substantial advance into the arable potentiality of the Vale in the twelfth and thirteenth centuries. But more than that dare not be said. Material proof is lacking. There is no survey, save the Domesday entries listed under Gloucestershire and Herefordshire, and they relate substantially only to lands between Usk and Wye. What land-charters have survived appear only in the late and dubious guise of the twelfth century *Liber Landavensis*.

Then again, in connection with the coastal strip, special problems arise to which no completely satisfactory answer can be given. It is no longer reasonable to suggest a period of complete isolation following the Roman withdrawal. Irish pirates were succeeded by Irish saints across the narrow seas. Recent archaeological work has emphasized the continued contact between the western shores of Britain and Merovingian Frankia. Merovingian glass has been found at Dinas Powis. Byzantine coins have been exhibited at Caerleon, though recent critical opinion has denied that they are the product of a Dark Age hoard; stray Carolingian coins have been found in the Gower. From the last half of the ninth century to the end of the eleventh century and beyond, Scandinavian raiders and traders from their settlements in Ireland and in the islands to the north and west of Scotland made their presence felt in South Wales, as indeed along almost every stretch of the British coast. Their imprint remains strong on the names of the islands and navigation points along the north coast of the Bristol Channel from Skokholm and Caldey to the Flat Holm and Steep Holm. In 914 A.D. they captured and held to ransom Bishop Cyfeiliog at a spot as far inland as Archenfield in the modern county of Hereford. During the reign of William himself we have record of an audacious raid in the course of which Scandinavians from the Scottish islands attacked the church of St. Gwynllyw at Newport, and so drew the wrath of the saint on their unfortunate heads. Some place-name forms inland like Homri in the parish of St. Nicholas, some names on the coast like Swansea and Womanby (Hundmanby) in Cardiff, have been taken as evidence of permanent Scandinavian settlement. There is nothing outrageously implausible in such suggestion. The Northmen set up their ring of fortified markets over the whole stretch of northern Europe in the ninth and tenth centuries from Rouen to Reykjavik, from Wexford to Kiev. There was heavy Scandinavian–Irish settlement in Cumberland and Lancashire in the tenth century, and some ambitious farmer-seamen may well have turned their attention south. There is slight literary evidence for a similar settlement in Pembrokeshire. The Vikings were slavers, and the Celtic lands provided a steady source of supply. They were accustomed to setting up temporary trading encampments that, given favourable conditions, could blossom into permanent settlements. The native kings and princes may have welcomed the establishment of coastal markets that would keep them in touch with the outside world. Yet unsupported, or poorly supported, evidence from place-names, particularly when the names occur in forms as late as is the case for the South Wales examples, provides weak foundation for the more elaborate hypotheses advanced in favour of heavy Scandinavian settlement in the area. Little is known of the date at which the names were first given. It could as well have been the Ostmen of Dublin in the twelfth century, as the Vikings in the tenth, who perpetuated our holms and -wics, our -eys and -bys. Many a prosaic Saxon -ton has been confounded with its more exotic northern cousin. Not proven is the fairest verdict to return in relation to the problem of significant Scandinavian settlement in the tenth and eleventh centuries.

But enough of questions to which as yet a satisfactory answer is lacking. There is more information relating to the political development of the area, on which positive light is thrown by royal genealogies, chronicle entries and later tradition.

In the first half of the seventh century the whole district from Tawe to Usk appears to have been under the control of a dynasty which traced its descent from a King Glywys. From him was derived the name Glywysing which applies strictly to the lands reputedly under his control. In the course of the seventh century a new dynasty arose, that of Meurig ap Tewdrig, under whose grandson Morgan ab Athrwys the name Glywysing was gradually replaced by that of Morgannwg. This kingdom was wider in extent than Glywysing. It included the ancient kingdom of Gwent, that is to say the lands between Usk and Wye which had taken its name from the Roman *Venta*, or modern Caerwent, still in the late ninth century a populous place, if the testimony of Asser may be accepted. Glamorgan itself, which is now thought of as the land limited on the east to the River Rhymney, appears in the *Liber Landavensis* of the twelfth century as a synonym of Morgannwg—Gulat morcant, Gwlad Forgan, the land of Morgan. To some degree most of the later rulers claimed descent from Morgan ab Athrwys, and although the area was subject to the customary practice of division and sub-division of inheritance, with Gwent often enjoying the rule of its own branch of the princely line, the political fortunes of Glywysing and Gwent were closely bound together in the larger kingdom of Morgannwg. But Morgannwg itself seems to have been somewhat outside and isolated from the fitful movements towards a larger Welsh unity. It remained outside the kingdom of Rhodri Mawr, outside the kingdom of Hywel Dda. Gruffydd ap Llewellyn, it is true, for a brief few years before his death in 1063, succeeded in uniting Morgannwg politically to the rest of Wales, but his work did not endure. In 1065 Harold conquered the greater part of Gwent and annexed it to his earldom of Hereford. His work was continued by the Norman earls from their new castle at Chepstow. In1086 most of Gwent was recorded in somewhat summary fashion under the Gloucester and Herefordshire folios of Domesday Book. There is even reference to lands held beyond the Usk. Possibly as a result of the political upheavals of the preceding generation, more probably as a culmination of a much longer period of autonomous Gwentian rule, the term Morgannwg was now narrowed to a smaller area than that occupied by the former kingdom of Glywysing. The Norman lordship of Glamorgan consists only of the lands between Tawe and Rhymney.

Yet at its widest extent Morgannwg undoubtedly stretched from the Tawe to the Wye. The whole kingdom was divided into seven cantrefs along the line of the rivers that run from the highland into the sea. Six of the seven may be identified clearly enough: Gorfynydd, the land between Tawe and Thaw; Penychen, the land between Thaw and Taff; Y Cantref Breiniol, between the Taff and the Rhymney; Gwynllŵg, which stretched from the Rhymney to the Usk; Gwent, split by Wentwood into Gwent Iscoed and Gwent Uchcoed, and lying between the Usk and the Wye. Concerning the seventh cantref there is not the same certainty. Sir John Lloyd suggested an area in modern Herefordshire, Archenfield and Ewyas Harold, which was still thoroughly Welsh at the time of the Domesday survey. The intense interest shown in this area by the church of Llandaff in the twelfth century helps to support this view. Like Dyfed in the west, Morgannwg was known as the land of the seven cantrefs. Only three of the seven were contained in the medieval lordship

of Glamorgan. Even Gwynllŵg, the land between Rhymney and Usk was administered as a separate lordship.

In one respect the area gives evidence of a vitality that suggests a reasonably well populated region: that is in the religious field. Exactly how deep-rooted was Christianity during Roman times is unknown. Emphasis now is generally placed on a sustained evangelizing movement from Gaul and from Ireland which brought about a thorough Christianization of South Wales in the fifth and sixth centuries. Evidence of stone crosses, of epigraphy, of church dedications all point to dissemination of the faith from the west. The monastic nature of the church also fits in well with the picture of derivation from Gaul and Ireland. Morgannwg, if we may anticipate the later name, had a vital part to play both in the first phases of this movement and in the consolidation that followed. Of all the monastic schools that abounded in Wales, that of Llanilltud Fawr, or Llantwit Major, has a certain pride of place. Though Saint David had little, if any, connection with Morgannwg, St. Illtud, St. Cadog, St. Dubricius, and probably St. Teilo, were busy in the region. In particular the foundations of Llantwit and Llancarfan exercised a great influence over the south. In the first instance these were monasteries, but developed into *clas* churches, governed by an abbot and served by men living according to rule. Pristine enthusiasm relaxed, as landed endowments increased. By the end of our period the mother churches were wealthy, and the Normans found it convenient to take over their endowments. Llancarfan itself passed to Gloucester; Llantwit to Tewkesbury. Llandaff presents a more difficult problem. In the twelfth century it was aggressively hailed as a Teilo foundation, and the *Liber Landavensis* also associated the church with St. Dubricius and St. Oudoceus. But critical, not to say sceptical, attention has been directed fiercely at the rag-bag of traditions, charters, forgeries and inventive hagiography that goes up to make the Book of Llandaff. Its object was blatantly to assert the claims of the new territorial bishopric of Llandaff over against the rival claims of St. Davids. Indeed Professor C. N. L. Brooke has recently suggested—with something of a flourish, it is true—that 'Urban's familia forged a book—the Liber Landavensis; they may also have forged a diocese'. The concern of the book with St. Teilo and St. Dubricius was occasioned by the weight of Teilo and Dubricius dedications in the lands under dispute in Ystrad Tywi and in Archenfield. Professor Bowen has suggested that Llandeilo Fawr, not Llandaff, was the centre of the Teilo cult. And much of the substance of Llandaff's ecclesiastical position seems in point of fact to have been taken over from the endowments of nearby Llancarfan.

Yet to fly to extremes and to deny Llandaff any ecclesiastical importance before the Norman period seems somewhat unjustified. There is good reason to suppose that Llandaff was a holy place throughout the Dark Ages. The site was well chosen on the road that linked Caerwent, Caerleon and Bassaleg with the west. A Teilo dedication is by no means impossible. One may agree that Llandaff was not of the stature of Llancarfan, Llantwit or Llandeilo Fawr, and that its true flowering period came with the advent of the Normans. But it is altogether reasonable to argue that the Normans built on sound foundations, and that Llandaff had its own religious traditions of high antiquity, probably with some Teilo connection.

The main point is, as Professor Brooke makes clear, that Llandaff should not be seen as a dominant episcopal see, exercising authority and jurisdiction over the kingdom of Morgannwg. Such a territorial authority was not in the nature of the Celtic church. It is doubtful if, for example, Bishop Cyfeiliog in the tenth century was bishop of Llandaff, as the term would now be understood. Episcopal functions were straitly limited in the Celtic world. Bishops were important as spiritual leaders, but were overshadowed in matters of ecclesiastical polity by the abbots of the most important mother churches. They were more truly bishops to a people than bishops of a territorial diocese. The impressive list of bishops from Teilo onwards loses a little of its force when viewed in that light. But there is no good reason why Llandaff should not have been among the favoured residences of the episcopate that served the peoples dwelling in Morgannwg.

In the cultural field the period has little tangible to offer, though later tradition tells of the strength of the schools of Llantwit and of Llancarfan, while there is evidence also of bardic activity at the royal courts of Morgannwg. Gildas has always been associated with Llantwit, but it is distressing to record that some acute modern critics are attributing part at least of his work to the late seventh or early eighth century and the school of Malmesbury. Some cultural exchange with the north Somerset coast is suggested by church dedications dating from pre-Saxon days, and indeed possibly by the vigour and prosperity of Glastonbury and of Malmesbury in the seventh century. Asser, the biographer of King Alfred, was probably no more than a bird of passage from the land of Dewi Sant to the court of the West Saxon king. A remarkable series of stone crosses with inscriptions in Latin denotes a tradition of skill in this art, particularly around Llantwit and Margam. A people who built in wood have left little for the archaeologists. Yet the lurid light of the Normans with their castles and great churches should not blind the historian to the unspectacular creators of the Christian kingdoms of Morgannwg. The strength of the Norman lords owes more than has always been appreciated to the work of their Welsh antecessors.

FROM THE NORMAN CONQUEST TO THE ACT OF UNION 1536

William Rees

Cardiff is so frequently regarded as a product of the industrial age that we are inclined to forget its role as a regional centre throughout historical times. Broadly the region occupies the southern slope of the Welsh plateau, its southward-flowing rivers traversing the fertile lowland plain to the Severn Sea. A country not unfavoured by nature, it offered from early times a highway into South Wales. The Roman was a relatively latecomer into the area, but his system of roads and forts provided the framework for the future, the fort on the banks of the Taff forming the nucleus of the first settlement at Cardiff.

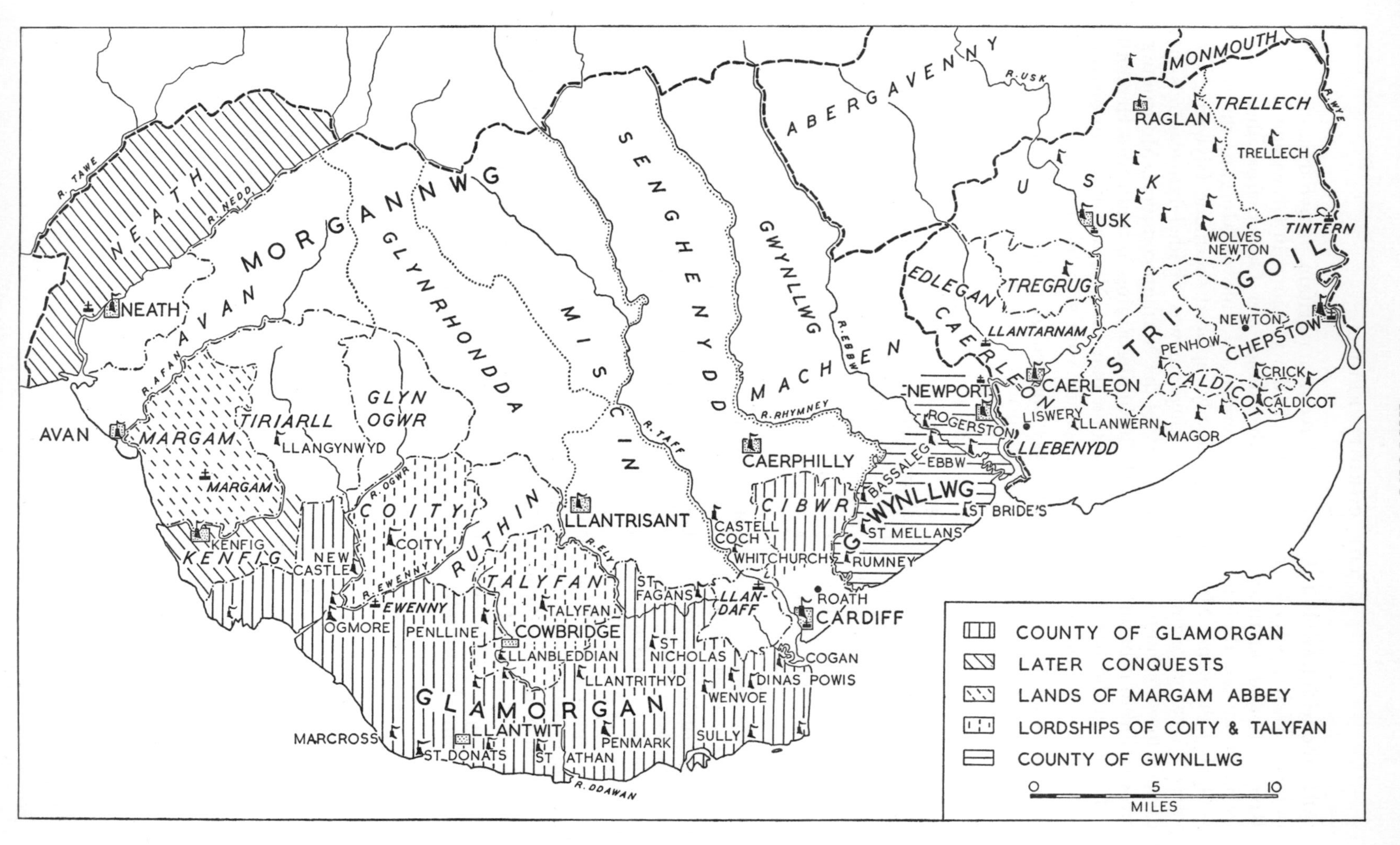

Fig. 16. Medieval Glamorgan and Gwent

After the withdrawal of the Roman forces from Britain, native dynasties arose in south-east Wales, petty kings of the line of Glywys ruling in Glywysing as far as the River Usk and, at times, extending their hold over Gwent, from the Usk to the Wye. It was in the eighth century, under the rule of Morgan, the son of Athrwys, that the name Morgannwg gradually replaced the name Glywysing. For purposes of local government, this early kingdom was divided into cantrefs and sub-divided into commotes, and, on the eve of the Norman conquest, Morgannwg–Gwent was said to contain seven cantrefs, including Erging in south-west Herefordshire. It was on the basis of this organization that the Norman built up his rule, replacing, however, the open Welsh court-house with a fortified castle.

The Norman conquest of England was followed by attacks upon the Welsh by Norman lords of the Border who sought in private raids to extend their territories. The grant of the earldom of Hereford to William fitz Osbern in 1067 opened the way for the seizure of Erging (Archenfield) and the invasion of Gwent, bringing about the fall of Cantref Iscoed and its conversion into the Norman lordship of Netherwent (Strigoil), with its castle at Chepstow. Before the death of William I (1087), Thurstan fitz Rolf, following the Roman road westward, had set up a castle within the Roman fort of Caerleon as the nucleus of the lordship there. A large part of southern Gwent had thus already fallen, and by the year 1100 the remainder of Gwent had been taken over by the lords of Monmouth, Abergavenny and Ewyas.

During the years 1090–93, Robert fitz Hamon, lord of Gloucester, crossed the Severn estuary to the conquest of Morgannwg, then under the rule of Iestyn ap Gwrgan. Seizing the cantref of Gwynllwg, fitz Hamon raised a castle mound at Stowe (Newport) and occupied the coastal lowland as far as the River Rhymney, leaving the hill country of Machen to the Welsh. Beyond the river the Roman walled fort on the Taff, long since abandoned, offered a defensible site and fitz Hamon raised here at Cardiff within the enclosure of the fort a moated mound with wooden palisade to serve as the keep of his castle. To it he attached the southernmost of the commotes of Cantref Senghenydd, viz. the commote of Cibwr, to form the lordship of Cardiff, the low-lying ground at Roath being cleared to provide the open fields for cultivation as a Norman manor. Within ten years a fully-constituted borough, to which all trade within the lordship was restricted, had grown up outside the castle, traders being attracted to settle as burgesses in the town by the grant of special privileges which before 1147 were incorporated in a charter.

The establishment of the castle at Cardiff was quickly followed by the conquest of the Vale of Glamorgan, fitz Hamon retaining in his own hands the greater part of Llantwit Major, which became the most important of his manors in Glamorgan, while the lands of the church of St. Illtyd there were granted to Tewkesbury Abbey and the former lands of the Cadoc foundation at Llancarfan to the Abbey of Gloucester. The remainder of the Vale, however, was granted out in estates to the knightly followers of fitz Hamon, each knight holding by the service of guarding the castle of Cardiff for forty days annually for each knight's fief at which his estate

was assessed, or by the payment of 6s. 8d. for *wardsilver* in lieu of the same. Many of the villages of the Vale today have their origin in these early grants. Each estate constituted a separate unit with its own castle and manor, this area of alien settlement being organized as the county of Glamorgan, subject to the county court presided over by the lord's sheriff. It is to this area that the name Glamorgan strictly applies. Along the northern fringe of this Normanized county, much exposed to the attacks of the Welsh, were the two lordships of Coity and Talyfan, held by the special tenure of serjeanty, whereby they were exempt from military service at Cardiff. Payn de Turbervill, who held by the serjeanty of hunting, was said to have acquired his lordship of Coity by marriage with a Welsh heiress of the line of Iestyn.

While the defeat of the Welsh ruler, Iestyn ap Gwrgan, had conferred on Robert fitz Hamon the feudal hold over all Glamorgan, it was more easy to assert the claim than to establish it. The first stage of occupation was confined broadly to the line of the River Ogmore, and on this temporary front it is significant that the castles of Penlline and Ogmore, the two westernmost of these early castles of the county, were built in stone rather than in timber.

Outside the bounds of the early county, fitz Hamon's hold was somewhat tenuous, dependent on the allegiance he could command from the Welsh of the interior. Something in the nature of an understanding seems to have been effected between him and the defeated Welsh royal family, for later we see sons and grandsons of Iestyn holding the hill commotes of Avan, Glynrhondda and Miscin and descendants of Einion ap Collwyn ruling the two commotes of Senghenydd. These lands they held from the Norman lord without the render of homage, the Welsh rulers recognizing none of the feudal links whether through military or other service, but by fealty only, with the payment of heriot at death. This region of native rule retained its name Morgannwg, standing in marked contrast with the feudal organization of the county, so that the official title of the lordship as a whole was *Glamorgan and Morgannwg*.

Wales was no part of the English realm and in the Welsh lordships, acquired piecemeal by private conquest rather than by royal grant, the English Crown, except in special circumstances, could claim no right of entry. The Norman lord took over the rights of the defeated Welsh ruler, exercising the royal prerogative in judicial and civil matters, issuing writs from his Chancery, creating boroughs, markets and fairs, the castle serving as the administrative centre.

In Glamorgan, the occupation of the Vale assured, the Norman sought to extend his hold beyond the limits of the River Ogmore into the western parts of the lordship. Newcastle was established in fitz Hamon's day, but later the new castle at Kenfig became the main base of operations. This was probably the work of Robert the Consul, the natural son of Henry I, who, by marriage with the fitz Hamon heiress, became Earl of Gloucester and second lord of Glamorgan (*c.* 1120–47). Before 1129 Richard de Granville had obtained a footing in Neath, founding there the Cistercian abbey, and before 1147 Earl Robert had founded the abbey at Margam, much of this frontier zone thus falling to the Church. The advance met with strong resistance from the Welsh who, taking advantage of Robert's pre-

occupation with the civil war in Stephen's reign, concentrated their attack on the new castles of Kenfig and Neath. The struggle was continued under William, Earl of Gloucester (1147–83), the castle of Cardiff being attacked in 1158 by Ifor, the Welsh lord of Senghenydd, when the Earl was carried off and released only on promise of redress of wrongs. By this time the local Welsh lords of Avan, Miscin and Senghenydd had the support of the Lord Rhys of Deheubarth and, on the death of the Earl, a concerted attack was made in 1184–5 on the Norman centres in Glamorgan, the town of Kenfig being twice burnt and its castle seriously damaged, as too were the town and castle of Neath. Even the town of Cardiff was burnt, its castle, and that of Newport, suffering heavily. Norman power, however, by this time was too strongly entrenched to be overcome, and with the drafting of troops into the area and with the death of the Lord Rhys, the revolt subsided.

Glamorgan passed in 1217 into the hands of the family of Clare which was later to play so prominent a part in the constitutional struggle in England, a struggle which gave opportunity for the emergence of the Princes of Gwynedd as leaders of the independent parts of Wales, bringing hope of aid to a new generation of Welsh rulers in Morgannwg. Under the protection of Llywelyn the Great, attacks on the Anglo-Norman settlements in Glamorgan were renewed causing widespread destruction from which even the abbeys of Neath and Margam were not immune. In 1231 the town of Neath was wiped out and Kenfig closely besieged. Llywelyn's attempt to win the allegiance of the local Welsh rulers was a major threat to the suzerainty of the Clares in their hill country. With the death of Llywelyn in 1240, however, and the defeat of Wales in the war of 1245–7, the threat passed, and the way opened for the gradual annexation by the Clares of the whole of the Welsh lordships in Glamorgan.

Occasion arose as the result of an attack by Hywel ap Meredydd of Miscin on Richard Siward, lord of Talyfan, during the years 1244–6 when Siward, traitorously breaking the truce arranged by Richard de Clare, was outlawed in 1246, his lordship being confiscated to become the important manor of Llanbleddian. At the same time, Clare confiscated Hywel's commote of Miscin, converting it into a lordship, ruled from his new castle of Llantrisant. Thus, by a single stroke, he greatly extended his hold over the centre of Glamorgan, a hold further strengthened about the same time by the building of a castle in the hill country of Llangynwyd in territory which now came to acquire the name Tir Iarll, the Earl's Land.

The suppression of the remaining Welsh lordships was linked up with the rise to power of the last Llewelyn and his recognition by the Welsh as Prince of Wales. Advancing southward, he seized the marcher lordships of the Border and by 1262 reached the boundary of Glamorgan. To counter this threat to his hill territory, the young Gilbert de Clare, the 'Red Earl', took possession of Senghenydd in 1266, imprisoning the Welsh lord Gruffydd ap Rhys and building a castle at Caerphilly. The first castle was destroyed by Llywelyn in 1270, and in 1271 the second great fortress, now in ruins, was constructed on the site according to the most advanced methods of castle building of the day. Joint pressure from de Clare and from the displaced Marcher lords of the Border forced Llywelyn to withdraw northwards,

[*Photo:* National Museum of Wales

Plate XX.—Megalithic chambered tomb at St. Lythan's, Glamorgan.

[*Photo:* National Museum of Wales

Plate XXI—Late Bronze Age cauldron from Llyn Fawr, Glamorgan.

[*Photo:* National Museum of Wales

Plate XXII.—Roman town wall with bastions at Caerwent, Monmouthshire.

Plate XXIII.—Early Christian cross with Crucifixion scene from Margam, Glamorgan.

[*Photo:* National Museum of Wales

only to be confronted on the accession of Edward I with the demand for homage, an issue which led to the Wars of Welsh Independence, 1277–83.

Senghenydd was henceforth administered direct by officials, the trade of the lordship being concentrated at the new borough of Caerphilly. Bound up with the fate of Senghenydd was that of Glynrhondda and indeed of Miscin, Glynrhondda being combined with Miscin. With the annexation of these Welsh lands, all Glamorgan became subject to the lord, and the full effect of the conquest realized. Only in Avan did the native family survive, to hold the commote from the lord as a sub-lordship by special tenure. The reversal of the policy of this family to one of 'co-existence' was probably the work of Morgan, son of Morgan Gam, and by a judicious trimming of sails, it was continued by his son, Lleison, now styled *de Avene*, Morgan himself signifying his acceptance of the new order by marrying in 1276 the daughter of Walter de Sully, lord of Wenvoe and a Sheriff of the county.

The spread of castle rule, with its accompanying abuses on the part of the lord's officials, brought widespread discontent which found expression in the revolt of 1294–5, constituting a formidable challenge to the 'Red Earl' on the eve of his death in 1295. He was succeeded by his young son, Gilbert, whose death on the field of Bannockburn in 1314 brought to an end the family of Clare in the male line, the wide estates in South Wales being administered for some years by the Crown. The action of successive Crown keepers, in their flagrant disregard of established custom, roused the Welsh to tragic, but unsuccessful, revolt under Llywelyn Bren, a member of the former royal family of Senghenydd. Until the days of Owain Glyndwr, no further outbreak took place.

The pattern of the lordship of Glamorgan was by now well defined. Yet it was no unitary structure with a single system of government. Rather was it a group of feudal lordships, the only bond of unity lying in a common allegiance to the chief lord. Hence it was sometimes regarded as a feudal 'honour' the feudal tenants-in-chief having representation in the county court, which court formed the chief element in the constitution of the lordship, concerned with all matters relating to feudal tenures and services. It was also a court of record in both civil and criminal causes, a court of first instance as well as of appeal, presided over by the Sheriff of the county and held commonly at the castle of Cardiff for which reason it is sometimes termed the 'county of Cardiff' or the 'county palatine of Cardiff', though frequently conducted near a site in dispute. The lordships of Neath, Kenfig, Llantwit and Llanbleddian, and the hill lordships, comprising the special domains of the Chief Lord, were, however, administered by the local bailiffs in the courts of these lordships, the courts baron and courts leet, while the boroughs of Neath, Kenfig, Llantwit, Cowbridge and Cardiff transacted their affairs in their town courts and in their gilds.

In the partition of the Clare estates in 1317, Glamorgan passed to Eleanor, the wife of Hugh le Despenser the younger, the favourite of Edward II, thus making of Glamorgan a cockpit in the stormy politics of that reign and the scene of the capture of that unhappy monarch. Gwynllwg was assigned to Margaret and her husband,

Hugh d'Audley, thus severing the ancient link between Gwynllwg and Glamorgan, while Caerleon, Usk and Trellech went to Elizabeth, wife of Roger d'Amory.

Of the later history of these lordships, Glamorgan continued under the Despensers, passing in 1423 by marriage to Richard Beauchamp, Earl of Warwick, and later to Richard Neville, the king-maker, and to Richard III, to be confiscated to the Crown after Bosworth in 1485. Gwynllwg descended to the family of Stafford to be forfeited on the attainder of Henry Stafford, Duke of Buckingham, in 1483. Usk, Trellech and Caerleon, formerly part of the great Strongbow-Marshal interest in Netherwent, had since 1245 assumed increased importance since their development into separate lordships by the Clares, each with its manor and borough. Through the grand-daughter of Elizabeth de Clare, these lordships descended to the Mortimer family and thus to the Yorkist branch of the royal family, later falling by forfeiture to Richard III and Henry VII. The remaining portion of Netherwent, the lordship of Strigoil, came by marriage with the Marshal heiress to the family of Bigod, Earls of Norfolk, and ultimately to Thomas Mowbray (created Duke of Norfolk and Marshal of England in 1386). Edward IV, to strengthen the Yorkist position in south-east Wales and to reward Sir William Herbert, Earl of Pembroke, for his service to the cause, raised his lordship of Raglan to the dignity of a lordship royal, Sir William also acquiring by exchange with John, fourth Duke of Norfolk, the lordship of Strigoil with its powerful castle of Chepstow. Herbert was beheaded after the battle of Edgecote in 1469, his estates descending later to his grand-daughter, the wife of Charles Somerset, who became in her right Baron Herbert of Raglan and Strigoil, later Earl of Worcester. After the suppression of the monasteries, the lands of Tintern went to swell the large estates of the family in South Wales.

During the Wars of the Roses, Yorkist influence was thus powerful in central Gwent, strengthened further by the Neville lands of Abergavenny to the north. On the north-eastern flank, however, in Monmouth, and in the Buckingham estates of Gwynllwg immediately to the west lay strong Lancastrian interests, thus dividing Gwent between the two powerful factions. The dislocation involved in the struggle for the Crown and the very scale of the disturbance pointed to the need for unity in the realm which the savage confiscations of rival victors during these years was helping to bring about. By the sixteenth century the growing State had become sufficiently conscious of unity to seek to subordinate all parts of the realm to its single rule. The lordships of the March, as separate units of jurisdiction rendering difficult the maintenance of law and order, conflicted with this unifying policy and, with many lordships now in Crown hands, the way lay open for the suppression of their royal rights and their incorporation into the English realm. By the Act of Union of 1536, the lordships of the March were merged to form shires on the English model, those of Glamorgan being combined to make up the shire of Glamorgan, and those of Gwent with Gwynllwg the shire of Monmouth, the name taken from the former royal lordship of Monmouth. Henceforth the Welsh shires were represented in the English parliament and local government taken out of the private hands of lords to be organized on public lines through parish, hundred and county.

FROM THE ACT OF UNION TO THE CIVIL WAR

GLANMOR WILLIAMS

The modern counties of Glamorgan and Monmouthshire came into being as a result of the determination of Henry VIII and his advisers fully to incorporate Wales into the realm of England. This was done by acts of parliament passed between 1536 and 1542 and usually known collectively as the Act of Union. An act of 1536 abolished all the formerly autonomous Marcher lordships and shired the whole of Wales. The county of Glamorgan was formed by the merger of the medieval lordships of Gower and Glamorgan, which throughout the medieval period had remained separate entities. It was an unnatural union. Gower, by history, tradition, dialect, and ecclesiastical affiliations, had much more in common with Deheubarth, or south-west Wales, than with Morgannwg. The boundaries of the county as then laid down, however, have remained in existence ever since. A sense of county loyalty and solidarity has grown up in the interim, but it is probably not fanciful to say that even today the eastern and western halves of the county do not lie too easily together.

The organization of the new shire, with its county town at Cardiff, was modelled on that of a contemporary English shire. It was given two members of parliament for the first time, one being returned for the shire and the other for the ancient boroughs within its boundary. Local jurisdiction lay very largely in the hands of the sheriff and the justices of the peace. Its successful working depended on the glittering prospects it offered of careers open to Welsh talents. The upper classes were quick to seize the chances of political and social advancement now offered to them. The families of landowning gentry who had been building up their possessions and positions amid the debris of medieval society now came quickly to the fore. Families like the Herberts, Stradlings, Carnes, Mansels, Lewises, Bassets, and others missed no opportunity of taking office under the Crown. For many generations to come theirs were the names which were to dominate the public life of the region. Some rose even higher. Sir John Herbert (1555–1617), one of two brothers whose ornate tomb still takes the eye in St. John's, Cardiff, became Second Secretary of State in 1600 and was one of the key figures in James I's administration; while Sir Robert Mansel (*c.* 1573–1656) rose to be Vice-Admiral of England and Treasurer of the Navy, as well as being an enterprising pioneer in the manufacture of glass.

Full of drive, initiative and public spirit as the gentry might be, they were also on occasion violent, grasping and unscrupulous. A sheriff of Glamorgan, Thomas Lewis of Llandaff, could in 1570 refuse to admit the election of two coroners of whom he disapproved and snap his fingers at the authority of the Council of the Marches, the body especially charged with the good government of Wales and the Border. Sir William Herbert, himself a member of the Council, in 1595 quarrelled with the bailiffs of Cardiff. The Court of Star Chamber found that his men, having attacked the bailiffs and freed two prisoners from gaol, spent 'divers days and weeks after this, walking and braving still up and down the streets in great troops and

companies both by day and night, weaponed and armed . . . without check or rebuke of their masters'.

Turbulent and hot-blooded as they sometimes were, the gentry in the main accepted responsibility for the changes of régime imposed upon them by the Tudor monarchy. Not the least or the easiest of these was the Reformation. Before 1529 there is little evidence of any hostility to the Church or criticism of it. Neither the older heresy of Lollardy nor the newer one of Lutheranism seems to have made much impact. In the popular religion there were some signs of vigour and liveliness. A good deal of building was going on in the churches and some of them were well-endowed with goods and possessions. St. John's, Cardiff, whose handsome tower was built in 1473, had, for instance, an array of costly vestments, a mass of plate and ornaments, a fine organ and a professional organist. Shrines like St. Teilo's at Llandaff Cathedral, or the very famous one of the Virgin at Pen-rhys, in the Rhondda, which had a fabulous reputation for healing, were much resorted to. Popular religious verses, known as *cwndidau*, were more numerous in the Vale of Glamorgan and its environs than anywhere else. They and the generous bequests to religious foundations made in contemporary wills testify to some extent to genuine devotion. Yet, when change was enforced, it was accepted without overt opposition by lay and cleric alike. The strong rule of the Tudors, the popularity they enjoyed as a Welsh dynasty, the solid advantages which their policies offered, combined with a certain supineness in contemporary religious life to prevent any rebellion against them.

Still, loyalty to Rome died hard in the area. Sir Edward Carne, though he had himself taken a prominent part in carrying out the dissolution of the monasteries and gained Ewenny Priory thereby, nevertheless became Queen Mary's ambassador to the Holy See, and died at Rome early in Elizabeth's reign, having chosen not to return home. Other leading families became notorious recusants during Elizabeth I's reign. In the year 1596, out of forty-five open Catholic recusants traced in the county of Glamorgan no fewer than sixteen bore the name of the ancient and influential family of Turberville. It was the determination of this clan more than any other which made the Vale of Glamorgan one of the strongest centres of hard-core papists in Wales. Side by side with this recusancy there was a persistent strain of Protestant radicalism. Cardiff seems to have been its focal point. In 1542, one Thomas Capper was burnt there—presumably for denying transubstantiation. In 1555 one of the three Marian martyrs of Wales, the Cardiff fisherman Rawlins White, was burnt at the stake. By early Stuart times a sizeable Puritan group existed in the town. In its parish churches William Erbury, one of the most powerful and esoteric of Puritan evangelists, and his curate, the ardent Walter Cradock, were preaching to sympathetic congregations. By and large, however, critics of the religion by law established, from right or left, were few in number. In the minds of most of those who were socially conscious and articulate, devotion to the State, patriotism and self-interest combined to keep them loyal.

Advantages there certainly were from co-operating with the régime. Economic opportunity as well as political authority came the way of those who did so. And

the gentry were hungry for new means of acquiring land and wealth. Marriages were managed adroitly by the dynastically-minded, and the hand of a great heiress like Barbara Gamage of Coity, who was married to Sir Philip Sydney's elder brother, Robert, in 1584, could become a matter of high politics involving personalities as august as Sir Walter Raleigh, Sir Francis Walsingham and the Queen herself. The Reformation brought monastic and other church lands into the market: Margam Abbey went to the Mansels, Ewenny to the Carnes, and the remains of the town house into which the Herberts turned the Grey Friary in Cardiff can still be seen. Estates were acquired by the pushing or the far-sighted from the unthrifty, the luckless or the weak; and holdings were consolidated. Purchase, lease, mortgage, litigation, chicanery, and even downright force were all weapons that came easily to the estate-builders. Everywhere in the more fertile lowlands, enclosures and improved farming went on apace.

Though land was still the main source of income and the exclusive fount of prestige, no one considered it beneath his dignity also to engage in industry or trade. Landowners on whose estates coal out-cropped conveniently near the sea either mined it themselves or leased the rights to entrepreneurs. Ironmasters from the Weald of Sussex, whose own timber supplies were far depleted, were attracted to Glamorgan and set up their forges there. The monopoly joint-stock company of the Mines Royal founded a smelting house at Neath for the refining of Cornish copper ore. They placed the enterprise under the direction of Ulrich Frosse, a German technician who made far-reaching experiments with the use of coal in the process of smelting.

Trading in the Bristol Channel was brisk, and centred on the western metropolis of Bristol, whose great St. James's Fairs were the highlight of the local commercial calendar. Memories of the Welsh traders and sailors who thronged that port are still preserved in the names of the 'Welsh Back' quay and the 'Llandoger Trow' tavern. There was a steady demand for Welsh store cattle, among which the Glamorgan breed rated high. Welsh wool sold well among the clothiers of the West of England. By-products of a pastoral economy—leather, cheese or butter—and the excellent corn grown in the Vale of Glamorgan, found a ready market in Bristol. Coal went across the Channel in considerable quantities, partly for industrial purposes, and even more for burning lime, a fertilizer heartily recommended by the most advanced agriculturalists of the age. Nearly all the coal went in the spring and summer months; a bulky cargo of this kind was in winter too risky for the small vessels engaged in the trade, the largest of which were never much more than sixty tons and the average nearer thirty or forty. Nor was traffic entirely legitimate. The Channel was in Tudor times a hotbed of piracy. The pirates were usually in collusion with the justices of the peace, and Cardiff was, in 1577, described as 'the general resort of pirates and there they are sheltered and protected'. But a major 'clean-up' of pirates took place in that year and thereafter the port laboured under no such evil reputation.

The changing economic scene was the backcloth of major social changes. The institutions and classes of medieval times were replaced by a newer pattern of landowner, small freeholder or tenant-farmer, and landless labourers, bound together by a cash nexus and not the ties of kin or feudalism. On the poor the inflation of the age often pressed hard and necessitated the introduction of a new poor relief to replace the charity formerly dispensed by the Church. For those who could keep their rents down or who farmed their own lands, rising prices were not unpropitious. But it was the relatively numerous class of small squires, from whose ranks lawyers and parsons as well as landlords were often drawn, who found this a golden age. A more peaceful social order and greater prosperity gave many of them the means of indulging a taste for literature and scholarship. Educated at the new grammar schools, they frequently went on to the Inns of Court or to the universities. Here they imbibed Renaissance notions of the complete man: scholar and man of taste, as well as soldier and man of affairs. They acquired a liking for English, French and Latin literature, though such inclinations were far from unknown among their forbears. Like their forefathers, also, many of them continued their patronage of the native literature. Poetry in *cynghanedd*, the traditional fixed metres, was composed by professional poets who went on circuit from one gentleman's house to another. Alongside it there flowered the newer growth of Welsh poetry in the free metres. But Glamorgan's most significant contribution to Welsh literature at this time was the prose turned out by a virile and gifted school of writers responsible for turning into Welsh, texts in English, French and Latin. Welsh antiquities also found distinguished exponents during the period. Rhys Merrick (d. 1586/7), a squireen of the Vale, is a minor figure characteristic of that Tudor scholarship which compiled county antiquarian surveys. Sir Edward Stradling (1529–1609) of St. Donats wrote an account of the Norman conquest of Glamorgan which until recent times misled historians about the true nature of that event. For all that, he was a fine scholar, a munificent patron, and the possessor of one of the finest private libraries in the land.

Some of the squirearchy's houses still survive. Small and unpretentious, the mansions of this period are none the less buildings of charm and distinction. The most notable is Beaupré, near St. Hilary, whose delightful Renaissance porch is the most beautiful thing of its kind in South Wales. The house at Cefn Mably, now a hospital, retains its handsome oak panelling and a reputed priest's hiding-hole. It may not be inappropriate that one of the best examples, St. Fagans, in this 'century of the common man' houses the Welsh Folk Museum. Flemingston Court, now a farm, Llansannor Court, and Llanmihangel Place, all near Cowbridge, are still privately inhabited. The last-named boasts a splendidly-panelled hall or dining-room, with a Tudor mantelpiece in which several coats of arms are carved in stone. What remains of these houses still speaks eloquently of the vigour, confidence, stability and good taste of that society soon to be shaken to its foundations by the outbreak of civil strife.

FROM THE CIVIL WAR TO THE INDUSTRIAL REVOLUTION

J. F. Rees

When the Civil War broke out in August 1642, Parliament had little prospect of any support in Glamorgan and Monmouthshire. It is true that Philip Herbert, Earl of Pembroke, who held a considerable part of the old lordship of Glamorgan, was a Parliamentarian; but his interests were elsewhere and he exercised no influence on the local situation. The leadership in the absence of one dominating personality therefore devolved on the chief families of the Vale of Glamorgan—the Stradlings of St. Donats, the Auberys of Llantrithyd, the Bassets of Beaupré and the Carnes of Ewenny. They were all staunch Royalists. In Monmouthshire it was different. There Henry Somerset, Marquis of Worcester, lived in semi-feudal state at Raglan Castle. He was one of the wealthiest men in the kingdom. As he was too old to take the field he was prepared to give the King most generous financial aid. But his eldest son, Edward, Lord Herbert of Raglan, was anxious to play an active part. The family was Catholic and the King knew that it would create a serious prejudice against his cause if he gave him a commission. He appointed William Seymour, Marquis of Hertford, Lieutenant-General of the Western Counties, including South Wales. On 3rd October he crossed from Minehead to Cardiff in some coal barges he found there and took possession of the castle. Steps were taken at once to levy forces for the King throughout South Wales. Some regiments had already been hastily raised and were sent to join him in his advance from Shrewsbury towards London. They were untrained and ill-equipped and suffered heavy casualties at the battle of Edgehill on 23rd October. William Herbert, of Cogan Pill, the member for Cardiff, was killed, and Sir Edward Stradling, of St. Donats, was taken prisoner.

The King, after the failure of the direct attack on London, withdrew to Oxford. Early in November Hertford made an attempt to take a large body of Welsh recruits there. Since both Gloucester and Hereford were then held for the Parliament he made for Tewkesbury; but there he was overtaken and forced to retreat. A second attempt was more successful. He reached Oxford with some two thousand men just before Christmas. Hertford did not return to Wales. There had been some friction between him and Lord Herbert of Raglan. The King now realized the importance of the financial help he was receiving from the Somerset family, and in defiance of anti-Catholic opinion he gave Lord Herbert of Raglan a commission as Lieutenant-General in South Wales and Monmouthshire. In return Lord Herbert engaged to raise at his own expense a sufficient force to take Gloucester. This project proved disastrous. The levies, about 1,500 foot and 500 horses, reached Highnam on the outskirts of Gloucester and encamped there. They were surprised by the Parliamentary General, Sir William Waller, who had crossed the Severn without their knowledge, and they surrendered on 24th March, 1643, without striking a blow. In an attempt to wipe out the reproach of this fiasco, Lord Herbert raised a much larger force some months later when he learnt that the King himself had decided to lay siege to Gloucester. The siege began on 10th August. The defence

by Lieutenant-Colonel Edward Massey and the relief by the Earl of Essex constitute one of the critical moments of the Civil War.

South Wales was no longer an easy field for the recruitment of infantry. When Prince Rupert, in the following year, attempted to raise reinforcements for the relief of York he found it necessary to appoint his own nominees as officers and to resort to impressment. Sir Charles Gerard was given charge of South Wales. He had seen service on the Continent and adopted the methods he had learnt there. The result became apparent after the Royalist defeats at Marston Moor (2nd July, 1644) and Naseby (14th June, 1645). The King made a personal appeal for further help. He spent the first fortnight of July as the guest of the Marquis of Worcester at Raglan Castle. He went to Cardiff on the 16th to meet the local Commissioners of Array. They were making such poor progress that it was decided to instruct the Sheriffs to call out all men fit for service. This proved a fatal move. The Glamorgan levies demanded redress of grievances before they would agree to any proposals. The King met them at St. Fagans on 29th July. They asked that the governor of Cardiff Castle, Sir Timothy Tyrell, should be removed and the post entrusted to a local gentleman. Also that the arrears of charges imposed by Sir Charles Gerard should be revoked. The meeting was adjourned to the next day when it assembled on Cefn Onn, north of Cardiff. The King agreed to remove Sir Timothy Tyrell, and Sir Richard Basset of Beaupré was nominated as his successor. Encouraged by this success they demanded that Sir Charles Gerard should be deprived of his command in South Wales. Again the King had to comply. Up to this point the opposition seems to have been unanimous ; but soon differences emerged between such Royalists as Sir John Aubery of Llantrithyd and Edward Carne of Ewenny on the one hand and Edward Pritchard of Llancaiach and Miles Button of Cottrell on the other. The latter had Puritan leanings. The matter came to a head in February 1646 when Edward Carne declared for the King. He stated that the understanding of the previous year had not been honoured. Men of no social standing had been appointed to the County Committee; in fact they included 'schismatics of several Kinds' and 'the Common Prayer Book had been commonly traduced and on several Sundays its use had been altogether omitted at Cardiff'. Carne hoped for help from a force of Monmouthshire Royalists from Raglan led by Sir Nicholas Kemys of Cefn Mably; but the intervention of Rowland Laugharne, the Parliamentary leader in West Wales proved decisive. The revolt was suppressed. The gentry of the Vale of Glamorgan made another demonstration in June 1647. The lead was taken by Sir Richard Basset of Beaupré and the Stradling brothers of St. Donats. Again one of the grievances was the partiality towards the new sects.

Meanwhile the Royalists had encountered difficulties in Monmouthshire. Sir Jacob Astley, who had succeeded Gerard as Royalist leader in South Wales, summoned commissioners to Abergavenny to urge them to assist against the Scots who were then besieging Hereford. They demanded that English officers should be deprived of all commands. When Astley tried to discover who were the leaders of the opposition, Sir Trevor Williams of Llangibby made a vigorous protest. There had long been a latent feeling against the dominance of the Somerset family. This

was now openly expressed by Thomas Morgan of Machen and William Herbert of Colebrook. The King decided to deal drastically with the malconents. At a further meeting at Abergavenny on 11th September, 1645, he committed Thomas Morgan, William Herbert, Sir Trevor Williams and others as 'hinderers' of the plan for relieving Hereford. The show of force had little effect. The Royalist cause had suffered such heavy defeats that there was a general disposition in favour of adjustment to the changed circumstances. Only Raglan Castle held out in South Wales. It was ultimately surrendered by the Marquis of Worcester to Sir Thomas Fairfax on 19th August, 1646. The uneasy peace which followed was marked by a crop of Royalist plots. These might not have had any effect in South Wales had not some of the former Parliamentary units resisted disbandment. Royalists threw in their lot with them. A large composite force, of which Rowland Laugharne assumed command, threatened Cardiff. On 8th May, 1648, their march was intercepted by seasoned Parliamentary troops near St. Fagans and they were completely defeated. The danger had been so great that Cromwell hastened to South Wales. He reached Cardiff on 16th May and continued his march to Pembroke where Laugharne held out until 11th July. He left Colonel Isaac Ewer to reduce Chepstow Castle, which had been seized by Sir Nicholas Kemeys of Cefn Mably and Monmouthshire Royalists. It was stormed on 25th May, Sir Nicholas being killed in the assault.

Reference has been made to the growing religious differences which led to dissension between the Glamorgan leaders in the later stages of the Civil War. Puritanism had made little progress in the region. Action had been taken in 1635 against William Wroth, rector of Llanvaches, near Chepstow, and William Erbury, vicar of St. Mary's, Cardiff, in the Court of High Commission for irregular practices. Erbury was forced to resign his living, and his curate, Walter Cradock, was deprived of his licence by the Bishop of Llandaff. William Wroth (died in 1641) spent the last few years of his life in ministering to a group of followers who formed a 'gathered church' at Llanvaches which was the first Independent cause in Wales. When the Civil War broke out the members fled to Bristol. The defeat of the King completely changed the situation. The wealth of the Church was now at the disposal of Parliament. On one charge or another many clergymen were expelled from their livings. But it was difficult to find suitable successors. Walter Cradock was appointed an itinerant preacher in Wales but he could make little headway. Parliament apparently had great confidence in him. When a large body of Welsh foot captured at Naseby had been marched through the streets of London and imprisoned in Tothill fields, he was sent to preach to them in their native language. It was probably on the advice of Cradock that in 1650 the Act for the Better Propagation of the Gospel in Wales was passed. He was one of the twenty-five examiners appointed to consider the suitability of those licensed to preach. The Act lapsed after three years, but the Puritan movement grew in strength during the years of the Interregnum. A number of 'gathered churches', Independent and Baptist, were formed, some of them greatly influenced by the impact of Quakerism. After the Restoration these dissenting bodies suffered under the Penal Laws until the Toleration Act conceded

freedom of worship, though it did not remove political disabilities. It is impossible to assess at all accurately the number of the adherents of the dissenting bodies. They were rent by so much theological disputation that their missionary zeal must have suffered. The established Church was hampered by its poverty. The tithes were largely impropriated and the lay holders paid such meagre stipends to the vicars that they were often forced to eke out their income by holding several livings, with consequent non-residence. The general picture of the early years of the eighteenth century is depressing; but this may be partly due to the contrast with the enthusiasm aroused by the subsequent Great Revival. The seeds of this revival were laid by the educational work of Griffith Jones of Llanddowror in Carmarthenshire, for Welsh Methodism, like that of England, was a movement within the established Church. Howell Harris, the leader, was opposed to secession and condemned a 'society' or 'experience meeting' which joined the dissenters. On the theological issue which divided John Wesley and George Whitefield—Arminianism and Calvinism—the Welsh Methodists adopted the latter. This was decided at an important 'association', which was a meeting of representatives of 'societies' held at the Watford near Caerphilly in 1743. The evangelizing work done by Howell Harris, Daniel Rowlands and others up and down the country left a permanent mark on the religious life of Wales. The eloquent itinerant preachers aroused an enthusiasm which was lacking in the formalism of the established Church and the theological niceties of the old dissenters. The Methodists found their position within the episcopal system increasingly irksome. Somewhat reluctantly they decided in 1811 to ordain their own ministers. They thus became a separate denomination with their own Confession of Faith (1823). The Great Revival had stimulated the old dissenting bodies to greater activity and nonconformity came to play a leading part in the religious, and indeed the political, life of the Welsh people, in the course of the nineteenth century. The disestablishment of the Church became an issue in the later years. Eventually a Bill to disestablish and partially disendow the Church was passed in 1914, but its operation was suspended until the end of the War; the Church in Wales came into existence on 31st March, 1920.

THE INDUSTRIAL REVOLUTION AND AFTER

J. F. Rees

Before the middle of the eighteenth century there was little indication of the future industrialization of the region. In the reign of Elizabeth I, shortage of fuel was driving the Sussex iron-masters to woodland districts where charcoal burners could supply their needs. There are several references to furnaces in Glamorgan, but they did not serve as a foundation for a permanent industry. Coal also had long been worked on a small scale, especially at outcrops. It was used locally and shipped across the Bristol Channel. Wire works were established at Tintern and experiments in tinplating were made at Pontypool. The region, however, remained agricultural in the lowlands and pastoral in the hill country. The density of population was

probably greater than that of Wales as a whole. There were market towns such as Cowbridge and Abergavenny, and ports with small tidal quays at the mouths of the rivers. The chief of these were Chepstow, Newport, Cardiff, and Aberthaw. The largest of the towns had less than two thousand inhabitants.

The beginning of the industrial revolution can be traced to successful enterprises in the Merthyr Tydfil area. In 1759 a partnership of nine persons, with a capital of £4,000, leased extensive mineral rights and proceeded to build furnaces on the banks of the Dowlais stream. Among them was Isaac Wilkinson, who had introduced the new process of coking coal as a fuel for smelting iron at his works in Bersham, near Wrexham. John Guest was appointed manager of the new venture. He came from Broseley in Shropshire, and it was obviously intended that he should experiment with the coking qualities of the local coal. At first progress was slow; but by 1782, when Guest was admitted to the partnership, the Dowlais Works was well launched on its successful career. Meanwhile, the projector, Anthony Bacon, had taken a lease on four thousand acres of a neighbouring estate. There he set up the first furnace at Cyfarthfa. In 1786, Richard Crawshay, a Yorkshireman who had a hardware business in London, got control and displayed great energy and resource in developing the enterprise. Thus were founded the two great dynasties of South Wales iron-masters—the Guests and Crawshays. There were two other ironworks in the neighbourhood—Plymouth and Penydarren—developed by the Hills and Homfrays, respectively. By 1815 there was a line of ironworks stretching from Hirwaun to Blaenavon along the northern outcrop of the Coal Measures. The advantages they enjoyed were abundant coal, easily worked, and the clay ironstone associated with it. Two new methods were exploited to the full, that of smelting with coke and the puddling process by which pig-iron could be reduced to malleable or wrought iron. The industry spread to the Monmouthshire Valleys—the Tredegar ironworks in the Sirhowy valley and the Ebbw ironworks in the Ebbw valley—while the ironworks at Nantyglo came to rival even those of Dowlais and Cyfarthfa. The first half of the nineteenth century was the great period of the iron industry. South Wales contributed about one-third of the total production of Great Britain.

The growth of Merthyr is revealed in the census returns. In 1801 it had a population of 7,705 and was by far the largest town in Wales (Cardiff 1,870; Newport 1,135). As late as 1861, Merthyr still led with a population of 49,794; but the ports now showed striking increases—Cardiff 32,954 and Newport 23,249. The natural outlet for iron and iron products from the Merthyr district was by way of the Taff gap at Tongwynlais. The iron-masters first projected an improvement of the roads, a means of transport slow and expensive when it depended on pack horses. Then they decided to promote the construction of a canal—the Glamorganshire Canal—which was opened for traffic in 1794. It ran from Merthyr to a tidal lock at Cardiff, a distance of over twenty-five miles in the course of which, owing to the contours, it passed through fifty locks. The canal was the most important factor in the development of Cardiff before 1840. But a new impetus was given to it by the second Marquis of Bute who, from his own resources, built the West Bute Dock which was opened in 1839. His enterprise was justified when the Taff Vale

Railway, completed from Merthyr to Cardiff in 1841, provided for an ever-increasing volume of traffic.

At that time it was not anticipated that the export of coal would play a significant part in the development of the port of Cardiff. The valuable steam coal of the hinterland had scarcely been touched. But in the 'forties considerable exploitation of it occurred in the Aberdare district, especially after a market had been found in France. In the next decade the pioneers turned to the Rhondda Valley where hitherto little coal had been worked. The first train of coal from the Rhondda was sent down to Cardiff at the end of 1855. Then began the transformation of a sparsely-populated pastoral area into an overcrowded industrial community. By the beginning of the twentieth century the population of the Rhondda was more than 112,000. The general extension of the use of steam for factories, railways and shipping made the sinking of coal mines a most profitable investment. New outlets were needed for the export of coal. Penarth Docks, closely associated with the Taff Vale Railway, were opened in 1865. Facilities at Cardiff were enlarged by the construction of the Bute East Dock (1859), the Roath Dock (1887) and was finally completed with the opening of the Queen Alexandra Dock in 1907. But the provision made at Cardiff had not satisfied the requirements of the trade. Complaints of the monopoly enjoyed by the Taff Vale Railway and the Bute Docks Company became insistent. In particular, it was alleged that it was restricting the development of the Rhondda valleys. A scheme was therefore promoted to construct a railway to Barry, where new docks were to be built. It was completed in 1889 at a cost of £2 million and was completely justified. The volume of trade required a second dock in 1898 and a third in 1914. In 1913 Barry docks achieved a record export of over eleven million tons of coal, which, in that year, exceeded that of Cardiff. Barry itself, which had a population of a few hundreds in the eighties, had reached 27,030 by 1901 and 33,763 by 1911.

Meanwhile the iron industry had experienced a complete technological revolution. The new processes of manufacturing steel made change inevitable. The challenge came in the 'sixties and was not immediately met. By the 'seventies, however, many of the smaller ironworks along the northern outcrop of the coalfield closed. Those in a stronger position—now converted into joint-stock companies—turned to steel. They—Dowlais, Cyfarthfa, Tredegar, Blaenavon and Ebbw Vale—remained on their original sites; but the growing dependence on imported iron ore made a movement to tidal water desirable. This was recognized by the Dowlais Company which built a branch of its works on the East Moors at Cardiff. The Cardiff–Dowlais Iron and Steel Works was opened in 1891. It was an indication of an ultimate general change in the location of the industry.

The dependence of the region on coal and iron and steel explains what happened after the end of the First World War. There were practically no secondary industries, for the advantages enjoyed by the heavy industries had naturally attracted the available capital and labour. The contraction of world markets and the growing competition of oil had serious consequences for the coal industry. There was heavy unemployment and persistent migration of workers and their families, particularly

to the Midlands and the London area. Between the census of 1921 and that of 1931 there was a net loss by migration of 230,000. A survey conducted by the University College at the request of the Board of Trade in the latter year estimated that there were still about 40,000 insurable workers surplus to the requirements of the region. Was it possible to revive the basic industries or to introduce new industries? Should labour transference be encouraged or not? If encouraged, what would be the social consequences for the region? These were the questions debated, investigated and reported upon in the inter-war years. The Special Areas Act came into effect in January 1935 and the Special Commissioner reported in July that he could see no prospect of reducing the unemployment in these areas to the national average. Meanwhile a South Wales Development Council had been established and was advocating the setting up of trading estates in order to diversify the industrial structure. Then a new threat caused great alarm. Richard Thomas and Company proposed to build a strip mill for making tinplate on the American method at Redbourn in Lincolnshire. South Wales had long enjoyed a virtual monopoly of this industry. The upshot of the resultant controversy was that the project was abandoned, and Richard Thomas and Company purchased the site of the steel works at Ebbw Vale, which had been closed for some time, and installed the new machinery there. The position in 1937 was distinctly better. More coal was raised and exported. There was increased production of steel. The scheme for a trading estate was making progress. A second industrial survey focused attention on possible new industries and indicated suitable sites for them. The policy of diversification was fully accepted. The Special Commissioner acknowledged that the supreme need was to bring new industries to South Wales and declared that it was an end to which he was devoting his time and attention. Migration, however, was still continuing, but at a lesser rate. The second industrial survey estimated that the net loss by migration between 1931 and 1935 was over 70,000.

The site chosen for the trading estate was at Treforest, some nine miles north of Cardiff. There factories could be built on level ground and the necessary services provided, while it was conveniently situated to draw off some of the unemployed from the valleys. The inducement to industrialists was that they could rent the factories and use their available capital on equipment and development. Applications came in from a wide variety of firms, and by the outbreak of the Second World War there were twenty factories in production, employing 2,500 workers. Notable among the new enterprises were those introduced by refugees from Austria and Czechoslovakia who were directed to the Special Areas. The war, as it proceeded, exercised a growing influence on the trading estate. Alternative accommodation was found for some of the less essential industries, and factories were enlarged and new ones built, particularly for the manufacture of aircraft components. By the end of the war the estate employed 17,000. At the same time, Royal Ordnance Factories provided a heavy demand for labour; that at Bridgend employed some 34,000, mostly women and girls. In all there were, at the peak, at least 130,000 at work in industries directly connected with the war effort.

The return to peace presented serious problems. With these the Welsh Reconstruction Advisory Council (which reported in 1944) attempted to deal. It

was naturally influenced by the experience of the inter-war years. Attention was drawn to what had been achieved under the Special Areas Acts. It was recommended that where there was likely to be substantial unemployment, steps should be taken to direct the location of industry. After the war, responsibility for reconstruction passed to the Board of Trade. The largest Royal Ordnance Factory in the region—Bridgend—was converted into an industrial estate on the model of Treforest. New factories were built with Treasury finance in advance of demand. The old sites at Cyfarthfa and Dowlais were cleared for new factories. Treforest became the headquarters of the organization which had the general oversight of the estates and individual factories reconditioned or built in Wales under the Distribution of Industry Acts. The annual reports on Government action in Wales provide statistics of the progress in diversification. In 1950 the total unemployment was 32,382, and in July 1955 it had fallen to 13,400, the lowest ever recorded in peace-time. There was a serious shortage of labour in the South Wales Coalfield. Wastage was not compensated for by recruitment. There were, of course, many factors other than direct Government action involved in the general position. These are revealed by an analysis of the present industrial structure of the region.

VII

THE GROWTH OF POPULATION

BRINLEY THOMAS

THE CITY

CARDIFF owes its existence to the age of steam coal in the second half of the nineteenth century; it was a creation of the Victorian era. Between 1801 and 1841 it had grown from an insignificant village of 1,870 people to a small township of 11,400; the centre of the industrial revolution in South Wales was the town of Merthyr Tydfil with a population of 35,000 in 1841. That year saw the opening of the Taff Vale Railway linking Merthyr and Cardiff, with connections to the Aberdare valley in 1846 and the two Rhondda valleys in the following decade. Cardiff was the natural outlet and it developed the largest coal-exporting trade in the world.

The rate of growth of population and the remarkable rise and fall of the coal export trade are given in Table I.

TABLE I

CARDIFF: POPULATION AND PORT TRAFFIC, 1841–1957

Year	*Population*[1]	*Exports of coal and patent fuel* 000 *tons*	*Total exports* 000 *tons*	*Total imports* 000 *tons*
1841	11,442	87	108	9
1851	20,258	708	827	92
1861	41,422	1,915	2,110	220
1871	57,363	1,945	2,284	374
1881	82,761	5,413	5,612	996
1891	128,915	7,246	7,387	1,406
1901	164,333	7,646	7,837	1,948
1911	182,259	9,910	10,199	1,885
1921	220,827	4,106	4,259	948
1931	226,937	5,743	5,900	1,402
1939	227,659	5,731	5,821	1,763
1951	243,632	1,221	1,366	1,952
1957	251,300	533	669	2,042

[1] The census figures have been adjusted as follows: 1841–1911 at 1921 boundaries; 1921–1957 at 1951 boundaries.

Sources: Population censuses; and the port traffic figures through the courtesy of the Chief Docks Manager, South Wales.

The pace of expansion in the sixty years 1851–1911 was phenomenal. The volume of coal exports went up fourteenfold and the population of Cardiff ninefold; and a corresponding extension took place in investment in railway and port facilities to handle the enormous flow of traffic.

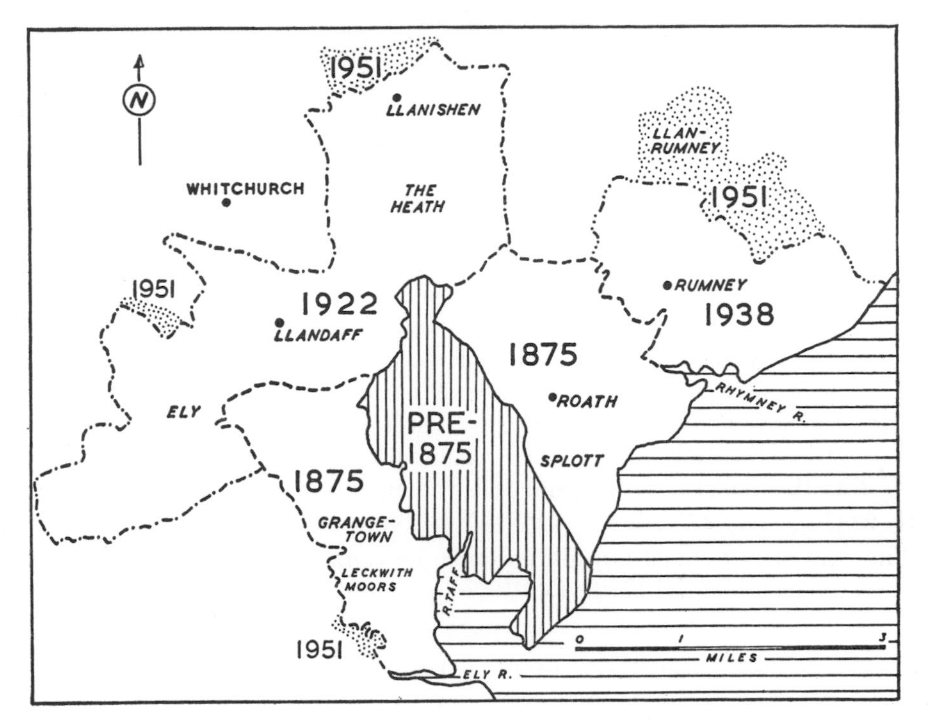

Fig. 17. CARDIFF: BOUNDARY CHANGES, 1875–1960

Up to 1875 the core was a relatively small area running north from the mouth of the Taff comprising the parishes of St. John and St. Mary. In 1875 an area comprising the parish of Roath and parts of Leckwith and Llandaff was added. An important addition occurred in 1922 when Michaelston-super-Ely, St. Fagans and parts of Whitchurch, Llanishen, Caerau, Llandaff and Llanedeyrn were incorporated. Minor changes in 1938 and 1951 brought in small parts of St. Mellons, Lisvane, Penarth and Radyr. The Whitchurch area shown in the map, although it lies in Cardiff Rural District, is virtually a part of the population unit which makes up the city.

With the turn of the century the rate of population growth began to diminish sharply. One reason was that the capacity built at Cardiff docks was inadequate to cope with the buoyant export demand for Rhondda and Aberdare coals, so that a new port had to be brought into existence at Barry. The effect may be seen in the following figures:

	Cardiff		*Barry*	
	1889	1913	1889	1913
	tons	*tons*	*tons*	*tons*
Coal exports	7,736,000	10,577,000	1,074,000	11,050,000
Total trade	9,701,000	13,677,000	1,106,000	11,736,000

By 1913 more coal was being shipped from Barry than from Cardiff itself. The population of Barry grew from 494 in 1881 to 33,763 in 1911.

In common with the rest of the coalfield, Cardiff attracted population from a wide area. The birthplaces figures of the 1911 census brought out the following picture:

TABLE II

BIRTHPLACES OF PERSONS ENUMERATED IN CARDIFF IN 1911

Place of birth	Population in 1911 Males	Females	Persons	Percentage distribution
				%
Cardiff	46,167	48,213	94,380	52
Glamorgan excluding Cardiff	6,311	8,388	14,699	8
Wales excluding Glamorgan ..	6,716	8,329	15,045	8
Total Wales	59,194	64,930	124,124	68
England	23,133	22,833	45,966	25
Scotland	996	686	1,682	3 (Scotland and Ireland)
Ireland	1,657	1,467	3,124	
Oversea British Empire ..	1,189	478	1,667	3 (Oversea British Empire and Foreign countries)
Foreign countries	2,740	1,054	3,794	
At sea	29	28	57	1 (At sea and Not stated)
Not stated	790	1,055	1,845	
Total	89,728	92,531	182,259	100

Source: *Census of England and Wales*, 1911, *County of Glamorgan*, Table 30, p. 77.

Only half the people living in Cardiff in 1911 had been born there; 25 per cent had come from England, 16 per cent from the rest of Wales, 3 per cent from Scotland and Ireland, and 3 per cent from foreign countries. The 5,400 from foreign or British Empire countries, the majority of them males, were mainly coloured people of many races who settled in the area around the docks.

After the First World War the long depression in the coal export trade entailed a formidable amount of surplus capacity at the ports; the drastic fall in outward traffic was only slightly counterbalanced by the increase in imports. The contraction continued after the Second World War and coal exports from Cardiff in 1957 were a mere 500,000 tons, even lower than they were in 1851. During the last forty-six years the population of Cardiff has risen by only 38 per cent; port traffic has receded to the background; and there have been significant changes in the balance of employment since 1945, with a considerable increase in manufacturing. What was a village of less than 2,000 people at the beginning of the nineteenth century is now the capital of Wales with a population of over a quarter of a million.

THE REGION

Pre-1913 Expansion

The development of the hinterland of Cardiff up to the First World War may be shown by examining the flow of migrants into the county of Glamorgan between 1861 and 1911.

TABLE III

ESTIMATED NUMBER OF MIGRANTS ENTERING GLAMORGAN (CIVIL COUNTY), 1861–1911

Area of origin	1861–71	1871–81	1881–91	1891–1901	1901–11
Welsh counties	16,300	31,400	47,900	44,800	42,900
South-west England	2,100	21,100	17,300	15,200	14,200
London and the South-east ..	400	3,600	5,900	4,700	12,400
Rest of England	1,900	17,600	32,800	21,900	53,400
Scotland and Ireland ..	300	1,000	4,600	7,800	5,600
Total	21,000	74,700	108,500	94,400	128,500

Source: Brinley Thomas, 'The Migration of Labour into the Glamorganshire Coalfield 1861–1911', *Economica*, November 1930, pp. 293–4.

As more capital was invested in the sinking of new pits, the radius from which labour was recruited became more extensive. In the sixties the majority of the 21,000 migrants came from Welsh rural counties; but in the eighties 16 per cent of the large total of 108,500 were drawn from Somerset, Devon and Cornwall, 36 per cent from the rest of England, and 4 per cent from Scotland and Ireland. During the boom years 1901–11 only one-third of the migrants came from the rest of Wales and nearly two-thirds from England. The coalfield had a very high fertility rate; the addition to the population of Glamorgan through excess of births over deaths rose from 61,000 in the decade 1861–71 to 169,000 in 1901–11. The natural increase in 1901–11 as a proportion of the population at the beginning of the decade was 19·9 per cent in Glamorgan as against 12·4 per cent in England and Wales. The most remarkable example of hectic expansion was the Rhondda valleys where population grew from 4,000 to 163,000 in the sixty years 1861–1921, and the density became no less than 23,680 persons per square mile of area built upon.[1]

A study of fluctuations in labour recruitment brings out an interesting difference between the evolution of the Welsh and the English coalfields in the era of rapid expansion. Investment in mining did not occur evenly in all coalfields. By distinguishing between areas concentrating on exports and those producing for home consumption, we find that the phases in their development did not coincide. Table IV sets out for the Glamorgan–Monmouth colliery districts on the one hand, and the English districts on the other, the net addition to the labour force every decade between 1851 and 1910.

TABLE IV

DECENNIAL NET GAIN (+) OR LOSS (—) BY MIGRATION (THOUSANDS), 1851–1911

Decade	*Glamorgan–Monmouth colliery districts*	*English colliery districts**
1851–60	+ 40	+ 64
1861–70	+ 11	+ 80
1871–80	+ 12	+ 72
1881–90	+ 87	+ 3
1891–1900	+ 40	+ 45
1901–10	+ 129	— 15

* Including Wrexham.

Source: A. K. Cairncross, 'Internal Migration in Victorian England', *The Manchester School*, Vol. XVII, 1949, p. 86.

[1] *Commission of Enquiry into Industrial Unrest, No. 7 Division, Report for Wales including Monmouthshire*, Cd. 8668, 1917, p. 14.

There is a clear inverse relation between the rate of growth of the Welsh and the English coalfields. In the sixties and seventies the major advance was in England; in the eighties Glamorgan–Monmouth overshadowed the rest; the English districts took the lead in the nineties, and in 1901–11 South Wales dominated the scene to such an extent that the English districts as a whole actually had a net loss by migration. The key to this interesting time pattern is to be found in the concentration of South Wales on exports; the opening up of the Glamorgan–Monmouth mining areas fluctuated in harmony with the British export sector, whereas the output of English coals mainly consumed at home was sensitive to the long swing in the rate of domestic capital construction. The evolution of the region of which Cardiff was the major port may thus be seen as part of the alternation of upswings as between the export sector and the home construction sector of the United Kingdom between 1850 and 1913.[1]

Inter-war Contraction

After the vigorous upsurge of activity up to 1913, the reaction caused by the depression after the First World War was severe; an area which had been attracting population on a large scale now experienced substantial outward migration. The following examples indicate the sharp reversal of trend in the inter-censal period, 1921–31:

	Population 1921	1931	*Amount of increase* (+) *or decrease* (—)	% *Decrease by migration*
Cardiff C.B. ..	219,580	223,589	+ 4,009	— 5·8
Merthyr Tydfil C.B.	80,116	71,108	— 9,008	— 16·9
Aberdare U.D. ..	55,007	48,746	— 6,261	— 16·4
Maesteg U.D. ..	28,917	25,570	— 3,347	— 22·1
Mountain Ash U.D.	43,287	38,386	— 4,901	— 21·2
Rhondda U.D. ..	162,717	141,346	— 21,371	— 21·7
Glamorgan Administrative County (with associated County Boroughs)	1,252,481	1,225,717	— 26,764	— 10·8

Source: *Census of England and Wales*, 1931, *County of Glamorgan* (*Part* 1), H.M.S.O., 1932, p. 1.

The Rhondda valleys, the heart of the steam coal area, lost one-fifth of their 1921 population in that decade; 52 per cent of the migrants were aged 15–29, and 19 per cent were aged 30–44. In South Wales as a whole a quarter of a million people were lost through migration.

[1] See Brinley Thomas, *Migration and Economic Growth* (Cambridge University Press, 1954), chapters VII, VIII, and XI.

The depression had a marked effect on the rate of fertility. The birth rate in the coal-mining districts of Glamorgan fell from 33·5 per 1,000 in 1913 to 17·6 per 1,000 in 1929. Whereas in 1913 the rate of fertility had been 34 per cent higher than the average for England and Wales, by 1929 it was only 8 per cent higher. The lower birth rate and the heavy emigration combined to raise the proportion of middle-aged and elderly in the population.

Recent Trends

In the last fifteen years Cardiff and its region entered a new phase of economic growth which is more firmly based than the expansion in the early years of the century. As shown in Chapter VIII, the former intensive specialization on export trade has been replaced by a more diverse economy. These changes are reflected in the industrial distribution of the insured population of Cardiff in 1958 as compared with 1938.

TABLE V

CARDIFF: INDUSTRIAL CLASSIFICATION OF INSURED PERSONS IN EMPLOYMENT, 1938 AND 1958

Industry Group	1938		1958	
	Males	Females	Males	Females
Metal manufacturing	4,883	183	8,857	639
General manufacturing	13,713	5,633	21,404	8,304
Transport	12,115	209	11,607	1,310
Distribution	10,203	6,256	8,563	9,553
Building	7,119	53	8,460	506
Gas, water, electricity	1,641	96	2,660	460
National and local government	3,373	1,010	4,517	1,190
Miscellaneous services	2,833	3,673	2,766	8,905
Professional services	1,479	1,019	6,703	9,868
Other	658	6	1,703	628
Ex-service not classified	—	—	74	4
Total	58,017	18,138	77,314	41,367

Source: Wales Office, Ministry of Labour.

Note.—Because of the change in the basis of insurance between 1938 and 1958 the figures are not quite comparable, but this does not affect the purpose in hand.

The most striking feature is the increase in the number of women workers who now comprise 35 per cent of the city's insured population; seven out of ten of them are in distributive, professional and miscellaneous services. The employment of men in manufacturing, including iron and steel, has gone up by nearly two-thirds, from 18,600 to 30,000. This is part of a general trend in Wales where manufacturing in the decade 1948–58 expanded twice as fast as it did in Great Britain.

In recent years there has been a steady increase in population in contrast to inter-war experience.

Area	1951 *Resident population* (*nearest thousand*)	1957 *Estimated home population* (*mid-year*) (*nearest thousand*)
Wales	2,584,000	2,611,000
Glamorgan ..	1,203,000	1,213,000
Cardiff ..	244,000	251,000

Net Loss (—) or Gain (+) by Migration 1951–57

Cardiff	Glamorgan	Wales	England	Scotland	N. Ireland	Eire
Annual Rate per 1,000 Mean Population						
— 0·9	— 2·2	— 1·9	+ 1·2	— 5·3	— 7·0	— 13·4

The rate of net loss by migration in Wales in 1951–57 was relatively low; the rate for Scotland was three times as high and that for Northern Ireland nearly four times. Cardiff's rate is less than half that of Wales, while the region's rate is slightly higher. With a slowly increasing population and a varied range of industries, Cardiff and its hinterland can expect to reap the advantages of a more balanced growth than in the past.

VIII

INDUSTRIAL STRUCTURE

LESLIE JONES

THE region which comprises the eastern valleys of the South Wales coalfield, the agricultural areas of east Monmouthshire and the Vale of Glamorgan, together with the ports of Newport, Cardiff, Barry and Penarth, lies almost entirely within the South Wales Development Area and contains over 40 per cent of the insured workers in Wales.

The nineteenth-century industrial development was greatly influenced by the natural resources of the region. It became an important centre of iron production and the greatest coal exporting region in the world, manufacturing industry being largely neglected. This simple, highly specialized, economy reached its fulfilment in the early years of the present century, but later it proved to be extremely vulnerable to the technological changes and general economic conditions of the inter-war years. For most of that period the region suffered chronic industrial depression and great social distress. In the 'thirties certain localities derived some benefit from the policy of diversifying industry pursued under the Special Areas legislation. By 1939 a variety of new industries had been introduced into the region and these gave employment to about 5,000 people, but when war broke out nearly 55,000, just over 16 per cent of the insured population, were unemployed.

The distribution of the insured population in 1939 and 1957 is given in Table I, which emphasises the specialized nature of the pre-war economy. Almost one-third of the insured population was engaged in coal mining. The service trades accounted for a similar proportion and a surprisingly large number was attached to the building industry. Employment in manufacturing was largely concentrated on metal manufacturing (mainly steel and tinplates) and heavy engineering. These industries employed a predominantly male labour force, consequently the ratio of women workers to the total was only 14 per cent as compared with double this proportion in the United Kingdom.

The tendency towards extreme specialization, so characteristic of the region as a whole, was most striking in the mining valleys. Here nearly 110,000, almost 60 per cent of the insured male population, were engaged in coal mining. Less than 24,000 were employed in manufacturing, and more than half of these were concentrated in metal manufacturing. Engineering was unimportant, and so was miscellaneous manufacturing. Indeed, building and contracting was more important than manufacturing. But in building there is much casual work which enabled unemployed miners and steel workers to drift into the industry. The new light industries were beginning to provide a greater variety of employment for women, but they formed only 8 per cent of the labour force, and the majority of them were in the service trades.

When we turn to the coastal area, we find that a much larger proportion of the male insured population was engaged in manufacturing. There was some diversity of activity within the sector, but steel and engineering, which was allied to ship repairing and waggon building and repair, were the major industries. While no single industry dominated the structure, there was a tendency to concentrate on a narrow range of industries—transport, distribution and general port services—the prosperity of which was closely associated with conditions in the coal and steel industries. In the region as a whole, too large a proportion of the total insured population was either directly or indirectly dependent on these two industries.

In 1946 industrial South Wales was scheduled as a Development Area, and the region's subsequent development is closely associated with the efforts made to rehabilitate the economy by reconstructing the older industries and introducing new industries. The task was greatly facilitated by wartime developments. These had created a nucleus of highly diversified industries around which further expansion could take place, and already by 1948 the efforts made to attract new industries were beginning to show results. The region had become less dependent on its traditional industries, the labour force was more evenly balanced between males and females and unemployment had been reduced considerably. Even so, there were 22,500 unemployed in a total labour force of 444,000, and there were localities which, because of their remoteness and general unattractiveness, had not shared in the process of development by attracting new industries. The major difficulty was the lack of suitable buildings, and a determined attempt was made to deal with the problem by a programme of Government-financed factory buildings coupled with other inducements to industrialists to settle in these localities. The success of these policies can be judged, first, in relation to the changes in the distribution of the insured population, and, second, on the level of unemployment in the region.

Post-war figures of insured population are not strictly comparable with those for 1939, but they are sufficiently so to show the broad changes that have taken place. Between 1939 and 1957 manufacturing activity was greatly expanded, and in so far as the introduction of new industries has reduced the dependence of the region on a narrow range of industries the policy of diversification has been a success. Mining, although the most important single industry, has ceased to dominate the economic and social structure of the region. Manufacturing is considerably more important and is also less dependent on steel making than formerly. The range of engineering production has increased; output being no longer confined to local markets and the requirements of the coal and steel firms. In addition, a wide range of miscellaneous manufactures has been introduced and these developments have created employment opportunities for women which were entirely lacking before the war, especially in the mining valleys.

These developments also had their effect on the general level of unemployment. Table II shows that 22,500 people, representing 5·1 per cent of the insured population, were unemployed in 1948. This was considerably above the national average, but not all localities were suffering to the same extent. In the mining valleys over 7 per cent of the male workers were unemployed, and unemployment among

women was higher than it had been pre-war. By 1957 the introduction of new industries had helped to reduce unemployment in the region to 2·1 per cent, but its incidence remains uneven as between different industries and localities. A special problem exists in those mining and metallurgical communities which will not benefit from the reconstruction of the basic industries. Frequently, too, there is a high degree of physical and psychological disability among the unemployed workers; the remoteness and general unattractiveness of some of these communities aggravates the problem still further. It is not easy to find suitable sites, nor the skilled labour required, which makes it difficult to apply the principle of taking work to the workers in these more remote districts. The cost of introducing new industries would be high in relation to the benefits that would accrue, and it must be recognized that beyond a certain limit the only solution lies in the greater mobility of labour.

There is also the question of whether the policy of diversification has rendered the region less vulnerable to cyclical unemployment. By broadening the basis of industrial employment it has undoubtedly provided some defence against a cyclical decline in activity. The region is much less dependent on coal mining, and the coal industry itself, because it is no longer a major exporter, is to some extent less vulnerable to fluctuations in world trade. The effects of a cyclical decline are now likely to be more indirect but they could still be serious because cyclically sensitive industries such as steel are very large consumers of coal. Moreover a large number of the 'new' industries have built up a strong export position. It may be that they will be able to maintain their exports better than the older industries, but one cannot predict what would happen in a serious recession. Unemployment among all workers rose in 1958 but in general, however, the recession of 1956–58 did not have any violent repercussions within the region, though there are certain aspects of the unemployment situation which give rise to anxiety. The 'pockets' of unemployment have already been referred to, and Table III shows further disquieting features. Of the unemployed males in the region, 20 per cent were in building, a further 16 per cent were in 'other services' and 7·6 per cent belonged to no particular industry. In other words about 45 per cent of the men out of work in 1958 were relatively unskilled. The great majority of unemployed women were in the valleys and, what is even more disturbing, a large proportion of them were in manufacturing.

The general prosperity which the region has enjoyed, and continues to enjoy in large measure, has sprung from two sources; the reconstruction of traditional industries, and the introduction on a fairly large scale of new manufacturing industry. Electrical equipment, aircraft controls, precision instruments, toys, glass, man-made fibres, light engineering products and a host of others are now being produced in the region. It is not possible to describe in detail the many firms which have contributed to this result, but a few examples will be sufficient to indicate the diversity, and success, of the new enterprises that have been established in recent years.

At Rogerstone, just outside Newport, the Northern Aluminium Company has the largest aluminium rolling mill in Europe, with a capacity of 75,000 tons annually. This modern continuous mill is an outstanding example of large-scale production methods. New equipment which is now being installed includes a 12-foot wide hot mill, the first of its size in this country, for rolling large plate, and a system of hot coiling under tension direct from the hot finishing mill. In the remelt section, furnaces have been modernized and considerable advances have been made in semi-continuous casting of ingots and billets for subsequent rerolling. In 1958 a new range of equipment for the processing and handling of aluminium alloy plate was put into service. This was specifically designed to supply the aircraft industry with high-strength quality-controlled thick plate, and welded shipbuilding plate up to 10 feet wide. New products are being developed continuously to meet the growing and changing needs of the aluminium-using industries and to maintain its position as one of the leading European aluminium fabricating works.

There is a flourishing electrical engineering industry, and several firms are now sending cable, switchgear and transformers all over the world. Among them is South Wales Switchgear Ltd., which from modest beginnings on the Treforest Trading Estate has developed into a major producer of electrical equipment employing 2,000 in its factories at Treforest, Blackwood and Aberbargoed. The firm entered the commercial switchgear field in 1945 and it is now producing a wide variety of switchgear and transformers. It was the first to develop air-insulated metalclad design switchgear, the success of which has led to a radical change in the engineering of certain types of electrical sub-stations, and has enabled the firm to build up a strong export position. Another firm which has made substantial progress since the end of the war is Standard Telephone and Cables Ltd. It took over the Royal Ordnance Factory in Newport for the development and production of telecommunication cables and equipment and all types of rubber and plastic insulated power cable. Later the manufacture of electronic control equipment for the Services was added to its range of products. During the last three years the company has been producing electronic data-processing equipment and it is already exporting its computers to many parts of the world.

The region is also making an increasing contribution to the production of man-made fibres, and over 3,000 men and some 600 women are employed by British Nylon Spinners Ltd. in their plant at Mamhilad, near Pontypool. Production of nylon yarn was started in 1948, and by 1954 output had reached 25,000,000 lb. per annum, which is considered to be the maximum output for a nylon production unit. The processes carried out at the plant fall into two main groups; the manufacture of textile yarns from nylon polymer, and the processing of nylon yarns for the textile industry. There was no nylon yarn production in this country before the war, and since the setting up of the Pontypool plant there have been considerable technical advances, some of them revolutionary, in yarn production, textile processing and quality control. New techniques have doubled productivity since 1948, while at the same time improved physical and chemical testing processes has led to a tenfold improvement in the quality of the yarn. The number and types of yarns

produced have also been increased and they now range from heavy denier tyre cord yarns to the finest yarn in the world, and a remarkable innovation is the production of nylon stretch yarns.

The Pontypool factory, as well as being the head office of the company and the centre of its administrative and distributive organizations, also houses the experimental plant and research department. The whole undertaking offers a variety of employment never known before in the locality. Its activities present a continuous pattern of improvement which has given it an unrivalled position in the production of nylon yarn.

Coal

When the mines were nationalized in 1946 the South Wales coalfield (which was grouped with the Somerset and Forest of Dean coalfields to form the South-Western Division of the National Coal Board) was divided into six administrative areas. Of these, the No. 3 (Rhondda), No. 4 (Aberdare), No. 5 (Rhymney) and No. 6 (Monmouthshire) areas fall within the region. More than half the number of pits in production in 1957 were situated in the region. They accounted for 67 per cent of the wage earners and produced 70 per cent of the saleable output of the South Wales coalfield.

The coal deposits of the region have been extensively worked during the past hundred years, and when the mines were vested in the National Coal Board the majority of the pits had been in existence for over fifty years. Many of them were badly laid out: few had been designed for mechanized coal cutting, and technical standards were low generally. Most of the easily accessible coal had already been mined, and large-scale reconstruction and new development was necessary to arrest the decline in productivity and output.

The main post-war trends are summarized in Table IV, which shows that the steps taken by the Coal Board to improve efficiency has increased productivity and raised output. Output per man shift (O.M.S.) has risen continuously and this has been due to two main factors. First, there has been a contraction in the scale of mining and the least productive pits have been closed. The number working in the region was reduced by one-third between 1948 and 1957, and a large proportion of the output is now obtained from relatively few collieries. The other factor in improving O.M.S. has been mechanized mining. There are now very few mines in the region where coal-cutting machines are not being used, and the proportion of the coal mechanically cut now exceeds 60 per cent of the output raised and weighed, and practically all of it is now mechanically conveyed. The improvement in O.M.S. has been more marked in some areas than in others, but this is not surprising when one realizes how widely pits vary in age, natural conditions and the type of coal mined.

The improvement in productivity helped to increase the output raised and weighed by just over two million tons; this figure would have been higher had the manpower situation been less difficult. Until recently there has been a severe

shortage of labour in the mines. Post-war fluctuations in manpower show that recruitment and wastage of mining labour are greatly influenced by the level of industrial production, and when manufacturing industry is booming there is strong competition for labour from the new industries which have been established in the mining valleys. The excess demand for mining labour was accompanied by a sharp increase in absenteeism which disorganizes production and causes severe loss of output especially in mechanized pits. In the same period the amount of saleable coal increased very little. This was due to two factors: firstly, an increase in the amount of dirt filled out with the coal, partly on account of the extended use of machines and partly through working a higher proportion of poorer seams; and secondly because of the expansion and improvement in coal cleaning and preparation plants.

It is unlikely that further mechanization and short-term reorganization will add very much to productivity in the future, but improvements in efficiency and output can be expected from new sinkings and the large-scale reconstruction of existing pits, some of which are now nearing completion. Since 1947 nearly £32 million, just over two-thirds of the capital expenditure on major schemes in South Wales, has been devoted to development within the region. At Nantgarw, in the Rhymney area, a major horizon mining project has been undertaken to work reserves of coking coal estimated to be 176 million tons, the greater part of the output to be treated in coke ovens on the site. In the Aberdare Area, the Maerdy pits are being reconstructed and developed to produce 4,000 tons per day of sub-bituminous dry steam coal. The reconstructions of the Cwm Colliery in the Rhondda Area will increase its output of high-grade metallurgical coal to over 5,000 tons per day, and a great deal of development work is being undertaken in the Monmouthshire Area where the reconstruction of the Hafodyrynys Colliery is nearing completion. While it is too early to judge the outcome of these projects, large-scale mechanization and reorganization has not improved efficiency and increased output to the extent expected. But it must be remembered that the absolute priority given to current output for many years after the war impaired the Coal Board's efforts to increase efficiency, and many pits with low productivity had to be kept going. But if output has been disappointing the region is now in much better shape technically and it has been operating at a profit since 1952.

Only one of the pits closed by the Coal Board in South Wales in December 1958, as part of its emergency measures, was situated in the region, and there was no difficulty in placing the redundant miners in other pits. Competition from other fuels may, in time, lead to further closures but the region has natural advantages, especially in its reserves of high-quality coking coals, which cannot be ignored. The expansion of the South Wales steel industry is a major factor inducing the reorganization and development of the coal resources of the region, and fully justifies the heavy capital expenditure involved in the reconstruction of pits producing metallurgical coal, and new coke oven capacity at the collieries. Moreover, the region, which was at one time the greatest coal exporting area in the world, is no longer dependent on the export trade and, provided employment is maintained

at home, it is unlikely that the industry will suffer the heavy unemployment of former years.

Steel

The South Wales steel industry has grown rapidly since the war. Between 1946 and 1957 the output of crude steel in South Wales rose by 91 per cent as compared with an increase of 66 per cent in the rest of Great Britain. Thus the South Wales share of total British steel production expanded from 21 per cent to 24 per cent.

There has been a marked increase in blast furnace productivity. In South Wales the output per furnace, at 236,000 tons a year, is much greater than the average of 146,000 tons for the United Kingdom as a whole. This has been brought about mainly by an increase in the size of blast furnaces and a more intensive use of capacity.

At the finishing end the emphasis is heavily on thin, flat products—sheets, tin-plate and light products. South Wales accounts for more than half of all British deliveries of sheets and for virtually all British deliveries of tin-plate. The 80-inch continuous mill at Port Talbot, the 56-inch continuous mill at Ebbw Vale, and the 48-inch reversing mill at Orb Works, Newport, account for over 85 per cent of present sheet output, the Newport works concentrating on electrical sheet.

The largest customer is the holloware industry, which in 1957 took 550,000 tons of steel, almost all of it tin-plate, or 15 per cent of total South Wales deliveries. The next largest consumer is the motor car industry. A quarter of the finished steel output of South Wales is exported.

The main feature of the next decade will be the development by Richard Thomas and Baldwins Limited of a new integrated strip mill plant at Llanwern, near Newport. By the end of the intermediate stage, say by about 1970, these works may have grown to approximately three million ingot tons a year—the size planned for the Steel Company of Wales' works at Port Talbot in the early 'sixties. It should then have a fully continuous hot strip mill and associated cold reduction mills and tinning capacity providing a mixed finished output of sheet, tin-plate and light plate. The nature of the additional steel capacity required to sustain the rate of output cannot yet be forecast, but it might include one of the latest steelmaking processes, such as the L.D. and Kaldo processes, not yet employed in South Wales. Some use might also be made of continuous casting of slabs, a process undergoing extensive development in Russia; but this innovation would be more likely to follow at a later stage when throughput was straining the capacity of the primary rolling mill. Newport may well grow towards an ultimate ingot output of some five million tons a year—equivalent to the whole of the output of the South Wales steel industry in 1957. This would make Llanwern the largest steelworks in Britain.

The pattern of industrial development is quite plain. Coal and steel are in the process of being brought to a high degree of modern efficiency and, although coal faces growing competition from other sources of power, there is no reason to suppose

that the industry here will face a sudden and sharp decline in demand, provided, of course, that employment generally is reasonably well maintained. In the steel industry there have been major changes. Modernization has transformed production techniques, and projected new works will increase output and employment in the region. Steel remains subject to fluctuations in world trade, but technical improvements have greatly strengthened the competitive position of local producers. This strong position has been reinforced by the expansion of manufacturing industry much of which has good long-term prospects.

TABLE I

INDUSTRIAL DISTRIBUTION OF THE INSURED POPULATION, 1939 AND 1957

Industry	Region				Valleys				South-East Coastal Belt			
	1939		1957		1939		1957		1939		1957	
	Males	Females	Males	Females	Males	Females	Males	Females	Males	Females	Males	Females
INSURED POPULATION:												
Metal manufacture	27,948	1,929	40,203	6,896	13,978	775	19,027	3,985	13,970	1,154	21,176	2,910
Engineering	12,874	1,817	37,035	10,767	3,363	593	16,646	6,899	9,511	1,224	20,389	3,868
Chemicals	1,090	158	10,224	2,248	430	69	5,191	1,000	660	89	5,033	1,248
Textiles and clothing	1,303	3,322	7,882	12,202	690	1,398	6,832	9,402	613	1,924	1,050	2,800
Miscellaneous manufacturing	15,882	6,033	24,408	13,265	5,179	1,528	11,914	6,696	10,703	4,505	12,494	6,569
Total manufacturing	59,097	13,259	119,752	45,377	23,640	4,363	59,610	27,982	35,457	8,896	60,142	17,395
Agriculture	5,157	145	3,295	622	1,790	31	840	114	3,367	114	2,455	508
Mining	110,024	191	76,029	1,433	109,343	184	75,298	1,221	681	7	731	212
Building	37,905	121	24,415	917	24,678	39	10,373	237	13,227	82	14,042	680
Transport	25,779	442	33,866	3,429	4,115	75	10,285	897	21,664	367	23,581	2,532
Distributive trades	25,832	17,902	19,384	24,578	11,186	7,169	7,136	9,773	14,646	10,733	12,248	14,805
Other services	25,663	15,146	48,014	51,992	10,545	4,818	18,700	16,522	15,118	10,335	29,314	35,470
TOTAL	289,457	47,206	324,755	128,348	185,297	16,672	182,242	56,747	104,160	30,534	142,513	71,602
PERCENTAGE DISTRIBUTION:												
Metal manufacture	9·7	4·1	12·3	5·4	7·5	4·6	10·4	7·0	13·4	3·7	14·8	4·1
Engineering	4·4	3·8	11·4	8·4	1·8	3·6	9·1	12·2	9·2	4·1	14·3	5·4
Chemicals	·4	·3	3·2	1·8	·2	·4	2·8	1·8	·6	·3	3·5	1·7
Textiles and clothing	·5	7·0	2·5	9·5	·4	8·4	3·8	16·6	·5	6·3	·8	3·9
Miscellaneous manufacturing	5·4	12·8	7·5	10·4	2·8	9·2	6·6	11·8	10·2	14·5	8·8	9·3
Total manufacturing	20·4	28·0	36·9	35·5	12·7	26·2	32·7	49·4	33·9	28·9	42·2	24·4
Agriculture	1·8	·3	1·0	·5	1·0	·2	·5	·2	3·3	·4	1·7	·7
Mining	38·0	·4	23·4	1·1	59·0	1·1	41·3	2·2	·7	—	·6	·3
Building	13·1	·3	7·5	·7	13·3	·2	5·7	·4	12·7	·3	9·9	1·0
Transport	8·9	·9	10·4	2·7	2·3	·4	5·6	1·6	20·8	1·2	16·5	3·5
Distributive trades	8·9	37·9	6·0	19·1	6·0	43·0	3·9	17·2	14·1	35·3	8·6	20·6
Other services	8·9	32·2	14·8	40·4	5·7	28·9	10·3	29·0	14·5	33·9	20·5	49·5
TOTAL	100·0	100·0	100·0	100·0	100·0	100·0	100·0	100·0	100·0	100·0	100·0	100·0

Source: Derived from data supplied by the Wales Office, Ministry of Labour.

TABLE II

NUMBER AND PERCENTAGE UNEMPLOYED, 1939, 1948 AND 1957

	1939			1948			1957		
	Males	Females	Total	Males	Females	Total	Males	Females	Total
Valleys	37,513	1,721	39,234	12,394	5,737	18,131	3,626	2,895	6,521
Coastal belt ..	13,201	1,871	15,072	3,581	938	4,519	2,407	800	3,207
Region	50,714	3,592	54,306	15,975	6,675	22,650	6,033	3,695	9,728
Valleys ..	20·2	10·3	19·4	7·2	12·6	8·3	2·0	5·1	2·7
Coastal belt ..	12·7	6·1	11·2	2·2	1·5	2·0	1·7	1·1	1·5
Region	17·5	7·6	16·1	4·7	6·1	5·1	1·9	2·9	2·1

Source: See Table I.

TABLE III

UNEMPLOYED, JUNE 1958 : INDUSTRIAL DISTRIBUTION

Industry	Region				Valleys				South-East Coastal Belt			
	Males		Females		Males		Females		Males		Females	
	Number	Per-centage	Number	Per-centage	Number	Per-centage	Number	Per-centage	Number	Per-centage	Number	Per-centage
Metal manufacture	324	5·4	189	5·1	206	5·7	163	5·6	118	4·9	26	3·3
Engineering	724	12·0	297	8·0	320	8·8	253	8·7	404	16·8	44	5·5
Chemicals	115	1·9	95	2·5	90	2·5	89	3·1	25	1·0	6	·8
Textiles and clothing	100	1·7	442	12·0	85	2·3	411	14·2	15	·6	31	3·9
Misc. manufacture	466	7·7	484	13·1	311	8·6	409	14·1	155	6·4	75	9·4
Total manufacture	1,729	28·7	1,507	40·8	1,012	27·9	1,325	45·7	717	29·7	182	22·9
Agriculture	126	2·1	13	·4	78	2·2	8	·3	48	2·1	5	·6
Mining	569	9·4	14	·4	557	15·3	14	·5	12	·4	—	—
Building	1,206	20·0	6	·2	873	24·1	1	—	333	13·9	5	·6
Transport	544	9·0	45	1·2	136	3·8	27	·9	408	17·0	18	2·3
Distributive trades	441	7·3	597	16·2	226	6·2	459	15·9	215	8·9	138	17·2
Other services	961	15·9	1,023	27·6	489	13·5	684	23·7	472	19·6	339	42·4
No Industry	457	7·6	490	13·3	255	7·0	377	13·0	202	8·4	113	14·0
TOTAL	6,033	100·0	3,695	100·0	3,626	100·0	2,895	100·0	2,407	100·0	800	100·0

Source: See Table I.

TABLE IV

TRENDS IN THE EASTERN SECTION OF THE SOUTH WALES COALFIELD, 1948–57

Area	Year	No. of mines	Output (52-week year)[1]		No. of mines using coal-cutting machines[2]	Percentage of raised and weighed output mechanically cut[2]	No. of wage earners[3]		Output per manshift		Percentage absenteeism		New investment major schemes (£'000)	Profit (+) or Loss (—) (£'000)
			Raised and weighed ('000 tons)	Saleable ('000 tons)			Total	Face[2]	Overall (cwts.)	Face (cwts.)	Overall	Face		
No. 3 .. .. (Rhondda)	1948	32	4,547·6	3,856·3	19	23·8	18,110	8,521	16·7	36·7	9·7	11·4	110·5	— 281·0
	1952	16	4,634·7	3,753·6	11	26·5	16,276	8,129	18·6	39·6	13·2	15·6	390·7	+ 363·0
	1957	15	4,293·0	3,246·3	12	43·8	14,580	6,546	18·7	43·2	15·6	17·1	3,356·4	+ 587·8
No. 4 .. .. (Aberdare)	1948	23	3,485·9	2,755·0	11	36·1	12,440	5,760	17·5	39·9	10·7	13·3	44·7	— 339·6
	1952	18	4,183·4	3,221·1	12	41·9	13,016	6,388	20·8	45·3	13·9	16·8	851·4	+1,369·6
	1957	18	4,942·8	3,624·0	16	61·0	14,438	6,312	21·1	51·5	16·5	18·5	612·1	+1,504·9
No. 5 .. .. (Rhymney) ..	1948	18	5,147·7	3,893·7	14	59·7	16,129	7,340	19·6	46·4	10·9	13·4	411·8	+ 619·8
	1952	16	5,170·5	3,716·9	14	59·4	15,683	6,956	19·4	47·9	13·4	16·2	1,305·4	+ 522·8
	1957	15	5,711·1	4,076·3	14	70·4	16,781	7,298	19·8	47·1	15·0	16·7	321·1	+ 145·0
No. 6 .. .. (Monmouthshire)	1948	40	5,999·9	5,111·8	30	59·4	24,570	11,106	16·3	34·8	9·6	10·7	—	— 568·1
	1952	33	6,747·6	5,491·3	28	62·8	23,691	10,476	18·2	43·4	11·5	13·2	30·2	— 537·2
	1957	28	6,367·3	4,878·3	26	81·8	20,403	8,152	19·6	50·0	13·9	14·8	1,008·2	— 781·3
Region	1948	113	19,181·1	15,616·8	74	46·8	71,249	32,727	17·3	38·5	10·1	11·9	567·0	— 468·9
	1952	83	20,736·2	16,182·9	65	50·6	68,666	31,949	19·0	43·7	12·7	15·2	2,577·7	+1,718·2
	1957	76	21,314·3	15,804·9	68	66·3	66,202	30,308	19·7	47·9	15·1	15·5	5,297·8	+1,456·4
South Wales ..	1948	203	26,550·1	22,274·3	119	41·3	106,187	46,185	16·7	39·1	9·9	11·5	857·3	—4,920·5
	1952	157	28,995·2	23,415·4	131	47·9	103,043	46,505	18·3	43·3	12·3	14·4	3,056·6	—1,949·4
	1957	141	29,256·9	22,496·1	120	63·6	98,628	42,144	19·1	46·4	14·5	15·9	10,119·8	—1,316·3

Notes.—[1] Figures for 1948 relate to calendar year.

[2] Data not available for 1948; the figures given relate to 1949.

[3] At end of year.

Source: Statistical Section, South Western Division, National Coal Board.

IX

AGRICULTURE

Emlyn Davies, John Davies, A. W. Prowel

THE Region consists of three distinct agricultural areas. The lowland area along the Bristol Channel — this stretches from Chepstow to Bridgend and varies in width from 4 to 10 miles. It consists of good agricultural land, although portions of it adjoining the Bristol Channel are in need of drainage and liable to considerable flooding. The area as a whole is devoted almost entirely to agriculture, the exception being the large towns along the Bristol Channel. In the north of the area is hill land rising to over 2,000 feet at the peak of the Brecon Beacons. The hill country consists of much poorer agricultural land, but underneath are large deposits of coal. This coal led to the industrial development that has taken place in the area over the last hundred years. Coal mines were sunk and other industries sprang up in the districts adjoining the coal mines, and docks were built along the Bristol Channel for the purpose of exporting this coal. Large towns have also grown up throughout the area as a result of this spread of industry, so that now more than half the population of Wales is concentrated in this area. In recent years opencast coal mining has also encroached on the area, producing large quantities of coal but disfiguring the land affected until such time as it is again restored to agriculture. To the north-east of this area is better quality land on red sandstone. This follows roughly across to the Wye and Usk Valleys and is again devoted almost entirely to farming.

The rainfall over the region varies from 35 to 38 inches along the Bristol Channel to 80 to 90 inches (sometimes as much as 120 inches in a wet year) in the upland areas. This rainfall has led to the construction of reservoirs in the upper reaches of many of the rivers to supply water to the industrial areas to the south.

The land falls steeply southwards from the Beacons for a distance of 30 miles towards the Bristol Channel. The swift-flowing rivers cut the region up into steep, narrow valleys, making transport from one valley to another difficult. The steep slopes were once well wooded but towards the end of the last century large quantities of the timber had been cleared. In recent years the Forestry Commission have replanted large areas.

The proximity of thickly populated areas has led to an increase in milk production and the main agricultural enterprise is the production of milk, even on very poor land in the mining valleys. In the days before the Milk Marketing Board there were very large numbers of producer retailers in these areas, but these have now been very considerably reduced in numbers owing to the improvement in transport and methods of handling milk.

SOILS IN THE AREA

Fig. 18 shows the variation in the types and character of the soils in the region.

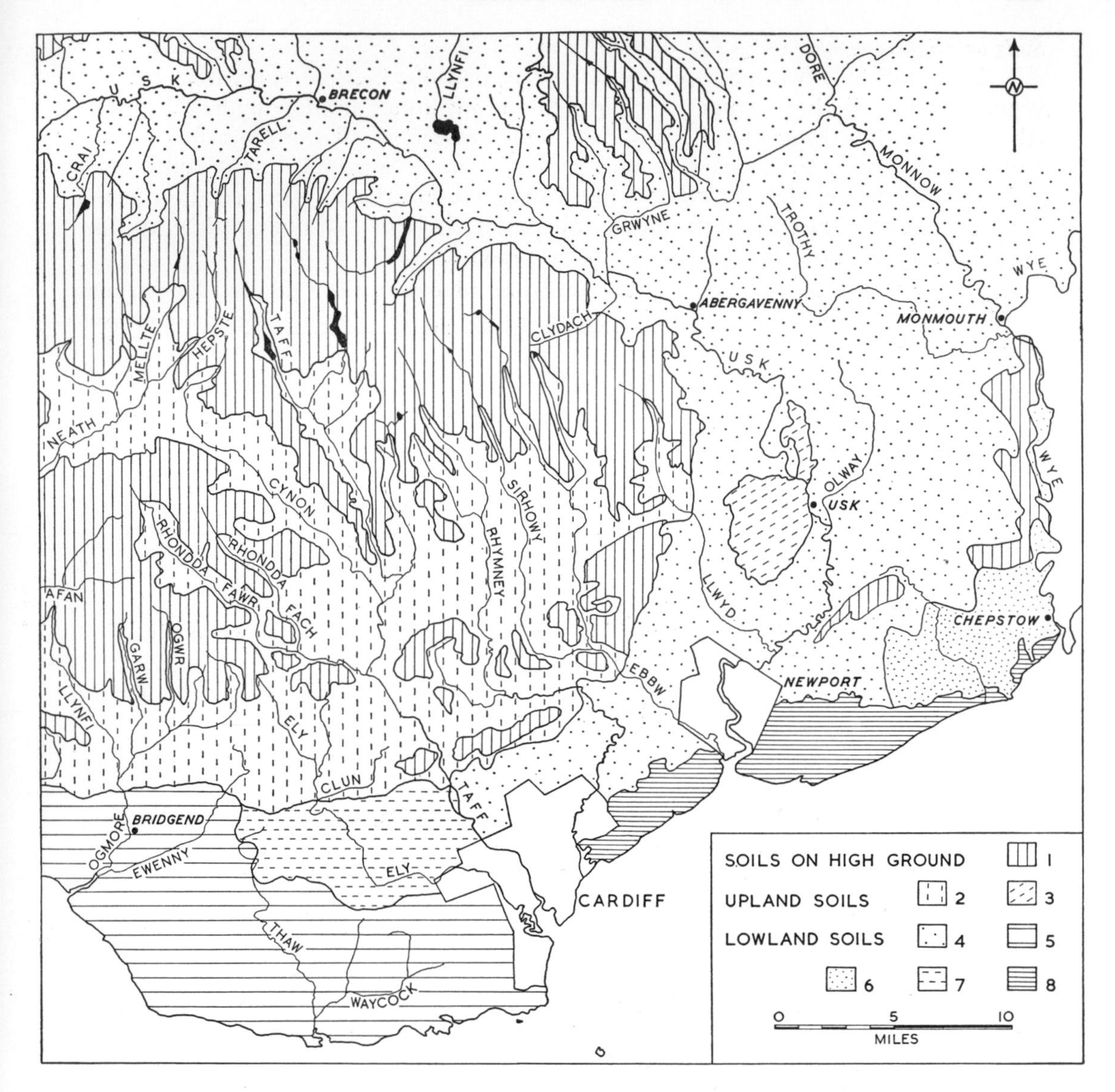

Fig. 18. Soils

Key to Shading on Map: 1. Open mountain rough grazing and afforested; podsolic and gley soils, usually peaty, and shallow limestone soils, formed on Old Red Sandstone, Carboniferous Limestone, Millstone Grit, and Carboniferous Sandstone. 2. Mostly grassland; brown earths and gley soils, formed on Carboniferous Sandstone and shales and associated glacial drifts. 3. Arable and grassland; brown earths, formed on Silurian shale, with limestone. 4. Brown earths on Old Red Sandstone. 5. Brown earths and gley soils formed on Lower Lias Limestone and shale, with some Carboniferous limestone and Triassic marl. 6. Brown earths formed on Carboniferous limestone and Triassic marl. 7. Brown earths formed on glacial drifts mainly of Carboniferous origin. 8. Gley soils formed on calcareous marine alluvium.

Soils on High Ground

These fall into two main groups: (i) peaty podsols, i.e. soils carrying a natural vegetation, usually bracken or gorse, formed on sandstones and having free drainage (the excessive leaching of rainwater has depleted almost all the bases in the soil, and it has a very acid reaction and is very low in available plant nutrients); (ii) peaty gleys, i.e. soils carrying a natural vegetation, usually rush, cotton grass, etc., formed on silty clays and shales, and having impeded drainage (they are less acid than the podsols, but otherwise are very poor).

Peaty podsols are formed on the sandstone phases of the Old Red Sandstone, the buff-coloured sandstones of the Millstone Grit, the Pennant Sandstone, and glacial gravels.

Peaty gleys are formed on the shales of the Millstone Grit, on shales of the productive Coal Measures, and on glacial boulder clay of mixed Old Red Sandstone and Carboniferous origin.

Reclamation work is resulting in the conversion of areas of deeper and less stony types of peaty podsol into brown earths, i.e. normal cultivated soils, and drainage work can effect the same change with peaty gleys.

Upland Soils

The cultivated soils in the coalfield upland are classed as brown earths, i.e. soils which have satisfactory drainage, but not so much as to result in rapid depletion of bases, either natural or added as lime over many years of farming practice.

These are mostly grassland soils, being reasonably deep and not excessively stony, and occur on the lower slopes of the hills and in valleys. They are formed from colluvial material, i.e. the residue of weathering rock which has collected on the lower slopes from natural movement down from higher ground, and from glacial drift material. Both these parent materials (i.e. materials which give rise to soils by weathering *in situ*) are derived from the sandstones of the productive Coal Measures, the Pennant Sandstone, and smaller amounts of the associated geological rocks, such as the Millstone Grit, Old Red Sandstone, etc.

The soils formed on the Silurian shale inlier near Usk are brown earths, and are better agricultural soils than those of the coalfield. They are mostly deep loams, light in texture but with a characteristic fine sand and silt content, and are formed from the Wenlock and Ludlow calcareous mudstones and shales, with small areas of Wenlock limestone.

Lowland Soils

The large area of central and north Monmouthshire and the Vale of Usk in Breconshire has good agricultural soils formed almost wholly from the Old Red Sandstone, and classed as brown earths. The texture of these soils varies from sandy loam to silty clay loams according to the lithology of the rocks and the extent of the superficial glacial gravels which occur in hollows and as mounds, giving rise to the characteristic rolling topography.

The Vale of Glamorgan soils are mostly the clay loams derived from the Lower Lias limestone and shales and are classed as brown calcareous soils, i.e. brown earths formed from a parent material sufficiently high in calcium carbonate to enable the topsoil to retain a high base status over the soil forming era. Although the texture of the topsoil is a clay loam, and that of the subsoil a clay or silty clay, the drainage is, on the whole, satisfactory.

In the south-east corner of Monmouthshire, and small areas elsewhere such as in the Vale of Glamorgan, the soils are derived from Carboniferous Limestone, together with varying amounts of material derived from Triassic rocks. Although there are areas of shallow soils, mostly they are deep, rich brown or red-brown loams, freely drained, and of excellent structure, and classed as brown calcareous soils. Because of favourable climatic conditions a high proportion of these soils are used for arable crops.

An area between the Vale of Glamorgan and the coalfield upland is covered by extensive glacial deposits, resulting in very mixed soils, mostly of light texture, but containing freely and imperfectly drained types. They would be classed as brown earths, but are of low base status, and agriculturally not as good as the adjoining Old Red Sandstone lowland soils.

South Monmouthshire has a characteristic coastal strip of marine alluvium, flat and below sea-level, with a sea wall and a system of reens to drain it. It is almost wholly grassland and the soils are silty clays, although the parent material is calcareous and support good pastures under normal conditions of rainfall.

The variation in the herbage of the grassland of the area is shown in Fig. 19.

THE FARMING PATTERN

The area is essentially devoted to the production of livestock and livestock products; arable cropping is complementary to livestock farming except for small acreages of wheat and potatoes and an insignificant acreage of sugar beet and vegetables sold off as cash crops. This picture was not always so, as there are records showing that during the eighteenth and nineteenth centuries the area of arable land was considerably greater than it is today and even supported an export trade of wheat through the port of Bristol. This arable cropping would have been concentrated in the lower good land areas.

However, during the last twenty years or so there has been no major change in the farming pattern except one of emphasis moulded by improved techniques and methods and economic pressures. The comparative statistics for Monmouthshire for 1939 and 1958 bear out this statement. (Statistics are not available for the parts of Glamorgan and Breconshire within the area, but the Monmouthshire figures can be taken as representative of the whole area.)

	1939 (*acres*)	1958 (*acres*)
Crops and Grass (excluding Rough Grazing)	210,473	208,158
Wheat	2,974	5,399
Barley and oats	4,244	8,031
Potatoes	885	1,841
Cabbage and kale, etc.	227	3,205
Clover and rotation grasses	6,383	29,405
Permanent grass	189,218	150,893

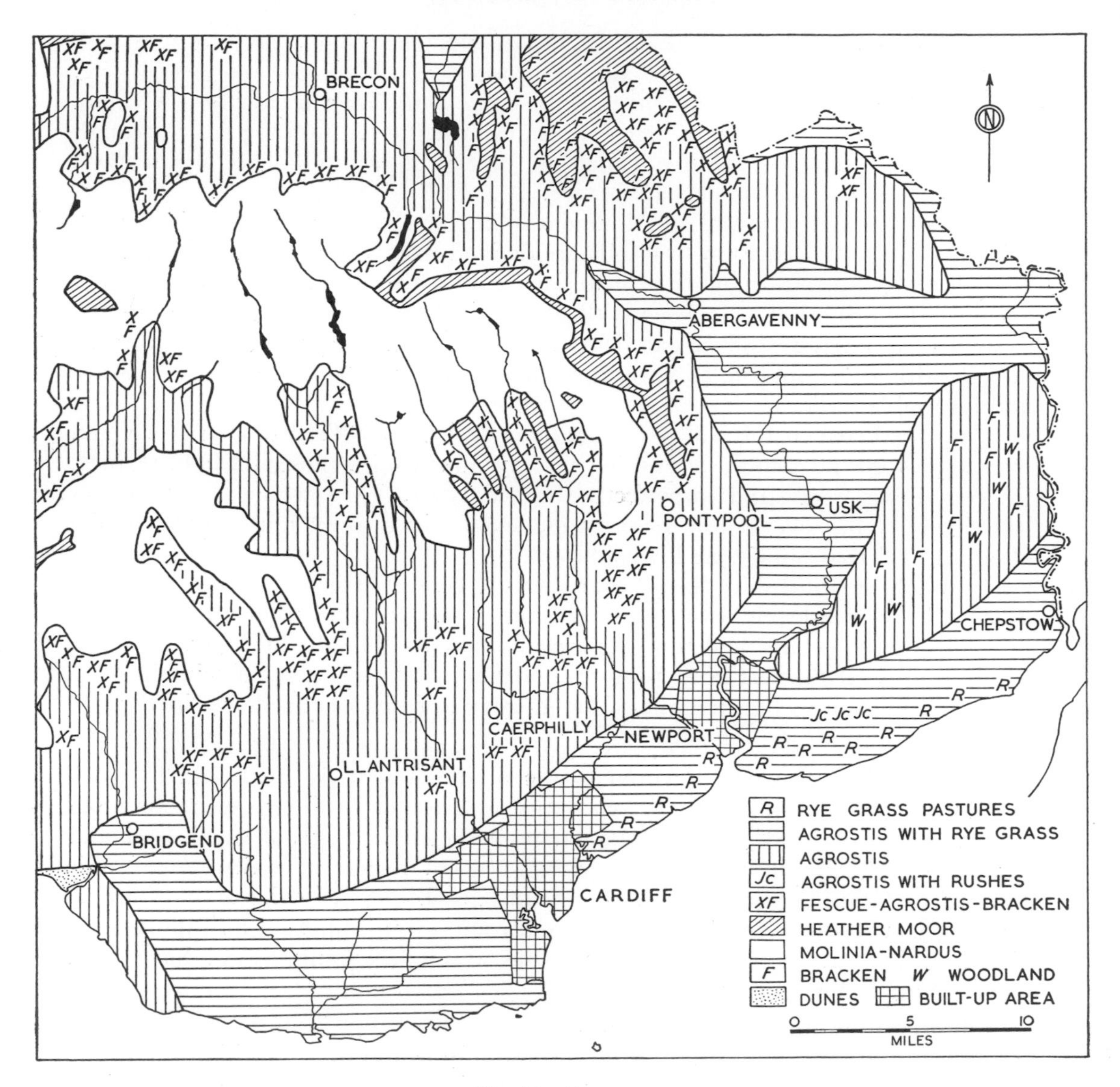

Fig. 19. Pastures

Livestock:	*Numbers*	*Numbers*
Cattle and calves	59,043	77,390
Cows and heifers in milk .. .. Cows in calf not in milk	20,876	28,205
Sheep and lambs	284,362	299,821
Total pigs	18,958	24,377
Total poultry	468,885	476,145

Other facts brought out by these figures, in addition to confirming the maintenance of the traditional pattern of farming, are (*a*) the reduction in the total crops and grass acreage (most of this will have been given up to industrial and urban development, for the demand for agricultural land near the larger towns and industrial centres is continually increasing); (*b*) the reduced acreage is supporting a greater output of crops and livestock which is in keeping with the considerable technical development that has taken place in British farming during this period; (*c*) the number of milk cows has increased and this trend is still, in effect, one of changing over from rearing and/or fattening to the more profitable enterprise of milk production (this is particularly so on the smaller farms (under 100 acres), both in the uplands and lowlands); (*d*) this change-over to more milk production has stimulated more than any other cause the adoption of a ley system of grassland production, coupled with an increased acreage of kale as vital to the economic production of milk. This is shown in the increased acreages of temporary grass and kale as compared with 1939. The permanent grassland figures for 1958 include permanent grassland listed in 1939 which is periodically ploughed out for improvement and reseeded to long-term leys.

Size of Holdings

Small farms predominate in the region. Out of a total of 6,927 holdings, 41 per cent are under 20 acres, 65 per cent under 50 acres and 84·5 per cent under 100 acres. The small farms (0–50 acres) are not evenly dispersed throughout the region, but are more concentrated in the mining valleys of the industrial uplands and the forest area of east Monmouthshire. These have existed during the last century as part-time holdings, the occupiers being wholly or partly employed in mining and other industry. With present-day 'full' employment, this system of occupation persists, although some of the better holdings in the 25–40 acre group have been developed as full-time holdings with one or more members of the family being employed in industry. This pattern is similar in some respects to the industrial Pennines, although the problem of the small farm is not so acute here. The larger and the more prosperous farms are to be found in the Vale of Glamorgan along the coastal belt, and within the area bounded by Usk, Abergavenny and Monmouth in Monmouthshire, and in the Brecon area.

FARMING REGIONS

Although there is no clear demarcation between the various systems of farming to be found in the area, an attempt is made to divide it into farming regions (Fig. 20).

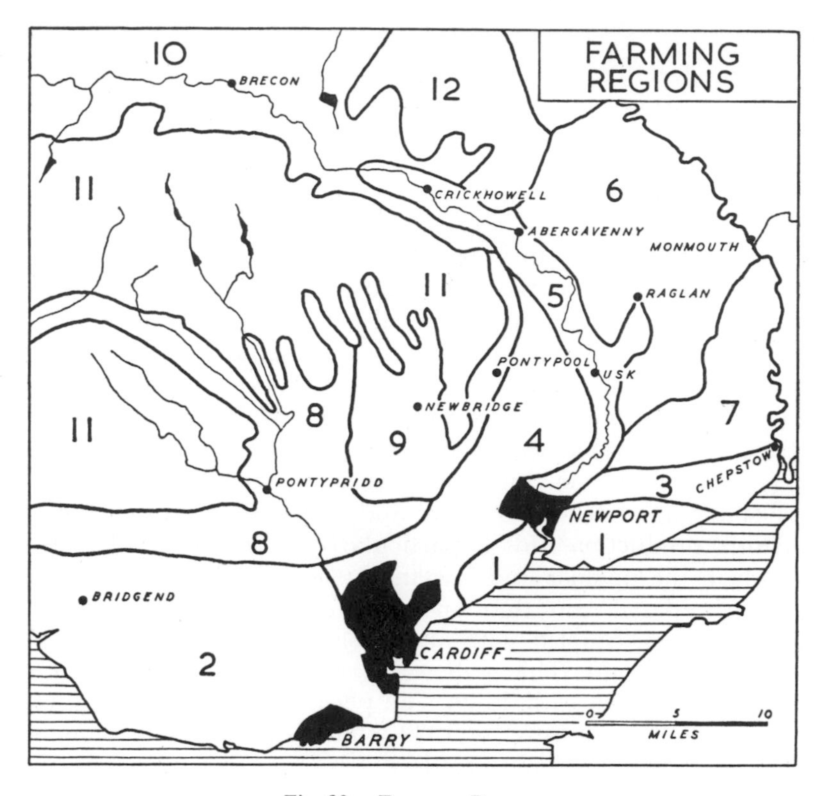

Fig. 20. Farming Regions
1. Caldicot and Wentloog Levels. 2. Vale of Glamorgan. 3. Chepstow Road· 4. Central Monmouthshire. 5. Usk Valley. 6. North-east Monmouthshire. 7. Eastern Woodland Region. 8–9. Coalfield Region. 10. Breconshire Upland Area. 11–12. Moorland Region.

Caldicot and Wentloog Levels

The Levels form a strip of low-lying, mainly marine alluvial soils bounded in the north side by the 50-foot contour and on the south side by a sea wall. The whole area is featurelessly flat, intersected with a maze of main ditches or 'reens' and smaller ditches. Most of this area is potentially highly productive as grassland, but this is governed by the effectiveness of the drainage system. The Levels known as the Monmouthshire Moors are believed to have been reclaimed from a marsh or lagoon subject to tidal flooding. When this reclamation took place is not definitely known, but it is thought that protection from the sea started in the fourth century and small improvements were carried out until the thirteenth century when the main drainage system was laid down. The present drainage system is not materially different from that developed in the thirteenth century.

The responsibility for the drainage and protection of the area from flooding now lies with the Usk River Board and the Internal Drainage Board for the area, and considerable plans are in hand to lower the water levels in the reens to give a normal free board in the farm ditches of at least 2 feet. This should prove of great

benefit to the farmers in the area, allowing them to exploit more fully the high potential of this land. This improvement will demand the full co-operation of all the farmers in the area in maintaining their own farm ditches in good condition. Unfortunately there are some less enlightened farmers on the moors who are insisting on their rights that the water be maintained at a high level within the farm ditches for the provision of water for livestock, as fences between blocks of land and for 'irrigation'. The high water level is maintained by a complicated system of sluices, and there is no doubt that if the full advantage of any improvement in the drainage system is to be obtained, these restrictive practices will have to be overcome.

The main system of farming is milk production. Parts of the area are farmed by farmers occupying holdings outside the region, and in such instances the land is used for the summer grazing of store or fattening cattle and sheep.

Vale of Glamorgan

This region lies along the Bristol Channel from Cardiff to Bridgend, and stretches inland for 8 or 10 miles. Here is found the most fertile agricultural land of Glamorgan and possibly of the whole area under review. The whole area is practically unbroken productive land. The soils are mostly clay loams derived from Lias limestone and shales forming brown earths of high calcium status. Burnt lime and limestone is produced in the area. Although the soils are varying textures of clay loam, the drainage over the whole area is generally good. They are suitable for arable cultivation and very productive, but the farming of the area is based mainly on grassland and livestock with some corn growing along the Bristol Channel. Milk production is now the main enterprise on most holdings, but some farms, particularly along the coast, are devoted to the rearing and fattening of cattle with mixed farming. The production of fat lamb and beef is a feature of many of these farms.

Chepstow Road

This region borders the main route joining Newport and Chepstow. Although it adjoins the Caldicot and Wentloog Levels, there is an abrupt change in landscape and agricultural use. The soils change from alluvial to generally fertile soils derived from Old Red Sandstone and Silurian shales with limestone. Agriculturally, this region is suitable for either arable or grassland farming, but like the Vale of Glamorgan milk production is the main system of farming, with mixed farming of arable cropping and fattening cattle secondary. Sheep for fat lamb production is an important enterprise on most farms.

Near Penhow is the Welsh Land Settlement Association farm — an experiment in co-operative farming.

Central Monmouthshire

This region covers the central area of Monmouthshire stretching from near Cardiff in the south, to just south of Abergavenny in the north, and bounded on the west by the coalfield and on the east by the Usk Valley bottoms. It can be

described as an undulating low hill region, varying in height between 50 and 400 feet. The higher western slopes come within the West Monmouthshire coalfield region. The soils are variable in character, of medium fertility, derived from Silurian and Carboniferous rocks and Old Red Sandstones. The agricultural value of the soils is, however, fairly homogeneous, being suitable for general mixed farming though the present-day emphasis is on milk production. The size of the holdings tends to be smaller than in the first three regions.

Usk Valley

This is a narrow strip of rich alluvial land bordering the River Usk and is nowhere much wider than 1 mile. Much of the area, particularly in the lower reaches, is liable to flood, and thus few complete holdings occupy this valley bottom the land being divided between farms in the other regions flanking it. This is first-class land used mostly as grassland, suitable for milk or beef production, but where flooding does not occur it can and does produce high yields of arable crops.

North-east Monmouthshire

Round hills of gentle slopes occur throughout the region, varying in altitude between 200 feet and 400 feet, but steeper slopes are locally dominant rising to about 500 feet. The soils are derived from the Old Red Sandstone and vary in texture from light to heavy loams. Generally they are not suited to arable cropping, so their use is mainly grassland which varies in quality from that on the steeper slopes, which is poor, to first-class fattening pastures in the valley bottoms. Arable cropping is confined to the production of fodder crops, although limited areas are found (e.g. the Raglan — Abergavenny area) where conditions are very suitable for the production of cash crops of wheat, barley and potatoes.

Traditionally, this is an area of livestock-rearing with some fattening on the better lands. Today, however, milk production is an important enterprise and variants between intensive milk production, mixed farming with milk, and rearing with some fattening is to be found. Sheep are common to most farms, their intensity being highest on the rearing and fattening farms. In recent years many cases of malnutrition in both cattle and sheep have been encountered and found to be due to trace-element deficiency of cobalt and/or copper. Remedial measures which have been taken have proved effective.

Eastern Woodland Region

Characteristic of this region is its patchwork of woodlands in addition to the forests shown on Fig. 22. The pattern of farming was mainly rearing, but, today, it is a mixture of rearing and milk production, together with sheep for fat lamb production. The soils are medium to poor in quality and generally 'hungry'. Arable cropping is limited on each farm to the production of fodder crops of oats, roots and green-crop. Unlike the remainder of east Monmouthshire a large number of small farms are to be found, particularly in the forest areas. No doubt these were developed for forest workers.

Coalfield Region

This area includes the East Glamorgan and West Monmouthshire coalfield regions. Both regions are similar in character, being intersected by deep valleys which are highly industrialized and urbanized. The soils are generally poor in natural fertility and combined with the comparatively high rainfall and difficult terrain they largely limit the land use to grassland which varies in quality from good cattle pastures in the valley bottoms to poor hill sheep grazings at the higher elevations. The economy of the farming in these regions has, over the last fifty years, been geared to supplying its urban population with milk, meat, eggs, poultry and vegetables, with many of the farmers retailing their own produce. The present-day system of retail trading and marketing has, to a great extent, reduced the inter-dependency between the farmer and the urban population, but the same general system of farming continues. On the better lowland farms, milk and fat lamb production is the main system, with eggs and pork or bacon production secondary. At the higher elevations, milk production is again a main enterprise, even under the most difficult conditions, but quite often on the larger farms it is coupled with rearing of either dairy or beef stores. The more inaccessible farms are devoted to livestock rearing. Many of the farms in this upper region have grazing rights on the open hill, and it is not uncommon to find smallholdings of under 40 acres of enclosed land grazing flocks of several hundred ewes on the open hill. These flocks are acclimatized to the hill, producing their own replacements; the surplus lambs are sold as stores.

The two main problems of these regions are the large number of smallholdings (many of which fail to provide a reasonable level of income and can only be classed as part-time holdings), and the inadequacy and very poor condition of the farm buildings.

Breconshire Upland Area

Compared with the two preceding regions, this region is much kinder, more fertile and less rugged. The soils are derived mainly from the Old Red Sandstone and in the lower regions are suitable for mixed farming, including milk production. On the larger, more upland farms livestock rearing is the main enterprise based on the single suckling by its own calf of Hereford cows and the production of fat and/or store lambs, depending on the land available to the farm. This system of single suckling and the sale of the calf as a weaner at about eight months old has developed in recent years as a sound and profitable system, not only because of the hill cow and calf subsidy obtained, but also because of the highly organized marketing arrangements for weaned calves which have been established in the counties of Brecon and Radnor.

Moorland Region

This is a region of hill land, rising over 1,200 feet. The soils are extremely poor, with a natural vegetation of associations of Molinia — cotton grass, Molinia — Nardus, Molinia — rushes, bracken, gorse and heather according to the soil type

and drainage. These regions are mainly open sheep-grazings, but store cattle and mountain ponies find some grazing during the short summer period of growth.

There are few holdings on the open moorland. The holdings using the moorland grazing are situated on its fringe in the valleys, surrounded by industrial and urban development. The system of farming is mainly livestock rearing, with sheep as the major enterprise. Milk is also produced on some farms under such adverse conditions that it is doubtful whether it is an economic proposition.

FARMING SYSTEMS

It has been stated previously that the land of the region is devoted mainly to the production of livestock and livestock products. Until the early thirties of this century the economy of the area, except near the industrial centres, was based on the production of fat and store cattle, and sheep, with livestock products of milk and butter being of secondary importance. Today, the position has changed to a reliance mainly on milk production, with sheep second in importance, to sustain farm incomes, and because of this widespread adoption of milk production there is no clear geographical demarcation between areas of milk and other systems of farming except perhaps the Moorland region which is unsuited to milk production. Fig. 21 shows at a glance the extent of milk production. The north and north-eastern parts of Monmouthshire and south Breconshire have a stronger tradition of livestocking-rearing farming; this system is maintained to a much greater extent than in the remainder of the region. Generally, the farms in these parts are larger and can produce a fair farm income from these extensive systems. Most of the smaller farms have, however, found their economic salvation in milk production.

Crops

The climatic conditions of the region are very suited to the farming of grass, and with the economy of the area being dependent on livestock most of the land is devoted to grass. Considerable strides have been made in the last decade or so in improving the production, management and utilization of grass; and ley farming, coupled with silage making, have become 'traditional' practices on many farms. This greater grass consciousness is evident through the whole region from the southern lowlands to the northern moorlands. But there is still a long way to go before the potentialities of modern methods of grassland farming in the economic production of livestock, and their products are more universally realized and accepted by farmers in the region.

Arable cropping is confined more or less to the production of crops (cereals, roots, kale, etc.) for the feeding of livestock on the farm. The proportion in relation to the total acreage of the farm varies in accordance with the type of livestock kept, suitability of the land and climate for arable crops, particularly harvesting, the size of farm, etc. Many farms of under 70 acres on the better land will produce a few acres of wheat and/or potatoes as a cash crop but it is on the larger farms over 100 acres that any significant acreage of cash cropping occurs. Even then the proportion rarely exceeds 25 per cent of the total acreage. On many of the more intensive dairy farms kale is the only arable crop grown.

Cattle

In the past the two main breeds in the region were the dual-purpose Shorthorn for the production of beef stores, milk and milk products, and the renowned Hereford for either beef stores for sale over the Border, or for fattening on the better land farms within the region. Today the Hereford has maintained its place as the primary beef breed, but the Shorthorn has lost considerable ground mainly to the Friesian and, to some extent, to other pure milk breeds. The Friesian is not only replacing the Shorthorn as the milk producer but, at the same time, because its beef qualities suit the present-day market, it is fulfilling the dual role of the Shorthorn. The contribution of the Friesian dairy herds to the beef industry is considerable by way of calves, either pure or as crosses with the Hereford for rearing for beef. On some upland and more exposed farms, where hardiness for out-wintering is important, the Galloway has been introduced in recent years, and on many farms Welsh Black cattle are being reintroduced after a very considerable period of absence.

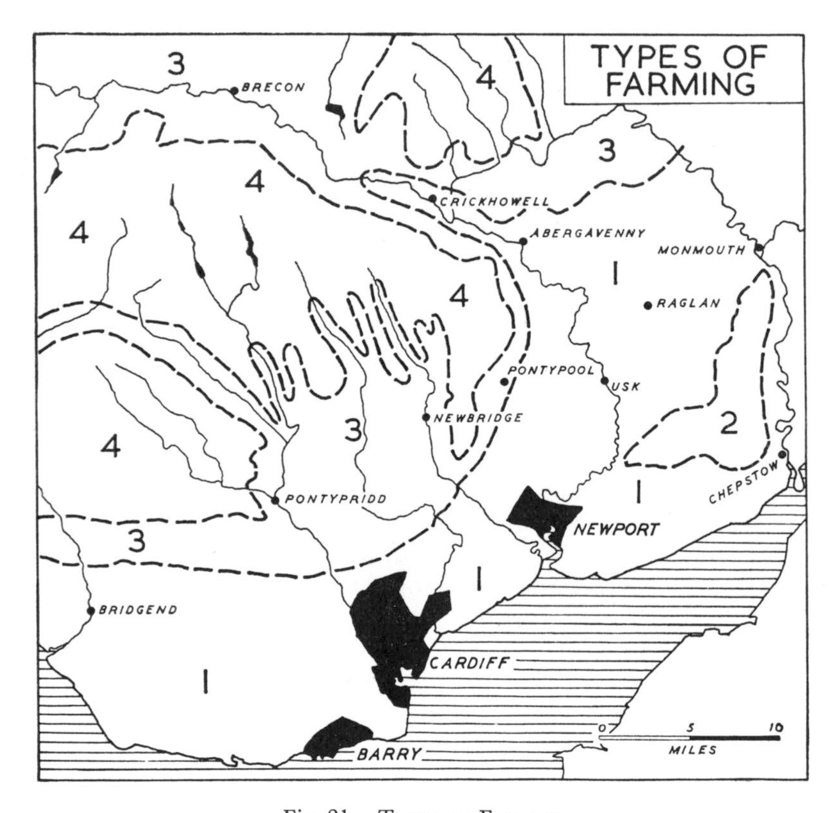

Fig. 21. Types of Farming
1. Mainly dairying with some mixed, rearing and fattening. 2. Dairying with livestock rearing. 3. Livestock rearing with some dairying. 4. Mainly hill sheep.

Sheep

Sheep are of secondary economic importance only to milk production. They are to be found on most farms, and it is not uncommon to find a stocking of

one and a half ewes to the acre on the larger mixed or rearing farms on the better lands. Where milk production is the main enterprise the concentration is much reduced, but even on the smaller milk farms sheep are kept. The system of management varies according to situation, the lowland and semi-upland farms producing mainly summer fat lamb, while the true hill-rearing farms sell store lambs to the lowlands for autumn or winter fattening and also draft hill ewes.

The breeds and crosses vary throughout the region. In the central Moorland area the white- or tan-faced Welsh Mountain (Nelson type) predominates. In the Black Mountains area the Radnor cross Welsh predominates, and on the better hills in the northern part of Monmouthshire, the Radnor. On the Glamorgan — Brecon border the Welsh with some Cheviot blood is found. These hill ewes are drafted during the autumn sales to the lowlands to be put to a lowland ram, generally a Suffolk, for the production of fat lamb. The ewe lambs of this cross may be kept on for breeding, to be crossed in their turn with the Suffolk, resulting in a heavier lamb than the first cross. Cluns are a common breed in the lowlands and particularly in the Usk Valley in the north part of the region, and crossing takes place between this breed and the Welsh, Radnor, Suffolk and their crosses; thus a black-faced ewe can be of very mixed ancestry.

Pigs and Poultry

Pigs and poultry are kept on most farms. The number will vary according to the likes and dislikes of the farmer and his family. Normally they play a very subsidiary part in the farm economy, but since the introduction of the deep litter system of management poultry numbers have increased, and on some farms flocks of up to 1,000 laying hens are found. There are few specialist pig or poultry holdings.

BUILDINGS

The condition and adequacy of farm buildings is on the whole poor, and not suited to the requirements of present-day farming. The change-over from store raising to milk production on a large number of farms was not accompanied by much change in buildings. As might be expected, the better farm buildings and houses found on the larger farms in the southern and eastern portion of the region give the impression of greater prosperity over the last hundred years, but, even on these holdings, the buildings, though structurally good, often need to be modernized. During recent years, advantage has been taken of the Farm Improvement Schemes to bring about some improvement, not only to get sufficient buildings in relation to stock numbers but also to improve labour efficiency and to improve the health of the stock. Nevertheless, more improvement is needed before the general standard of farm buildings can be considered satisfactory, especially in view of the fact that out-wintering of stock is difficult owing to high rainfall and wet soils.

FORESTRY IN THE REGION

In this part of South Wales there was not a great deal of forestry until shortly before the 1939–45 war, with the exception of the Wye Valley. Since 1947

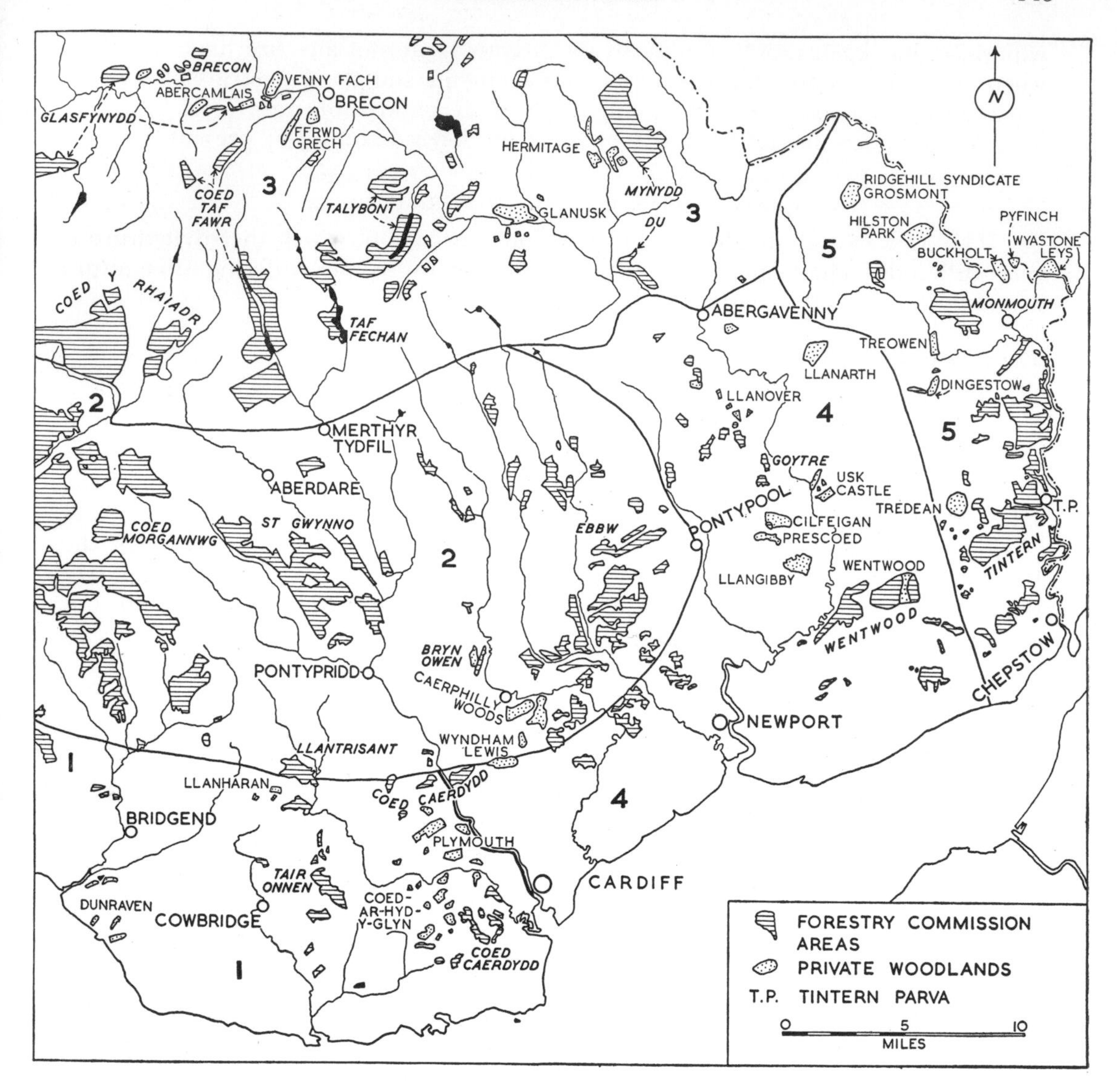

Fig. 22

1. The Vale of Glamorgan. 2. The Coalfield. 3. The Brecon Beacons and Black Mountains. 4. The Usk Valley. 5. The Wye Valley.

expansion has been rapid; almost all the private estates of any size have put their woodlands under some form of forest management, and the Forestry Commission areas have been increased and planted up at a considerable rate (Fig. 22). The total areas under plantation and scheduled for forest planting at present are:

Private Estates	7,500 acres
Forestry Commission	66,000 acres

The area can be divided into five regions, in each of which the silviculture is very different. The regions are distinct geologically as the differing silviculture is mainly due to soil variations.

The Vale of Glamorgan

This low coast plateau of Triassic and Jurassic age west of Cardiff is similar to many parts of lowland England but quite different from most of the rest of South Wales. Forestry here is confined to small, scattered areas of rather poor hardwoods on sites unsuitable for agriculture and little cared for since wartime fellings took place. These are being rehabilitated by private estates and the Forestry Commission, and a wide variety of species can be grown. East of Cowbridge, in the centre of the Vale, the largest Welsh nursery owned by the Forestry Commission is situated. It produces about five million plants per year. It is not an ideal nursery site but has a well-established labour force.

The Coalfield

The Pennant Sandstone and Coal Measures give rise to the poorest soil in the area. The region is quite suitable, however, for the less exacting tree species such as Japanese larch, Sitka spruce and *Pinus contorta*. Scots pine and Corsican pine grow well at lower elevations, but Douglas fir and European larch are unsuited and are not planted. The region is dissected by steep-sided valleys, heavily industrialized in the bottoms. The valley sides are mainly covered with bracken and, in places, the remains of scrub oak and birch. They are little utilized except for forestry, for which they are quite suitable. The flat molinia-covered ridge-tops between the valleys are moderate grazing and also good plantable land.

There used to be fears that fumes would damage plantations in the Coalfield, and pre-war acquisitions were therefore limited, but this is now known to be not quite so serious or widespread as originally anticipated, and expansion of Forestry Commission areas is rapid. The dense industrial population provides hazards by way of vandalism and fire danger. The latter is particularly serious as the outbreaks, which are difficult to spot from towers, occur on the lower margin of plantations and sweep rapidly up the steep hillsides. The problem is largely one of time, and in plantations which have existed for some years and are accepted by the local people there is less likelihood of damage. At Llantrisant, which is the oldest forest in the region, there has been no fire, other than a railway fire, since the war. It is perhaps significant that this area carried a timber crop, belonging to the Marquis of Bute, before acquisition by the Forestry Commission in 1921.

There is very little private forestry in the region.

The Brecon Beacons and Black Mountains

This Old Red Sandstone area is in marked contrast to the coalfield immediately to the south of it. The soil is fertile, the rainfall high (100 inches on the Beacons) and the exposure considerable. Sitka spruce and Japanese larch are still the predominant species, but Douglas fir, Norway spruce and Scots pine are also widely used. Recently the newer exotics such as the *Abies* species, *Thuya*, *Tsuga* and *Pinus contorta* have been used fairly extensively. As elsewhere in South Wales, European larch is not now planted, but there are some good plantations of this species at Tal-y-bont and Hay.

Forestry Commission work in this region started in 1927, and about 20,000 acres are now under management. Further large increases are unlikely as prosperous sheep farming is a keen competitor for land, and almost all the moorland round the existing forests is common land.

Private forestry has flourished in the past more than elsewhere, and the break-up of large estates has not been so marked here. Private woods are therefore well managed and on fertile land well integrated with agriculture.

The Usk Valley

This region includes Silurian shales, Devonian sandstones and marls and Carboniferous limestones. It is therefore fertile and suitable for the more valuable coniferous species such as Douglas fir, *Tsuga*, *Abies grandis* and hardwoods. Poplars are well suited in certain localities. As in the Vale of Glamorgan almost all the areas being planted are old woodland sites, now covered with poor quality hardwoods. There is a market for the best of this material at the new hardwood pulp mill on the Severn estuary at Sudbrook.

The Wye Valley

This is mainly an area of Old Red Sandstone with some Carboniferous limestone near Chepstow. The valley is very fertile in the bottom but tapers off to a poorer soil on the higher slopes where quartz conglomerate occurs. Much of the region has always been woodland and has been associated with, and influenced by, the adjacent Forest of Dean. Tintern Forest is an old Crown Woodland, and around Tintern itself there are about 5,000 acres of oak and beech in advanced stages of conversion from coppice with standards. Some of this was felled during the last war, and oak has been the main species used for replanting. Near Chepstow, on the limestone, about 2,000 acres of beech have been planted. On the poorer soils higher up the valley sides Norway spruce, Douglas fir, and Japanese larch are grown with Corsican pine on dry heath sites.

The Wye Valley forests, older than the other forests in the area, are supplying a wide range of produce from fencing material and pit-props to pulp wood and mill timber of both hardwoods and softwoods.

Most of the private estates in the region have a well-established tradition of forestry, hardwoods and larch being the predominant species.

Acknowledgements are due to the staff at the National Agricultural Advisory Service Sub-Centre, Cardiff, and the Forestry Commission at Cardiff for information supplied by them.

X

THE WELSH LANGUAGE

Ceri W. Lewis

ORIGINS

WELSH is a member of the Celtic branch of the Indo-European family of languages, its closest relations being Cornish and Breton. It is sometimes convenient to divide the Celtic languages geographically into the two broad divisions of Continental Celtic (or Gaulish), which became extinct in the early Christian era, and Insular Celtic, although such a geographical division really obscures fundamental differences of phonology within the insular group. (See below, for example, on Q-Celtic and P-Celtic.)

The term 'Gaulish' is usually used loosely to denote the widely-scattered remains of Celtic speech on the Continent, in Cisalpine and Transalpine Gaul, the Iberian Peninsula, Central Europe to the Black Sea, and Galatia in Asia Minor, as a result of the settlement of the Celtic *Galatae* in Northern Phrygia, subsequent to their incursion into the Balkans. The bulk of the surviving material, however, derives from Gaul, and very little is known of the Celtic dialects spoken farther east.

'Insular Celtic', as the term implies, refers to the two varieties of Celtic speech introduced into Britain and Ireland, namely Goidelic and British (or Brythonic). Goidelic was the parent-language of (*a*) Irish, (*b*) Scottish Gaelic (in the Highlands of Scotland and the Western Isles), derived from the Irish speech (or 'Common Gaelic', as it is sometimes called) brought to Scotland about the end of the fifth century by the Dalriadic colonists from north-east Ireland who settled in Argyll, and (*c*) Manx, derived similarly from the speech of the Irish settlers who came to Man, possibly sometime in the fourth century, although this is far from certain. The latter is now virtually extinct. British (or Brythonic), the other variety of Celtic speech introduced into this island, was the parent-language of (*a*) Welsh, (*b*) Cornish, which was in grave danger of becoming extinct even as early as the latter part of the eighteenth century (enthusiastic but somewhat belated attempts have been made to revive it during the present century), and (*c*) Breton, introduced by British immigrants who, as a result of Anglo-Saxon pressure, fled in successive waves to the Armorican peninsula from the middle of the fifth century to the early seventh. The fact that many of these refugees, particularly during the middle and second half of the sixth century, came from Devon and Cornwall, accounts for the close relationship between Cornish and Breton, and for the various phonological and morphological features which, during successive periods in their development, these two languages shared to the exclusion of Welsh.

These two varieties of insular Celtic speech represent the P and Q branches of Common Celtic, distinguished by the way in which they treated the IE.[1] labio-velar consonant q^{u}. In Goidelic labio-velar q^{u} was preserved, but it later lost its labialization in Irish, becoming the velar tenuis *k* (*c*) which, under certain conditions (e.g. when it occurred intervocally in the interior of words), was lenited to *ch*. In British, on the other hand, IE. (and Common Celtic) $q^{u} > p$, apart from certain instances where the labialization was lost; when subject to the conditions of lenition this $p > b$. Thus W. *pedwar* 'four', Co. *peswar*, Br. *pevar* are etymologically related to O Ir. *cethir* from IE. *q^{u}*ĕtu̯ŏres*; cf. Lat. *quattuor*.

The P branch of Celtic also embraces Gaulish; but compare, for example, the forms *Sequani* and *Sequana* (Seine), or the form *Equos* 'February' in the famous Coligny Calendar. However, the theory postulated by some philologists, on the basis of these forms and other similar examples, that there were some Celtic dialects in Gaul which retained IE. q^{u} has been vigorously challenged. Whatever truth may be in such a theory, it is abundantly clear from the bulk of the material which has survived from Gaul that the language or related Celtic dialects spoken there belonged pre-eminently to the P branch of Celtic, so that the speech of the Gauls, as Tacitus asserts, could not have been greatly dissimilar from that of the Britons. So with W. *pedwar* etc., O Ir. *cethir*, cf. Gaul. *petuar*[*ios*] 'fourth', *petor-ritum* 'four-wheeled cart', and (with different vowel-grade) *Petru-corii* 'the four hosts'. It is extremely unlikely that the change $q^{u} > p$ occurred independently in British and Gaulish, and some authorities thus find it convenient to use 'Gallo-British' or 'Gallo-Brittonic' as a generic term for the various P-Celtic dialects spoken on the Continent in the pre-Christian era by widely-dispersed Celtic tribes, sections of whom ultimately crossed to Britain and settled there, thus introducing the P variety of Celtic which we know as British (or Brythonic).

The most important of the phonological developments which marked the differentiation of Common Celtic as a clearly-defined sub-group from Indo-European were: IE. *ē* > *ī*: Lat. *rēx*, Gaul. *rīgo-*, W. *rhi* 'king', O Ir. *rí*. IE. *ō* > *ā* in non-final syllables: Lat. *nōtus*, Gaul. *Eposognatus* 'familiar with horses', W. *gnawd* (aw < *ā*) 'customary', O Ir. *gnáth*. IE. *ō* in final syllables > CC. *ū* (> Brit. *ǖ* > Late Brit. *ī*), except that IE. *-ōm* > *-ŏm* (> *-ŏn*) in CC., owing to early shortening of a long vowel before a nasal; cf. IE. **k̂u̯ō* > W. *ci* 'dog', O Co. *ki*, Mn.Co. *ky*, Br. *ki*, O Ir. *cú*: Skt. *śvā*, Lat. *canis*. IE. *ei* > *ẹ̄* (a long close *e*): Gk. στείχω 'I walk', Goth. *steigan* 'to ascend', W. *-twy* as in *mordwy* 'movement of the sea' > 'sea-voyage' (wy < *ẹ̄*, cf. Gaul. *Moritex*), O Ir. *tégi* 'thou goest'. IE. *r̥*, *l̥* > *rĭ*, *lĭ* before mutes and sonants: Skt. *bhr̥ti-ś* 'a bearing, maintenance', W. *bryd* 'mind', Co. *brys*, Gaul. *vergobretus* (with

[1] The following abbreviations have been used in various places for the names of languages:

Br.	Breton	Ir.	Irish	O Ir.	Old Irish
Brit.	British	Lat.	Latin	ON.	Old Norse
CC.	Common Celtic	Lith.	Lithuanian	OW.	Old Welsh
Co.	Cornish	ME.	Middle English	Osc.	Oscan
Gaul.	Gaulish	Ml.Br.	Medieval Breton	Slav.	Slavonic
Gk.	Greek	Ml.W.	Medieval Welsh	Skt.	Sanskrit
Goth.	Gothic	Mn.W.	Modern Welsh	Umbr.	Umbrian
IE.	Indo-European	OE.	Old English	W.	Welsh

-re- instead of *-ri-*), O Ir. *breth*, *brith*, verb-noun of *berid* 'bears'; Skt. *pṛthú-š* 'broad', Gk. πλατύς, W. *llydan* 'broad', Co. Br. *ledan*, O Ir. *lethan*, the Celtic forms being derived from **lĭtano-*, cf. Gaul. *Litano-briga*. IE. *p* in initial and intervocalic positions disappears: Skt. *pra*, Gk. πρό, Slav. *pro*, Goth. *fra*, Lat. *pro-*, Gaul. *Ro-talus*, W. *ry*, Co. *re*, Br. *ra*, O Ir. *ro*, *ru*. But IE. *pt*, *ps* fell together in Celtic with *kt*, *ks* > χ*t*[1], χ*s*. IE. *gᵘ* (the labio-velar media) > *b* initially, except before *u*; also post-consonantally in medial positions; but intervocally and before consonants IE. *gᵘ* > *g*; as an example of the regular development in initial positions cf. Lat. *vīvus*, W. *byw* 'living', Co. *byw*, *bew*, Br. *beo*, O Ir. *beo*, the Celtic forms being derivatives of IE. **gᵘĭ-* from the root **gᵘei-* 'to live'. IE. *gᵘh* > *g* initially according to Irish forms, but there are Brit. forms where *gw̯-* appears for *g-*.

These were the major changes which marked the differentiation of Common Celtic as a sub-group from Indo-European. Celtic, in common with a number of other IE. languages, did not distinguish between the palatal and velar series of the IE. consonantal phonemes, while the IE. tenues fell together in an early period with the voiceless aspiratae, and the mediae generally fell together with the voiced aspiratae.

It has frequently been observed that there are a number of special features which Celtic and Italic share, often to the exclusion of the other IE. languages. These features, it has been argued, reflect very early dialectical affinities, and some philologists have thus been led to postulate an Italo-Celtic dialect (or group of dialects). Attention has usually been concentrated, with varying degrees of emphasis, on the following features: Assimilation of IE. *p* . . . . *qᵘ* > *qᵘ* . . . . *qᵘ*; e.g. IE. **penqᵘe* > Italo-Celtic **qᵘĕnqᵘe*: O Ir. *cóic* 'five' (< Goidelic **qᵘŏnqᵘe*), OW. *pimp*, Ml.W. *pymp*, Mn.W. *pump*, Lat. *quinque*; but Gk. πέντε, Skt. *pañca*, Lith. *penki*. The genitive singular of *-o*-stems ended in *-ī*; e.g. Lat. *dominī*, *virī*, Gaul. *Segomari*, *Dannotali*, *Cantli* etc., Ogam *MAQQI*, *MAQI* 'of the son', *NETACARI* etc., O Ir. *fir* (gen. sg.) < **u̯irī*; but the genitive singular of *-o*-stems in Greek and Sanskrit had an ending which probably went back to IE. **-o-si̯o*, cf. Gk. ἵπποιο, Skt. *açvasya*. The impersonal forms of the verb in Celtic and Osco-Umbrian are characterized by an *r*-ending: Umbr. *ferar* 'one must bear', W. *cerir* 'one loves', *gwelir* 'one sees'. The same ending also characterizes the deponent and passive forms in Celtic and Italic, e.g. Lat. *sequor*, *sequitur*, O Ir. *sechithir* 'follows', and cf. the deponent forms *bwyr*, *awyr*, *edrychuir* etc. which occur in the early Welsh poetry. Other features common to Celtic and Italic are: the *ā*-subjunctive, the sigmatic subjunctive, and possibly the *b*-future; the formation of superlative adjectives by means of the suffix *-(i)sm̥o-* (with variations in Italic); the nominal suffix *-tūt-*, cf. the formation *virtūs*, *virtūtis* in Lat. with O Ir. *be(o)thu*, W. *bywyd* 'life' < Celtic **bĭu̯o-tūt-s*, a derivative of IE. **gᵘi-*, from the root **gᵘei-*. The change IE. *eu̯* > *ou̯* has also been regarded by some philologists as another peculiarity; e.g. Osc. *touto*, Gaul. *teu̯to-*, *tou̯to-*, W. *tud* 'people, land', O Ir. *túath* 'tribe, people', but Goth. *þiuda*. Some scholars have also maintained that an analysis of the vocabulary shows

[1] χ = a velar voiceless spirant; cf. *ch* in Scots *loch*, or German *nach*. This sound is written *ch* in Modern Welsh.

that there are a number of words which are exclusive to Celtic and Italic. The interpretation of these features, however, has been much disputed. It has been pointed out, for example, that the _r_-endings mentioned above occur in other IE. languages, in Hittite, Tocharian, and Phrygian, while Marstrander has argued that there are really great divergences of vocabulary which militate against the theory that there was once a very close connection between the Celtic and Italic peoples. Moreover, it has been observed that there exist a number of features common to Celtic and Germanic (which is hardly surprising when one remembers that the Celts had an early centre in south and south-western Germany on both sides of the Rhine), or common to Italic and Germanic, or even to all three. As a result, some authorities, while not necessarily rejecting or impugning the points of resemblance outlined above, have challenged the conception of a close prehistoric association between the linguistic ancestors of the Celtic and Italic peoples which would seem to be implicit in the theory of an Italo-Celtic dialect (or group of dialects).

Welsh, then, belongs to the P branch of Celtic, being a descendant of British (or Brythonic), the language or group of related dialects spoken by the Celtic inhabitants of Britain both before and during the Roman occupation. Those who spoke this language called themselves *_Brĭttŏnes_ (> W. _Brython_), and their language *_Brĭttŏnĭkā_ (> W. _Brythoneg_). The Welsh, however, now call their national language _Cymraeg_ (accented on the final syllable < _Cym-rá-eg_), and they refer to themselves as _Cymry_ (< Brit. *_Kŏmbrŏgī_ 'men of the same region, fellow-countrymen'), singular _Cymro_ (< Brit. *_Kŏmbrŏgos_, cf. the first element in _Cumber-land_). This name, however, probably only became current as a national appellation after the Britons of Wales had been effectively separated from those of the Dumnonian peninsula by the English penetration into the Severn valley which followed the battle of Deorham (or Dyrham), near Bath, in 577. The name probably became current in this connotation during the bitter struggle in which the Welsh participated with the Britons of Strathclyde against the encroaching English, a struggle which culminated in the fateful battles of Chester (613) and Winwaed Field (655), which finally separated the Welsh from their north-western compatriots. The British language was thus spoken throughout the areas now known as England and Wales, and in parts of southern Scotland, before the Roman occupation. And it continued to be spoken in Roman Britain, in both the Highland and Lowland Zone. The old catastrophic picture of the complete disappearance of British speech over large areas of the Province has now been abandoned. Latin must have been the language of government, of civil and military administration, of trade and commerce, of education and the Christian religion and, to a marked degree, of the great civil settlements and of the market and garrison towns. But the vast majority of the rural peasantry probably spoke British, and this is certainly true of the less-intensively Romanized regions of the highland west.

As British was thus spoken over so wide an area, there must inevitably have been some dialectical variations. Unfortunately, however, hardly anything is known of the British language or dialects spoken in eastern Britain. In the west, on the other hand, it is possible on phonological grounds to distinguish between a West and South-western dialect of British. The former was the parent of Welsh and the

closely-related speech of Cumbria, while South-western British was the ancestor of Cornish and Breton. It was probably not until the fifth to sixth centuries that these dialects began clearly to diverge, although, according to the most recent work on the phonology of the British languages, there are some slight indications of possible dialectical differentiation as early as the first century (Jackson, 1953). It is impossible, however, to pass a confident judgment on any phonological differentiation during this early period, as the direct information for studying British is extremely meagre, our knowledge being largely obtained by inference. Not one sentence of British has survived, nor is there any inscription written entirely in that language. Apart from the information which can be gleaned from the inscriptions on the coins which were occasionally minted by pre-Roman kings and princes, our direct knowledge of early British is confined to place-names, personal and tribal names, and a few common words, which occur in Classical sources. This is hopelessly inadequate. Fortunately, however, there is one source of inestimable importance for understanding the structure and development of British, namely the Latin words which were borrowed by the ancient Britons during the Roman occupation and which have survived in the vocabularies of Welsh, Cornish and Breton. When British decayed and became Welsh, etc., the loan-words underwent the same phonetic developments as the basic Celtic vocabulary. By comparing the Latin words with the forms into which they subsequently developed, the philologist can deduce what were the regular phonetic changes which ultimately transformed the dialects of British into Welsh, Cornish and Breton. With this information at his disposal, and guided further by the overall picture presented by the Celtic remains on the Continent, it is possible for the philologist to trace the various elements in the Welsh, Cornish and Breton vocabularies back to their original forms, and thus reconstruct hypothetically certain features of the parent British language.

According to the picture thus created, British was a synthetic language, in the same stage of development as Latin, to which it bore some striking resemblances in its sound-system and morphology, so that the borrowing of Latin words could have presented no great difficulty for the ancient Britons. (A study of Old Irish, however, provides us with the salutary warning that there must also have been fundamental differences between the two languages). British was, no doubt, a fairly stable language in the first century, and as such it could not have been drastically dissimilar in its phonology from Common Celtic. It was the Roman occupation which probably led in the first instance to its gradual deterioration, a fact which has usually been ascribed to the loss of official status and cultural prestige suffered by the native inflected language during this period, as well as to the removal, as a result of the political degradation of the British upper classes, of any conservative influence which may formerly have been exercised on the native speech, so that greater freedom was given for the increasing percolation of the more 'developed' and corrupt type of British spoken by the lower orders. According to some authorities, the collapse of Roman organization in the early fifth century, and the social upheaval caused by the Anglo-Saxon conquest and settlement, acted as a catalyst on the phonetic developments of the first four centuries, thus leading to a considerable acceleration in the rate of linguistic change, and ultimately to the complete trans-

formation of British into Welsh, Cornish and Breton. Professor Binchy (1958) has recently suggested, albeit tentatively, that the drastic phonetic changes which resulted in the breakdown of Primitive Irish were likewise due to a period of social stress and upheaval, to which there are vague references in some sagas and genealogical tracts, as well as to the more frequent inter-relationship of Goidel and Brython which followed the introduction of Christianity. Similarly, the drastic linguistic changes which marked the transition from Old to Middle Irish can be attributed to the disruption of the old order under the impact of the Norse invasions, while the subsequent change to Modern Irish is usually connected with the advent of the Anglo-Normans. And students of English are familiar with the thesis that the impact of the Norman Conquest was in a large measure responsible for the rapid deterioration of Anglo-Saxon and the change to Middle English.

The various phonetic changes which ultimately transformed a dialect of British into Welsh are clearly reflected in the development of the Latin loan-words in British. Briefly, the most important of these were:

(*a*) A series of vowel changes, e.g. *ẹ̄* (a long close *e*) > *wy*; *ā* > *ǭ* (a long open *o*) > *aw̯* (*au̯*) in monosyllables and final (originally accented) syllables; *ọ̄* (a long close *o*) > *ü*, originally a rounded central vowel (later unrounded), which is written *u* in Welsh from the earliest sources; etc. Cf. *cēra* > *cwyr*, *rēte* > *rhwyd*, *ăltāre* > *allawr* (later *allor*), *părātus* > *parawd parod*, *fōrma* > *ffurf*, *ōrdo* > *urdd*.

(*b*) A series of consonant mutations comprising (1) lenition, or the 'soft mutation' as it is called in Welsh, whereby between vowels in the interior of words, or initially when they formed a close speech-liaison with the final vowel of the preceding word, or (with certain exceptions) between vowels and *l*, *r*, *n*, the single voiceless plosives *p*, *t*, *c* were voiced to *b*, *d*, *g*, while the voiced plosives *b*, *d*, *g* became the voiced spirants *f*,[1] δ,[2] ʒ,[3] and *m* > *ṽ*.[4] Cf. *u̯īpĕra* > *gwiber*, *Aprīlis* > *Ebrill*, *cīu̯ĭtas* > *ciwed*, *pŭtris* > *pwdr*, *lōrīca* > *llurig*, *băcŭlus* > **băc'lus* > *bagl*, *lăbōr-em* > *llafur*, *Fĕbruārius* > *Chwefrawr Chwefror*, *fĭdes* > *ffydd*, *fŭga* > *ffo*, *mărgărīta* > *meri̯erid mererid*, *gĕmĕllus* > *gefell*, *cŏlŭmna* > *colofn*; (2) the nasal mutation, whereby *mb* > *m*(*m*), *nd* > *n*(*n*), *ŋg*[5] > *ŋŋ*, and, later chronologically, *mp* > *m*(*m*)*h*, *nt* > *n*(*n*)*h*, *ŋc* > *ŋ*(*ŋ*)*h*. Cf. *Ambrŏsi̯us* > *Emreis Emrys*, *ăscĕndo* > **ăscĭndo* > *esgyn* (*esgynnaf* 'I ascend, I mount'), *ăngĕlus* (≡ *ăŋgĕlus*) > *angel* (≡ *aŋŋel*), *ĭmpĕrātor* > *ymherawdr ymherodr*, *fŏntāna* > *ffynnawn ffynnon* (pl. *ffynhonnau*), *căncĕllārius* > *canghellawr canghellor*; (3) the spirant mutation whereby, for example, the geminates *pp*, *tt*, *cc* became the voiceless spirants *ff*[6](*ph*), *th*,[7] *ch*,[8] and *rp*, *rt*, *rc* > *rff*, *rth*, *rch*, while *lp*, *lc* > *lff*, *lch*. Cf. *clŏppus* > *cloff*,

[1] A labiodental (originally bilabial) voiced spirant ≡ English *v*.

[2] A dental voiced spirant (written *dd* in Modern Welsh) ≡ English *th* in *this*, *then*.

[3] A velar voiced spirant; generally this disappeared later, or became in certain cases *i̯*, i.e. a semi-vowel ≡ English *y* in emphatically pronounced *yes*.

[4] A strongly nasal *v*; the nasality was later lost, thus giving Welsh *f* ≡ English *v*.

[5] *ŋ* represents the *ng* in English *singing*.

[6] A labiodental voiceless spirant ≡ English *f* in *for*, or English *ff* in *staff*.

[7] A dental voiceless spirant ≡ *th* in English *thin*, *thing*.

[8] A velar voiceless spirant ≡ *ch* in Scots *loch* or German *nach*; it is articulated with a slight uvular vibration.

săgĭtta > *saeth*, *pĕccātum* > *pechawd pechod*, *cŏrpus* > *corff*, *pŏrta* > *porth*, *ărca* > *arch*, *Alpīnus* > *Elffin*, *călc-em* > *calch*.

(*c*) Vowel affection, a phenomenon analogous in certain respects to Germanic umlaut, whereby a short vowel in British (and in Latin loan-words) was affected by a sound in a succeeding syllable. Thus, to take final *ā*-affection as an example, *ĭ* or *ŭ* in the penultimate syllable in British were lowered to *e* and *o* respectively when followed by *ā* in the ultimate. Or, as a result of final *i*-affection, *a*, *o*, *u*, and *e* in the penultimate were raised to e^i (> *ei*) or *y*,[1] as the case might be, with palatalisation of intermediate consonants. The Latin borrowings again reflect this change quite clearly. Cf. *mănĭca* > *maneg*, *grămmătĭca* > *gramadeg*, *cŏlŭmna* > *colofn*, *bŭcca* > *boch*, *brăcchịum* > *breich* (later *braich*), *ăngĕlī* > *engyl*, *ĕpĭscŏpī* > *esgyb*, *cŭneus* > **cŭnịus* > *cŷn*.

(*d*) The loss of final and unstressed internal syllables, including the syncope of unstressed composition vowels. Cf. *trīnĭtắt-em* > *trindawd trindod*, *caụĭtắt-em* > *ceudawd ceudod*, *aụ(c)tōrĭtắt-em* > *awdurdawd awdurdod*.

Without doubt, the most important of all the various phonological changes which characterized the transition of the Western dialect of British into Welsh was the disappearance of final and unstressed internal syllables, a process which resulted in the complete disintegration of the British case-terminations and which inevitably brought about a profound transformation in the whole syntactical and morphological character of the language.[2] These linguistic changes, it must be emphasized, did not all occur simultaneously, and they were, of course, gradual developments, albeit quickened in some measure, according to some authorities, by the disturbed conditions of the immediate post-Roman period, which brought the various phonological changes to their culmination. The date when the old synthetic British language had so far decayed as to give rise to the new analytic language, Welsh, has been the subject of vigorous discussion and debate. It was once commonly believed that proper names, retaining their final (inflected) syllables or composition vowels intact, which occur in various inscriptions from the mid-fifth to the end of the seventh century, represented forms which were still current in the contemporary living speech, so that the language then spoken could not have been Welsh, as it was still essentially an inflected one. Modern scholarship, however, has decisively refuted this argument, and informed opinion now accepts an earlier date for the emergence of Welsh as a new analytic language from British. Sir John Morris-Jones (1918) demonstrated that the proper names in question were really traditional archaising Latin forms—in much the same way as *Henricus* occurs in modern documents

[1] A clear retracted *i*-sound.

[2] 'British became Welsh when the unaccented medial syllables, and the unaccented terminations were dropped; the medial consonants during this process underwent regular changes or mutations, so that *-c-* became *g*, *-m-* became *v*(*f*), and *-t-* became *d* in the word we are studying. Both the dropping of the unaccented vowels and the various mutations of consonants were gradual processes, and several centuries passed away before the orthography was adapted to the changed pronunciation. When, however, these changes had taken place in the living speech, British may be said to have become Welsh.'—Sir Ifor Williams, 'When did British become Welsh?', *Transactions of the Anglesey Antiquarian Society and Field Club*, 1939, p. 30.

or inscriptions as a Latinization of *Henry*[1]; and the practical identity of Old Welsh and Old Breton proved that the considerable linguistic reconstruction involved in the growth and development of the new linguistic entities had occurred before the effective separation of Welsh and Breton. Sir John Morris-Jones (1918) therefore confidently asserted that 'the new language was already in existence in the first half of the sixth century'.[2] The major conclusions of Sir John Morris-Jones have been confirmed and amplified by the monumental scholarship of Sir Ifor Williams who, after analysing some fifth- and sixth-century names in various Anglesey inscriptions, concluded that they 'are in favour of the theory that British at this period was not the spoken language of the men who wrote these inscriptions'.[3] Sir Ifor was firmly convinced that St. Patrick swore in Welsh in the fifth century![4] These conclusions give greater significance to the important references to Welsh poetic tradition made by Nennius (or Nemnius) in his *Historia Brittonum* (*c.* 800) where, after referring to Ida, king of Northumbria, 547–59, he goes on to say:

> [T]unc dutigirn. in illo tempore fortiter dimicabat contra gentem anglorum. Tunc talhaern tat aguen in poemate claruit. et neirin. et taliessin et bluchbard. et cian qui uocatur gueinth guaut. simul uno tempore in poemate brittannico claruerunt.

Unfortunately, not a single line of the poetry composed by Talhaearn (*c.* 550) has survived. But the reference to him as *tat aguen*, i.e. *Tad Awen* 'Father of the Muse', is significant. He is probably the first in a long line of *Welsh* (as distinct from *British*) poets, so that his standing in Welsh poetic tradition can with some justification be compared with that often assigned in English literature to Chaucer, 'the father of English poetry'. Such a comparison reflects the great chronological differences in the evolution and development of the two languages. It is now generally agreed that the Welsh language had been in existence long enough, and had gathered sufficient tradition behind it, to enable the poems attributed in thirteenth-century manuscripts to Taliesin and Aneirin to be composed by them in the new analytic language in the second half, and towards the end, of the sixth century. These poets are thus appropriately known in Welsh poetic tradition as the *Cynfeirdd*, the 'First (or Original) Poets'; they sang, as Sir John Morris-Jones so aptly phrased it, 'the birth-song of the new speech'.

The loss of the old final syllables resulted in the disappearance of case-inflections in the British dialects. Traces of the British oblique cases survive, however, in a few Welsh forms. Thus in *beunydd* 'daily', a lenited form of *peunydd* < **peu-n dydd*, the form **peu-n* represents the accusative of *pawb*; cf. *beunoeth* 'nightly' and the later

[1] The situation may not have been quite as straightforward as this, according to some authorities; but there is no doubt that Sir John Morris-Jones was correct in his main thesis. *Vide* J. Morris-Jones, 'Taliesin', *Y Cymmrodor*, XXVIII, pp. 28–31.

[2] John Morris-Jones, op. cit., p. 31.

[3] *An Inventory of the Ancient Monuments in Anglesey*, p. cxvii.

[4] *Transactions of the Anglesey Antiquarian Society*, 1939, pp. 37–9. But see Jackson, op. cit., p. 633. Professor Jackson has attempted, in a work of monumental scholarship, to date the various sound-changes which took place in the evolution of the British languages. He suggests that the Welsh language had come into existence by the second half of the sixth century. It is impossible to enter here into a detailed discussion of this subject, but it is significant that, in the light of modern scholarship, even the most conservative estimate would not ascribe the evolution of Welsh from Brythonic to a date later than the second half of the sixth century.

formation *beunos*. Again, *erbyn* 'by (a certain time or event), against' is a composite preposition formed from the preposition *er-* (*ar-*) 'before, in front of, opposite', < Brit. **are-* < Celtic **ari-* (cf. Gaul *Aremorici*, O Ir. *air*) and the dative of *pen* 'head, end' < Brit. **pĕnno-* < Celt. **q*^{u}*ĕnno-*; cf. O Ir. *cenn*. The form of the dative singular in Celtic would be **q*^{u}*ĕnnū* (cf. O Ir. *ciunn*, dative of *cenn* 'head') > Brit. **pĕnnū* > Late Brit. **pĕnnī* which, as a result of final *i*-affection, would regularly give W. *pyn* as in *erbyn*; cf. O Ir. *ar-chiunn* 'in front', Co. *erbyn*, *er dhe byn*. The adverb *fry* 'up', a mutated form of **bry* (cf. *obry* 'beneath, below') probably derives from the dative of Brit. and Celt. **brĭgā*, which regularly gave W. *bre* 'hill, brae, highland' (cf. Gaul. *Admageto-briga*, *Litano-briga*). In some instances two distinct forms have survived in Welsh from British personal names, the oblique cases of which differed appreciably from the nominative singular. Thus, for example, the nominative singular **Măglŏkū*, a composite personal form from **măglo-*, the stem of the noun **măglo-s* 'prince' (cf. O Ir. *mál* 'prince', 'noble', Ml.W. *mael*, O Br. *Mael*) and **kū* 'dog hound' (cf. O.Ir. *cú*, W. *ci*), in the sense of 'warrior, hero, defender', would regularly give *Meilyg* in Welsh. But the stem in the oblique cases **Măglŏkŭn-* (e.g. Brit. accusative singular **Măglŏkŭnan*, genitive singular **Măglŏkŭnos*) would regularly give *Maelgwn* in Welsh. *Tudyr* (> *Tudur*) and *Tudri* are also a related pair in precisely the same way as *Meilyg* and *Maelgwn*. However, apart from a sprinkling of forms such as these, the British case-inflections have completely disappeared in Welsh. The fact that pairs such as those noted above are felt to be different words and are so regarded, and not different cases of the same word in Welsh, shows that the existence and significance of the British case-inflections was rapidly forgotten in the new analytic language.

It is clear, therefore, that the really fundamental changes in the history and development of the Welsh language were those involved in its evolution from the synthetic parent tongue. No changes of comparable magnitude have occurred since. This is not to imply that the language has since ceased to change and develop. Indeed, it is convenient, for purposes of study, to divide the language into the following periods:

(1) Early Welsh, from the time when the language had developed from British to the end of the eighth century. Mere fragments survive from this period, such as the forms *Car Legion* (for *Caerlleon*, Chester), *Ban-cor*, *Brocmail*, *Dinoot* which occur in Bede.

(2) Old Welsh, from the beginning of the ninth to approximately the end of the eleventh century. The Old Welsh remains consist of a number of glosses (e.g. the glosses in the Liber Commonei, Bodleian MS. Auct. F. 4. 32, on various Latin notes discussing weights and measures, known as *De Mensuris et Ponderibus*, or the glosses in the Corpus Christi College, Cambridge, MS. of the *De Nuptiis Philologiae et Mercurii* by Martianus Capella); some pieces of prose (e.g. the *Surexit*-memorandum and the *Ostenditur hic* entry in the Book of St. Chad, a manuscript containing a Latin text of the Gospels of St. Matthew and St. Mark, and part of that of St. Luke, now in the possession of the Cathedral Church of St. Chad at Lichfield); some fragments of anonymous verse (cf. the two poems, one consisting of three verses, the other of nine, in the Juvencus MS., Cambridge University Library, Ff. 4. 42). In addition, Old Welsh forms have survived in the Genealogies, in the *Historia Brittonum* (Nennius), in the Latin Life of King Alfred written by the Welshman Asser, in the *Liber Landavensis*, a twelfth-century compilation

containing an important collection of Latin charters and various other documents pertaining to the church of Llandaff, with Welsh names, and often land boundaries given in Welsh; etc. The 'Computus Fragment', a passage of prose written in the tenth century as a commentary on one of Bede's astronomical tables, proves conclusively that the language was already a fitting medium for the precise and lucid exposition of the most abstruse subjects.

(3) Medieval Welsh, from approximately the beginning of the twelfth to the end of the fourteenth century and, in some instances, somewhat later. There was considerable variation in the orthography during this period, from which a wealth of material, both prose and poetry, has survived. The best known examples of Medieval Welsh prose are probably the eleven stories traditionally called the Mabinogion, which are preserved in the White Book of Rhydderch (*Llyfr Gwyn Rhydderch*), written down *c.* 1300–25 and now in the possession of the National Library of Wales, Aberystwyth, and in the Red Book of Hergest (*Llyfr Coch Hergest*), *c.* 1375–1425, now preserved in the Library of Jesus College, Oxford. These prose compositions often reflect a technical competence and sense of proportion, or a conscious literary artistry, of the highest order. They have been described as being 'among the finest flowerings of the Celtic genius and, taken together, a masterpiece of our medieval European literature' (Jones, 1949). The Laws, the texts of which survive in a large number of manuscripts, are a model of utilitarian prose; comparatively advanced legal principles are defined clearly and unambiguously, and it is obvious that the language could draw during this period on a great wealth of technical terms and phrases. The great body of panegyric poetry composed in the strict metres during this period, and later, which survives in a great number of miscellaneous manuscripts, reflects a conception of society and of the bard's function therein which is virtually unique in the European literary tradition.

(4) Early Modern Welsh, from the *cywyddau* of Dafydd ap Gwilym (*fl.* 1340–70) to the sixteenth century.

(5) Late Modern Welsh, from the sixteenth century (the translation of the Bible in 1588) to the present day.

It must be emphasized that the dates suggested for the various divisions outlined above are only approximate, and there must inevitably be some overlap. But they serve as a convenient guide for purposes of study. Nevertheless, whatever differences may divide these periods from one another, they are by no means as drastic or as fundamental as those which divide Old English from Middle English, or both from the language of the modern period. Talhaearn in approximately the mid-sixth century, be it remembered, was the father of the Welsh Muse.

VOCABULARY

The basic vocabulary is Celtic (and Indo-European), and the cognate forms can generally be recognized without any serious difficulty in Cornish and Breton, the sister British languages, but usually with somewhat more difficulty in Irish, owing to important differences in phonological development. During the Roman occupation a considerable number of words were borrowed into British from the living Latin speech of the Romans and, generally speaking, they reflect the impact of a superior civilization. These borrowings, for the reasons already adduced, are a source of inestimable importance for the Celticist. Nor are they devoid of all

interest for Romance scholars. In a detailed analysis of the Latin element in British, Professor Kenneth H. Jackson has demonstrated that the phonology of the Latin spoken in Britain was on the whole conservative and archaic when compared with contemporary Continental standards. The forms into which these Latin loan-words subsequently developed in the three British dialects prove the continuance in Roman Britain of pronunciations which had elsewhere vanished from colloquial use, in some instances as early as the first century. Professor Jackson has argued, on the basis of this evidence, that these borrowings are derived from a somewhat 'stilted' and artificial Latin, which had been acquired as a second language at school, a language in which the rather refined and archaistic pronunciations tended, on the whole, to conform not with those current in ordinary Vulgar Latin, but with the more literary or classical standards advocated by the schoolmasters and grammarians. Whatever reservations must be attached to this hypothesis, it is obvious that the Latin loan-words in British are an important source for estimating the degree of the Romanization of the Province. In addition to these early borrowings the Welsh vocabulary also contains a number of 'learned' loans, i.e. words borrowed and adapted during later periods from literary Latin sources. These later 'book' loans can very often be detected by some irregular features in their phonological development when compared with the regular sound-changes which occurred in the early borrowings.

There were intimate contacts between Wales and Ireland from a very early period. Irish immigrants settled in the north-western and south-western extremities of Wales during the Roman occupation, and the presence of Irish elements in the population is attested by the distribution of the Ogam-inscribed stones. The intimate relationship of Welsh and Irish continued into the medieval period, so that it is by no means surprising that a number of Irish words have found their way into the vocabulary. Note, e.g., *brat* 'rag, clout, apron' < O Ir. *brat*; *cochl* 'mantle, cloak, robe' < O Ir. *cochull* (< Lat. *cucullus*); *cadach* 'rag, piece of linen or cloth, handkerchief, etc.' < O Ir. *cadach* 'calico'; *cleir(i)ach* 'aged person, decrepit old man' < Ir. *cléireach* (< O Ir. *clérech*) 'clergyman, cleric'; *croesan* 'jester, jongleur, minstrel' < O Ir. *crossán* 'lewd, ribaldrous rhymer; a mimic, buffoon'; *cnwc* 'hillock, knoll' < O Ir. *cnocc*. Irish elements are also attested in place-names; e.g. Roath (W. *Y Rhath*) from Ir. *ráth* 'fortified enclosure, rampart, mound'.

There are also a few traces, in the vocabulary, of Old Norse relations with Wales. Thus *carl*, diminutive *cerlyn*, 'churl, miser, skinflint' could be a borrowing from ON. *karl*, although the Old English *carl* is not to be ruled out, while *iarll* 'earl' is probably a borrowing from ON. *iarl*. It has also been suggested that *gardd* 'garden' comes from ON. *garðr* 'yard, enclosed space'. As various sections of the Welsh sea-board were subjected to Scandinavian attacks from approximately the mid-ninth century to the end of the eleventh, it is hardly surprising that ON. elements can be attested in Welsh place-names, particularly the islands, creeks, bays and headlands which served as navigational guides along various stretches of the coast. Unfortunately, however, it is often impossible to obtain precise information with regard to the period of borrowing, and some elements which have usually been

regarded as direct loans from Old Norse could just as easily be of Old English provenance. (See the chapter on Place-names.)

The most prolific source of borrowing has undoubtedly been English, from the Anglo-Saxon period right down to the present day. It would be quite impossible to enumerate or to classify here the hundreds of words borrowed in the modern period, especially those which are of a distinctly technical or scientific nature. Some of the very early borrowings retain unmistakable traces of the Old English inflectional system. Thus, for example, *tarian* 'shield', *cwpan* 'cup', *sidan* 'silk', *capan* 'cape, cloak, cope, surcoat' and *hosan* 'hose, stocking' reflect quite clearly the OE. *-an* ending of the so-called 'weak-declension', being derived from one of the oblique cases of OE. *targe*, *cuppe*, *side*, *capa* (*cæppe*) and *hosa* respectively. Another interesting feature is that the Welsh forms often retain sounds and occasionally preserve meanings which have disappeared or changed in the source-forms. Thus in W. *cnoc* < English *knock*, or *cnaf* < Middle English *knave*, *cnafe*, the (hard) *c-* is clearly pronounced. Cf. also *rhonc* 'rank' (adjective), 'out-and-out, stark' < ME. *ronke*, *ronk*, and *clep* 'babble, chatter, gossip; bang, clap' < ME. *cleppe* 'clap, noise, chatter'. An interesting example of the way in which the Welsh form has preserved the older meaning while that of the English has changed can be seen in Welsh *sad* 'firm, steady', cf. ME. *sad*, *sadde*. Again, words which have become obsolete in English, or which may now survive only in some dialects, still occur as living forms in Welsh; cf. *barclod* 'apron' < OE. *bearmclāþ*, or *llidiart* 'gate' < OE. *hlidgeat* (the intrusive *r* in the Welsh form can be attributed, according to some authorities, to the influence of English *yard* in some form or other).

Some words have also been borrowed from French, particularly from Norman French, while the translation of the Scriptures introduced a sprinkling of Hebrew and Greek words into the language.

ACCENTUATION

The accent falls regularly on the penult in Welsh polysyllables, while there is secondary stress on the first syllable in words of four syllables or more: *cáraf* 'I love', *carédig* 'kind', *càredígrwydd* 'kindness'. The exceptions to this rule represent only a fraction of the entire vocabulary. Words accented irregularly on the ultima are often forms in which the final syllable represents a late contraction, e.g. *Cymraeg* < *Cym-rá-eg*, *paratoi* 'prepare' < *pa-ra-tó-i*. In these forms the accent fell regularly on the penultimate before the contraction. Some forms borrowed from English also retain their original accentuation. So, e.g., the forms *apêl* 'appeal', *perswâd* 'persuade' are accented on the ultima, while *testament*, *polisi* 'policy', *melodi* 'melody', and *paragraff* 'paragraph' are accented on the ante-penultimate.

Care should be taken in pronouncing place-names. The Language and Literature Committee of the Board of Celtic Studies of the University of Wales has recently issued *A Gazetteer of Welsh Place-Names* (Davies, 1957) in which it has attempted to establish a standard rational orthography for Welsh place-names. The principle generally adopted was that a hyphen should be used in those forms where the stress, instead of falling regularly on the penult, is thrown forward on to the last

syllable. Hence *Brynáman*, *Llanbádarn*, but *Bryn-glás*, *Pen-y-bónt*. Hyphens have not been used, however, to indicate the stress in some forms which are widely known. Thus *Caerdydd* (Cardiff) and *Pontypridd*, although written as one form, should be pronounced *Caer-dýdd* and *Pont-y-prídd* respectively. The *Gazetteer* also provides (pp. xxvii–xxxi) a simple but effectively clear guide to the correct pronunciation of Welsh vowels and consonants, a subject into which it is impossible to enter here for considerations of space.

VOWEL AND CONSONANT CHANGES

Few features present greater difficulty for those who are beginning to learn the language than the various vowel- and consonant-changes which can do so much to transform the appearance of words.

Vowel mutation (*gwyriad*) is a change certain vowels or diphthongs undergo by changing their position in a word, so that vowels or diphthongs occurring in the ultima and in monosyllables are regularly modified when, by the addition of new syllables, they change to non-final positions. Thus *ai* in monosyllables and in the ultima regularly becomes *ei* in other syllables, e.g. *gair* 'word', pl. *geiriau*. A similar alternation according to their position is seen in *au – eu*: *haul* 'sun', *heulog* 'sunny'; *amau* 'to doubt, to suspect', *amheuaeth* 'doubt, suspicion'. *aw – o*: *awr* 'hour', pl. *oriau*. *w – y* (*ə*)[1]: *dwfn* 'deep', *dyfnder* 'depth'. *y*[2] *– y* (*ə*): *dyn* (≡ *dyn*)[2] 'man', pl. *dynion* (≡ *dənion*); *mynydd* (≡ *mənydd*) 'mountain', pl. *mynyddoedd* (≡ *mənəddoedd*). *uw – o*: *buwch* 'cow', pl. *buchod*. These sound-changes can be explained by reference to the accent-shift which took place towards the end of the Old Welsh period, probably in the eleventh century. In British, certainly in Late British, the accent fell regularly on the penultimate, so that after the loss of British final syllables the accent must have fallen in Early Welsh on the new ultimate. This explains, for example, the alternation *aw – o* noted above. For British *ā* (< IE. *ā* and IE. *ō* in non-final syllables) and Lat. *ā* (except for some instances where *ā* > *ă* in Vulgar Latin unstressed syllables) developed in Late British into an open *ǭ*. In non-final, i.e. pretonic, syllables this Late Brit. *ǭ* was shortened to *ǫ̆*, thus giving *ŏ* in Old, Medieval and Modern Welsh in non-final syllables. But the *ǭ* remained in Early Welsh in final (i.e. stressed) syllables and, of course, in monosyllables, and was later diphthongized to *aw̯* (*au̯*). This diphthong has remained in Welsh monosyllables to the present day. But after the accent had shifted back to the Welsh penultimate, *aw̯* (*au̯*) was reduced to *ŏ* towards the end of the Old Welsh period in the now unaccented final syllables. Again, British (and Latin) *ŭ* and *ĭ* in unaccented syllables were reduced ultimately to *ə*, written *y* in Welsh. But in final (originally accented) syllables and in monosyllables *ŭ* remained, written *w* in Welsh, and *ĭ* regularly developed into the clear retracted *i*-sound, written *y* in Welsh. The Latin borrowings reflect the difference in development quite clearly. Thus *plŭ́mbum* > *plwm*, *Sātŭrnus* > *_Sătŭ́rnus_ > *Sadwrn*; but *cŭltĕ́llus* > *_cəlléll_ > *cə̂llell* (written *cyllell*). Compare also *ĭnĭ́tium* > *_ənýd_ > *ə́nyd* (written *ynyd*). Thus the obscure sound of *y* (i.e. *ə*), which had developed

[1] An obscure sound like the *e* in English *hammer*, or, when long, like the *u* in English *further*.

[2] A clear retracted *i*-sound. In ordinary written and printed Welsh the character *y* is used to represent both the clear and obscure sound.

from the reduced varieties of *ŭ* and *ĭ* in (originally) pretonic syllables, remained even when, as a result of the accent-shift, they now bore the stress.

The other important change which vowels undergo is vowel affection (*affeithiad*), i.e. a change in a vowel or diphthong due to a sound which follows it, or which once followed it, in the word. Reference has already been made to this change in outlining the major changes involved in the deterioration of British. (See also some of the remarks under Accidence and Syntax.)

The initial consonants undergo regular changes or mutations under certain conditions, a feature which is common to all the Celtic languages. There are nine consonants which can be modified by initial mutation, and there are three types of change, namely the soft mutation (lenition), the nasal mutation and the spirant mutation. These mutations can best be illustrated by means of the following table:

Radical	*p*	*t*	*c*	*b*	*d*	*g*	*m*	*ll*	*rh*
Soft	*b*	*d*	*g*	*f*	*dd*	—	*f*	*l*	*r*
Nasal	*mh*	*nh*	*ngh*	*m*	*n*	*ng*	No change		
Spirant	*ph*	*th*	*ch*	No change			No change		

For example, *cath* 'cat': *dy gath* 'thy cat', *fy nghath* 'my cat', *ei gath* 'his cat', *ei chath* 'her cat'. The science of comparative grammar has established beyond any reasonable doubt that these initial mutations are in origin phenomena of sandhi. Compare the three systems of initial mutations in Old Irish, generally known as aspiration (or lenition), eclipsis and gemination. The mutations in Welsh have become, however, an essential feature of grammar and syntax. (See some of the remarks under Accidence and Syntax.)

ACCIDENCE AND SYNTAX

It is only possible here to refer briefly to some of the more prominent features. Welsh has no indefinite article; the definite article, *yr*, *'r* or *y* (OW. *ir*, *-r*), which seldom occurs in the earliest poetry, although it becomes more common from the period of the Old Welsh glosses on, can probably be related etymologically to the forms of the definite article in the other Celtic languages, being based on an old demonstrative **sindo-*, **sindā*. The noun has two numbers, singular and plural; and two genders, masculine and feminine. The plural can be formed from the singular by vowel change, or by the addition of a termination, or by both methods combined. The plurals formed by umlaut are derived from the *-o*-stems; the nominative plural of this class of nouns ended in *-ī* (cf. Lat. *dominī*, *virī*), and it was this ending which affected the (short) vowel of the preceding syllable. Thus the nominative singular **bărdo-s* > *bardd* 'poet', **mărko-s* > *march* 'horse, stallion', **tăru̯o-s* (cf. Gaul. *TARVOS*) > *tarw* 'bull'; but, as a result of final *i*-affection, the nominative pl. **bărdī* > *beirdd*, **mărkī* > *meirch*, **tăru̯ī* > *teirw*. The affected forms,

however, can also be derived by regular sound-change from some of the other cases, e.g. from the genitive and dative singular of the *-o*-stems. But after the loss of the British case-endings the umlaut came to be regarded as a characteristic feature of the plural formation, and then spread by analogy to nouns which belonged originally to other stems. The plural terminations, on the other hand, can generally be derived from the stem-endings of British imparisyllabic nouns. With the loss of British final syllables these stem-endings did not survive in the form which regularly developed from the old nominative singular, although they were retained in the plural. Thus *-au* (Ml.W. *-eu*, OW. *-ou*), which is the commonest of the various plural terminations in Welsh and Breton, can be derived from the plural endings of *-u*-stems; e.g. Brit. nom. sg. **kătu-s* > *cad* 'battle', nom. pl. **kătou̯-es* > *cadeu*, *cadau*. This ending later spread by analogy to nouns of other declensions, particularly when, after the loss of the British case-endings, no distinctive form for the plural had survived in Welsh. Again, the plural termination *-ed* can be derived from the *-t*-stems. Thus, e.g., nom. sg. **mĕrket-s* > *merch* 'girl', but the stem **mĕrkĕt-* in the oblique cases (e.g. nom. pl. **mĕrkĕtes*) would regularly give *merched*, the plural form in Welsh. Many of the other plural terminations are similarly derived, sometimes from old collectives, cf. Ml.W. *pyscawt* 'fish', Mn.W. *pysgod* < Lat. *pĭscātus*. Welsh also makes use of singular terminations, *-yn* (masc.), *-en* (fem.), which can be added to the stem, so that the corresponding plural form derives from the stem, without any plural termination; cf. *adar* 'birds' < Brit. **(p)ătăr-*, sg. *aderyn* (< *adar* + *yn*); Brit. **mi̯ár-* > *mwyar* 'blackberries', sg. *mwyaren*. Traces of an old dual can be seen, particularly in Medieval Welsh, in the lenition of the initial consonant of an adjective after a noun denoting two of a particular kind, or a pair, a phenomenon originally caused by the old vocalic ending of the nominative dual; cf. also the lenition of the initial consonant of a noun after the numerals *dau*, *deu-* (masc.), *dwy*, *dwy-* (fem.), and of the initial consonant of the numeral after the definite article: *y ddau beth* (*y ddeubeth*) 'the two things', *y ddwy fil* 'the two thousand'. Names of parts of the body which are in pairs are often expressed in Modern Welsh as compounds with the numeral 'two'. Traces of an old British neuter can be seen in some nouns of uncertain or vacillating gender, e.g. *braich* 'arm' < Lat. *brăcchium*. Some of the old neuters have different genders in Medieval and Modern Welsh; thus *chwedl* 'story', feminine in Modern Welsh, but masculine in the medieval period, is cognate with O Ir. *scél n-*, a neuter noun belonging to the *-o*-stems < Celtic **skĕtlo-n*. Again, the non-lenition of certain forms after *dau* 'two' may be a relic of an old neuter formation.

The genitive is conveyed by placing the noun which is in the genitive case and (if such occur) the article or prefixed pronoun immediately after the noun on which it depends, or (if such occur) after the adjective or adjectives which qualify that noun; e.g. *esgid bachgen* 'a boy's boot', *ystafell yr athro* 'the teacher's room', *lliw coch y llyfr* 'the book's red colour'. It will be observed that whereas the dependent noun in this construction can be preceded by its own article, the latter is omitted before the noun on which it depends, e.g. *cadair y tad* 'the father's chair', literally 'chair the father', *cadair tad y bachgen* 'the boy's father's chair'. The indefinite partitive genitive is conveyed by connecting the nouns with the preposition *o*: *rhan o'r ystafell* '(a) part

of the room', *y trydydd dydd o'r mis* 'the third day of the month'.

The attributive adjective usually follows the noun it qualifies, and if the noun is feminine singular the initial (mutable) consonant of the adjective is lenited, a phenomenon which can be attributed to the fact that a great number of the feminine singular nouns had a vocalic ending in British, usually *-ā* or *-ī*. After the loss of the old case-endings, this lenition spread by analogy to adjectives following all feminine singular nouns; the mutation thus became morphemic. (The fact that the old demonstrative **sindo-*, **sindā* was originally inflected for case, gender and number accounts for the rule in Welsh that the initial consonant of a feminine singular noun is lenited after the definite article, *ll-* and *rh-* being exceptions to this rule owing to provection). Adjectives can also be inflected for number, gender and comparison. The plural is formed from the masculine singular by vowel change, or by adding the ending *-(i̯)on*, in some cases with vowel change. Those plurals formed by umlaut are derived from the British adjectives with *-o*-stems. Thus singular **lĭtăno-s* > *llydan* 'wide, broad', **i̯ou̯ănko-s* > *ieuanc* 'young'; nom. pl. **lĭtănī* > *llydein, llydain*, **i̯ou̯ănkī* > *ieueinc, ieuainc*. When its plural has been thus formed by vowel affection, the adjective often agrees with the noun in number, although there are exceptions to this rule; agreement is optional in those instances where the plural has been formed by the addition of a plural ending. Some adjectives have no distinctive plural forms. There are no feminine plural forms, nor have the equative and comparative degrees any plural formations. The attributive adjective agrees with the noun in gender, but this is not always true of a predicative adjective; cf. *llym awel* 'keen (is) the wind' where, although *awel* is feminine, we have the masculine form of the adjective *llym* (fem. *llem*). The gender inflection whereby (usually, but not exclusively, in monosyllables) *w* or *y* in the masculine form are changed to *o* or *e* in the feminine is derived from those adjectives which belonged to the British *-o-* and *-ā*-stems. In British, as in Latin, the *-o*-stems were masculine-neuter, with a corresponding feminine in *-ā-*; cf. Lat. *bonus, bonum*, fem. *bona*; *tener, tenerum, tenera*. Thus Brit. **u̯ĭndo-s* (masc.), **u̯ĭndo-n* (neut.) > *gwyn(n)* 'white' by regular sound-change. But the nominative singular of the feminine form, as we have seen, originally ended in *-ā*, and as a result of final *ā*-affection the feminine **u̯ĭndā* > *gwen(n)*. Similarly, **dŭbno-s* (masc.), **dŭbno-n* (neut.) > *dwfn* 'deep', but **dŭbnā* (fem.) > *dofn*. This gender inflection then spread to other adjectives, whatever their original declension; cf. *crwn*, fem. *cron* 'round', which is cognate with Irish *cruind*, an adjective belonging to the *-i*-stems < Celtic **krund-i-*. The equative, comparative and superlative degrees are formed from the positive by the addition of *-(h)ed*, *-ach* and *-(h)af* respectively. Before these endings provection of the final voiced plosives (*b, d, g*) of the positive occurs, even when the positive form ends in one of these mediae plus a liquid or nasal. This provection occurred originally in the equative and superlative, owing to the *-h-* of the suffix, but by the Modern Welsh period it had spread to the comparative. Thus the three degrees of comparison of *teg* 'fair' would be *teced, tecach* (Ml.W. *tegach*), *tecaf*, and of *budr* 'dirty': *butred, butrach, butraf*. Some examples occur, more particularly in Medieval Welsh, where the endings of comparison have been added to the feminine positive; cf. *gwenned, gwennaf, tromaf, berraf*. But these forms never became general, and in Modern Welsh

there are no distinctive feminine forms for the derived degrees. The adjectives which do not take the various endings of comparison can be compared periphrastically by placing *mor*, *mwy* and *mwyaf*, respectively, before the positive. The adjectives which are compared irregularly are of particular interest to the Celticist, as many of these reflect quite unmistakably the original IE. formation whereby the suffix of comparison was added to the root of the positive (sometimes with different vowel grade), and not to the stem.

There are a number of interesting features in the numeral system. The numerals can be used adjectivally and are placed before the noun, which is in the singular: *tri dyn* 'three men' (lit. 'three man'). Many examples occur in Medieval Welsh, however, and in the language of the bards, of the regular plural form of the noun after numerals above 'one' (*un*): *teir chwioryd* 'three sisters' (sg. *chwaer*), *pump gwraged* 'five women' (sg. *gwraig*). There are a few traces of this construction in early Biblical Welsh, while the old plural form *diau* (earlier *dieu*) 'days' is still used in *tridiau* 'three days', and the plural form *blynedd* < IE. **blĭdnĭi̯ās* occurs regularly in *tair blynedd* 'three years', etc. Compare also the plural form *saint* (sg. *sant* 'saint') after the numerals *tri* 'three' and *pump* 'five' in the place-names *Llantrisaint* (> *Llantrisent* > *Llantrisant*) and *Llanpumsaint* respectively. The general use in the modern period of the singular form of the noun after the cardinals above 'one' probably reflects the influence of the old dual. In the *-o*-stems the British dual, by regular phonological development, ultimately gave the same form in Welsh as the old British nominative singular; but in certain other stems the form which had developed in Welsh from the dual was identical with the plural. It was inevitable, therefore, that there would be some fluctuation in the use of singular and plural after 2, this tendency being further helped by the fact that in some instances (e.g. in the *-o-* and *-ā*-stems) there was no distinction in Welsh between the form which had developed from the British nominative singular, the nominative plural and the nominative dual. The singular form ultimately predominated, so that it became the rule for the singular form of the noun to be used after all adjectival numerals. The cardinals can also be used substantivally, followed by the preposition *o* and a plural noun or pronoun: *saith o blant* 'seven children', *pump ohonynt* 'five of them'. The cardinals 'two' (*dau*), 'three' (*tri*) and 'four' (*pedwar*) have separate feminine forms, namely, *dwy*, *tair* and *pedair* respectively, and the same is also true of the ordinals. The numerals 11–19 reflect two distinct constructions. Thus *deuddeg* '12' and *pymtheg* '15' are old compounds (now indivisible) formed from the units 2 and 5 respectively plus 10. This construction must formerly have been more widespread, as is shown not only by similar formations in the other British dialects, but also by some 'fossilized' examples in early Welsh texts, e.g. OW. *naunec-* in the form *naunecant* 'a period of 19 years', and Ml.W. *undec* 'eleven'; cf. also Mn.W. *pythefnos*, *pythewnos* 'fortnight' (lit. 'fifteen nights'). However, with the exception of the old compounds which are still preserved in 12 and 15, Welsh has adopted another construction in the numerals 11–19. Thus 11, 13 and 14 are conveyed by the construction numeral + the preposition *ar* 'on' + *deg* 'ten': *un ar ddeg* '11', *tri* (*tair*) *ar ddeg* '13', etc. The digit is followed by the singular form of the noun: *un bachgen ar ddeg* '11 boys'; or the plural form of the noun follows the composite formation

plus the preposition *o*: *tri ar ddeg o fechgyn* '13 boys'. The numerals 16–19 follow a similar pattern, except that the addition here is to *pymtheg* 'fifteen': *un ar bymtheg* 'sixteen', *dau lyfr ar bymtheg* 'seventeen books', etc. In addition to the construction *tri ar bymtheg* 'three on (plus) fifteen', the numeral '18' can also be conveyed by multiplication: *deunaw* '2 × 9'; cf. Breton *triouec'h* '3 × 6'. The general pattern described above is preserved after '20', except that the digit is now added to *ugain* 'twenty': *un ar hugain* '21', *dau ar bymtheg ar hugain* '37', etc. There are clear examples of a Celtic vigesimal system: *deugain* 'forty' (lit. '2 × 20', cf. Ir. *dá fichit*), *trigain* 'sixty' ('3 × 20', Ir. *tri fichit*), *pedwar ugain* 'eighty' ('4 × 20', cf. French *quatre-vingts*), *saith ugain* 'one hundred and forty' ('7 × 20', cf. Ir. *secht fichit*), etc.

One of the most interesting features in the syntax of the personal pronouns, which Welsh shares with the other Celtic languages, is the construction in which the object pronoun precedes the verb, being infixed, for example, after such proclitics as the relative *a*, affirmative particles such as *fe*, the negative, or conjunctions such as *o* 'if', *oni* 'if not', etc. So, in Job X, 18, *O na buaswn farw, ac na'm gwelsai llygad!* ('Oh that I had given up the ghost, and no eye had seen me'), the accusative pronoun *'m* (1st. sg.) is infixed between the verb *gwelsai* and the negative *na*. There are also some comparatively early examples of a construction which has not survived in Modern Welsh where the pronoun object is placed immediately after the first element in a compound verbal form in which a preverb has been placed before the verbal root; e.g. Ml.W. *dymkyueirch pawb* 'everyone asks me', where the pronoun object *-m-* is infixed between the preverb *dy-* and the compound verbal form *kyueirch*. There is a similar construction in Old Irish. There are also examples in the medieval texts of the infixed pronouns being used in the dative case with the verb 'to be' conveying 'to have': *vn tat a-e bu* 'they had the same father' (lit. 'one father there was to them'). This construction, however, has now been replaced by a prepositional construction: *y mae gennyf, y mae imi* 'I have'. Another interesting feature is to be seen in the prepositions which, as in all the Celtic languages, have 'conjugated' personal forms. This feature can be attributed to the early agglutination of the prepositions and the personal pronouns which they governed, so that the compound forms ultimately developed into inflexions. The simple form of the preposition is used when the object is other than a personal pronoun, and many prepositions have also an adverbial form.

The verb has four tenses in the indicative mood, the present (which is frequently future in meaning, and predominantly so in the spoken language), the imperfect, the past (aorist or perfect), and the pluperfect. There are two tenses of the subjunctive mood, present and imperfect, although the distinction between the forms of the imperfect subjunctive and the imperfect indicative can be seen in only a few irregular verbs in Modern Welsh. There is also an imperative. With the exception of the latter, which naturally has no first singular, each of these tenses is inflected for the three persons, singular and plural. Each tense has also an impersonal form which, with its accompanying object, is often translated into English by a passive verbal formation with its subject: *gwelir fi* 'I am seen'. Relics of the deponent survive in the earlier Welsh poetry, these forms being generally characterized by the *r*-ending which is a conspicuous feature of the Latin passive and deponent. But the

only form of the old deponent which now survives in Welsh is possibly *gŵyr* 'knows', cf. Co. *gor*, Ml.Br. *goar*, O Ir. *-fitir*. Each verb has also a verbal noun, which can sometimes be etymologically different from the finite verb. The verbal noun governs the genitive, not the accusative, and it can generally be used like any ordinary noun. With the preposition *yn* and the various tenses of the verb 'to be' (*bod*) it forms a periphrastic conjugation: *yr wyf yn canu* 'I am singing', *yr oeddwn yn canu* 'I was singing', etc. This construction is particularly prevalent in the spoken language. Most verbs have also verbal adjectives, cf. *caredig* 'kind': *caru* 'to love'. The preterite forms of the regular verb reflect quite clearly the *-s*-preterite, which is probably derived from a formation going back to the IE. *-s*-aorist. The preterite forms of certain other verbs reflect the *-t*-preterite, which is generally held to be derived from the 3rd singular of the consonantal stems of the IE. aorist, whence it later spread in the Celtic languages to other personal forms. There is also clear evidence of the suffixless preterite (sometimes with reduplication). The *-h-* which originally characterized the subjunctive stem, and which has left its mark in Modern Welsh in certain forms with provection (cf. *maco*, 3rd sg. pres. subj. of *magu* 'to breed, to rear, to nurse'), is derived from the sigmatic subjunctive, which is well attested in three Medieval Welsh forms, *duch* 'may bring', *gwares* 'he may succour', *gwnech* 'he may do'.

Normally the verb stands at the beginning of the sentence, as in Irish, followed by the subject (when expressed), the object, and the remainder of the predicate. The position of the adverb or adverbial phrase varies, and it is possible for this to stand at the head of the sentence. The verb can also be preceded by a particle, this being generally the rule in the spoken language. The rule generally observed in Modern Welsh that the subject, when it immediately follows the verb, retains its radical while the initial consonant of the object undergoes lenition is, in addition to the regular word-order of the normal sentence, a further convenient aid for distinguishing subject from object. The subject is itself lenited, however, when separated from the verb (e.g. by an adverbial expression), while the object invariably retains its radical after impersonal forms. A particularly striking feature is the non-agreement in number between verb and subject. For the verb, when followed by an expressed subject other than a personal pronoun, is always in the third person singular; e.g. *Gwêl y bechgyn geffylau yn y cae*, lit. 'Sees the boys horses in the field', but *Gwelant* (*hwy*) *geffylau yn y cae* 'They see horses in the field'. In the second example, where the verb *gwelant* 'they see' is 3rd pl., the termination *-ant* in the verbal form, with or without the auxiliary affixed pronoun *hwy*, conveys the pronominal subject of the verb. Similarly, *gwelaf* (*fi*) is 'I see' and *gwelwch* (*chwi*) is 'you see'. There are many examples in Medieval Welsh, however, and in some of the material derived from the Old Welsh period, showing concord in number between verb and subject. For example, in Medieval Welsh we find *doethant y llygot* 'the mice came', or *kychwynnassant yr yniueroed hynny*, 'those hosts set out', where the verb is 3rd plural. Examples of a similar agreement occur in Old Irish. This usage, however, has completely disappeared in Modern Welsh.

Many examples also occur in Medieval Welsh and in the old poetry where the verb in a non-emphasizing construction is preceded by some other part of the

sentence, e.g. by the subject or object. The freer word-order which is evident in the early poetry probably reflects, to some extent, the greater syntactical freedom possessed by words in the synthetic British language, which could convey the various grammatical relationships by means of its inflectional endings, without recourse to an invariable word-order. It was thus possible, as the Gaulish inscriptions indeed confirm, for the subject or object to precede the verb at the head of the non-emphasizing sentence. Note the following example from Old Welsh, where the subject stands at the head of the sentence: *dou nam riceus un guetid*, 'two lords can converse, one speaks'; or the following example where the object comes first: *grefiat guetig nis minn tutbulc hai cenetl*, 'a title-deed afterwards Tudfwlch and his people will not require'. There are examples in the early poetry, again confirmed by the Gaulish inscriptions, of the order subject + object + verb, e.g. *meiryon eu tretheu dychynnullyn*, 'stewards their taxes gathered'. When the object in sentences of this type happened to be a personal pronoun, the latter could be infixed between the subject and the simple (uncompounded) verb by means of the meaningless particle *a*: *Duw a-m difero* 'may God defend me'. Sentence-patterns of this type could hardly fail to influence those where the order was subject + verb + noun object. The result was that the meaningless particle *a* spread by analogy and was used even in the absence of an infixed pronoun. In this way there arose the so-called 'abnormal sentence', subject (or object) + the meaningless particle *a* + verb, which is extremely common in Medieval Welsh prose, e.g. *Bendigeiduran uab Llyr a oed urenhin coronawc ar yr ynys hon*, 'Bendigeidfran son of Llyr was crowned king over this Island'. The 'abnormal sentence' occurs very frequently in Biblical Welsh. The spread of the meaningless particle *a* to sentences of this type was also materially facilitated by the close interaction there must have been between them and the so-called 'mixed sentence'. For when any word or phrase other than a finite verb is to be emphasized in Welsh, it is placed at the beginning of the sentence (preceded in the earlier periods by the copula, of which it formed the predicate), and is followed in the remainder of the sentence by a proper or improper relative clause. So, for example, in a poem in the twelfth-century Black Book of Carmarthen we find *Oed Maelgun a uelun in imuan*, 'It was Maelgwn whom I saw attacking', where the relative pronoun *a* introduces the proper relative clause. Instances abound in Old Irish of a similar construction with the copula, e.g. *is rann din deacht ad-gén-sa*, 'it is (only) a part of the Godhead which I know'. The copula, however, has long disappeared in Welsh, so that in the modern period the word or phrase which is emphasized stands at the beginning of the sentence, e.g. *Y bachgen a laddodd yr aderyn, nid y gath* 'It was the boy who killed the bird, not the cat'. The same is generally true of Medieval Welsh — although 'mixed sentences' with the copula do occur — and there are a few interesting examples in Old Welsh which show that the copula was beginning to disappear even then, e.g. *Salt emmiguollig hinnith ir bloidin hunnuith*, '(It is) the Saltus which prevents that that year'. Sentences of this type, after the disappearance of the copula, bear a striking resemblance to the 'abnormal sentence' already described. There must inevitably have been a close interaction between the two constructions, a factor which further facilitated the spread of the particle *a* to the non-emphasizing 'abnormal sentence'. The spoken language, however, would make

a clear distinction between the two types of sentence, as the emphasizing or 'mixed sentence' would have a different stress and intonation. The fact that Welsh is particularly sensitive to various and often subtle shades of emphasis probably accounts in some measure for the unusual word-order and intonation of the English spoken by many Welsh people. The relative construction also provides a further example of the non-agreement in number between verb and subject mentioned above, for the verb is always in the 3rd person singular when the relative pronoun is the subject of the affirmative relative clause. But when the negative form of the relative pronoun refers to a plural antecedent the verb in the relative clause will also be plural in form.

Welsh, like Irish, has probably inherited an old Indo-European usage in placing the verb at the head of the normal sentence. The preference which both the insular Celtic languages have shown for such a construction was probably strengthened, according to Professor Vendryes's theory (1911–12)[1], by those constructions where an accusative pronoun was infixed after the first preverb in a compound verbal form, or, when the verb was a simple uncompounded form, after the negative or an affirmative particle. Professor Vendryes has argued that constructions of this kind gave rise to a definite pattern for opening a sentence, namely preverb or particle + pronoun object + verb + subject. The pattern thus evolved ultimately influenced those sentences where the object was not a personal pronoun but a noun, thus giving rise to the order preverb + verb + subject + noun object, or, when the verb was a simple uncompounded form, verb + subject + noun object.

It should be noted that literary Welsh is remarkably conservative when compared with the colloquial language. For example, final *-nt* in the ending of the 3rd person plural of the verb is regularly mutated to *-nn(h)* in the spoken language. There is no doubt that the mutation had occurred as early as the twelfth century at least, as the 3rd. pl. forms *dygan* 'bring', *deuthan* 'came' and *kuynan* 'lament, complain' occur in a poem in the Black Book of Carmarthen where they rhyme with such forms as *(g)welugan*, *Elgan*, *tarian* and *kyulauan*. Nevertheless, although it is probable, as the 3rd plural form *treidin* in the Juvencus *englynion* suggests, that this mutation had taken place before the beginning of the medieval period, the standard literary language still adheres religiously to the ending *-nt*, so that the three forms noted above are written *dygant*, *daethant* and *cwynant* respectively. Again, the diphthongs *ai* and *au* in final (unaccented) syllables are generally levelled with *e* or *a* in the dialects. Thus, in Powys, Dyfed and large areas of Morgannwg the words *perffaith* 'perfect' and *pethau* 'things' are regularly pronounced *perffeth* and *pethe* respectively, while in Gwynedd and Gwent the same forms are pronounced *perffath* and *petha*. These, and other similar dialectical variations, have not been accepted into the standard literary language, which is based on the language of the Bible. In his translation of the latter, which appeared in 1588, Dr. William Morgan (*c*. 1541–1604), while not by any means rejecting entirely the forms of the living speech, took generally as his medium not the contemporary living language, nor

[1] Compare also the discussion by Professor Henry Lewis (1942), especially pp. 266–9. Professor Lewis's lecture is the best general discussion of the subject.

even the flexible language of poetry composed in the free metres, but rather the majestic language of the classical *cywydd*-writers, the poets who sang in the strict metres. The latter devotedly studied and fostered the language from generation to generation in their bardic schools, and clung tenaciously to its unsullied purity. In the new and revised edition of the Bible which appeared in 1620 — probably the work of Dr. John Davies (*c.* 1567–1644), incumbent of Mallwyd, and generally regarded as one of the greatest of Welsh scholars — the language was made yet purer, emendations being made to Dr. William Morgan's text whenever the latter had strayed from the exacting standards of the literary language. Hence the translation of the Bible, although it established a standard of correctness in writing which is often extremely conservative when compared with the colloquial tongue, gave the Welsh nation a standard literary language, excelling any dialect, and with centuries of unbroken tradition behind it. The essential continuity of that tradition can perhaps best be illustrated by the fact that a *cywydd* composed today by a poet who sings in the strict metres would, as far as its language is concerned, be remarkably similar to one composed in the fourteenth century by Dafydd ap Gwilym, traditionally regarded as the greatest of Welsh *cywydd*-writers.

Yet this language, with such a wealth of tradition behind it, and which can boast one of the oldest extant literatures in Western Europe, is now struggling for its very existence. The steady decline in the number of people able to speak the language is clearly mirrored in the various census reports. In the census returns for 1951 the figure given for those persons aged three years and over who were able to speak Welsh was 714,686, compared with 909,261 in 1931, the total population aged three years and over being just under two and a half million at both dates. This shows a decline within a period of twenty years of 194,575 or 21·4 per cent. Almost all those persons recorded as being able to speak Welsh were also able to speak English, only 41,155 being recorded as speaking Welsh only. This latter figure showed a sharp decline when compared with the 1931 returns, when 97,932 were recorded as speaking Welsh only, representing a decrease of 56,777 or 58·0 per cent in twenty years. The present century has witnessed a steady and appreciable decrease in the proportion of persons speaking Welsh, from 49·9 per cent in 1901 to 43·5 per cent in 1911, 37·1 per cent in 1921, 36·8 per cent in 1931, and 28·9 per cent in 1951. A particularly depressing feature is the fact that the unrelenting decrease in the proportion of persons speaking Welsh only, from 15·1 per cent in 1901 to 8·5 per cent in 1911, 6·3 per cent in 1921, 4·0 per cent in 1931, and 1·7 per cent in 1951, was appreciably greater than the decrease in the proportion able to speak both Welsh and English. The serious reduction in the number of monoglot speakers can only lead to a progressive corruption of idiom, syntax and vocabulary, a feature which is immediately apparent to any observant Welshman who has more than a mere superficial command of his native language. It must, of course, be remembered that there are very many thousands of Welsh-speaking Welshmen in England, the United States of America, Patagonia, etc., and various Welsh societies exist in scores of places in many countries. One of the most moving moments in the National Eisteddfod, which is held every year during the first week in August in North and South Wales in turn, is the ceremony of

extending an official welcome to the '*Cymry Alltud*' or '*Cymry ar Wasgar*', those Welshmen from overseas who have returned home, sometimes after many years 'in exile', for the great national festival. But the existence of such Welshmen, who still speak their native language in many lands, does not really offset in any way the alarming decrease, as reflected in the successive census reports, in the incidence of Welsh speaking which has taken place over a long period.

Some of the factors which have thus resulted in the progressive anglicization of Wales are not difficult to seek — the tremendous expansion in the power and range of English publicity; the fact that the language, in spite of small concessions, has no official status of any significance, so that English is inevitably regarded as the language of material advancement; the accumulative effects of an English system of elementary education which all too often in the past studiously neglected the Welsh linguistic, cultural and historical tradition; the close economic integration of Wales and England, coupled with successive waves of English immigration into Wales and, during periods of intense industrial depression, of Welsh emigration to England, with the result that the anglicization of the heavily-populated industrial regions of South Wales has proceeded at an alarming pace during the present century; the decline in traditional religious observances, so that the Nonconformist chapel, with its Welsh services and literary meetings, has ceased to act as a social focus in many communities. The picture, however, is not one of unrelieved gloom, for there is some evidence in recent years of a more enlightened outlook and policy in official circles. The language now has a staunch supporter in the Welsh Department of the Ministry of Education, while the University of Wales has recently manifested its desire to recognize the cultural value of the language by deciding to appoint to its staff people who are qualified to teach certain subjects through the medium of Welsh. The Welsh Departments of the four University Colleges have for many years lectured and held their examinations in that language. Moreover, Welsh works on literary and linguistic subjects are published regularly, improved editions of the early poetry, the medieval prose, and of several of the great classical *cywydd*-writers have appeared, the result of many years of painstaking linguistic and textual study, and the classical prose-writers have been made more accessible to the Welsh-reading public. As a result, the Welsh literary tradition has been rediscovered and reinterpreted, a feat which has made a deep impression on the intellectual life of Wales. Linguistic research, as already suggested, has played an indispensable part in opening up the treasures of the past, and the Board of Celtic Studies of the University of Wales is now issuing in parts a standard dictionary of Welsh. Creative literary works of all kinds continue to appear, sometimes of a very high standard. Welsh news bulletins and miscellaneous Welsh programmes are regularly broadcast in the Welsh Home Service of the B.B.C., and Welsh is still the only language of worship for many thousands. In recent years a determined attempt to arrest the steady decline in the number of those able to speak the language has been made by the establishment of schools where the medium of instruction is entirely Welsh. But, important as these measures are, there are many who now feel that, if the Welsh language is to survive, more radical and far-reaching measures are necessary. There is, in brief,

a growing body of opinion which holds that the difficulties which beset the language are basically political, and that therefore they can only be effectively countered by political means.

REFERENCES

Baudiš, J., 1924. *Grammar of Early Welsh*, Oxford.

Binchy, D. A., 1958. Review of *Language and History in Early Britain*, by Kenneth H. Jackson, *Celtica*, iv, pp. 288–92.

Caradar (A. S. D. Smith), 1925. *Welsh Made Easy*, 3 parts, Cardiff.

Davies, Elwyn, 1957. *Rhestr o Enwau Lleoedd: A Gazetteer of Welsh Place-Names*, Cardiff.

Dillon, Myles, 1944. 'Italic and Celtic', *American Journal of Philology*, LXV, pp. 124–34.

——, 1947. 'Celtic and the other Indo-European Languages', *Transactions of the Philological Society*, pp. 15–24.

Dottin, Georges, 1920. *La langue gauloise*, Paris.

Evans, Simon D., 1951. *Gramadeg Cymraeg Canol*, Cardiff.

Holder, Alfred, 1896–1913. *Alt-Celtischer Sprachschatz*, Leipzig.

Hudson-Williams, T., 1935. *A Short Introduction to the Study of Comparative Grammar (Indo-European)*, Cardiff.

Jackson, Kenneth H., 1953. *Language and History in Early Britain*, Edinburgh.

Jenkins, Myrddin, 1959. *A Welsh Tutor*, Cardiff.

Jones, 1949. *The Mabinogion*. Translated by Gwyn Jones and Thomas Jones, London.

Jones, Stephen, 1926. *A Welsh Phonetic Reader*, London.

Lewis, Henry, and Pedersen, Holger, 1937. *A Concise Comparative Celtic Grammar*, Göttingen.

Lewis, Henry, 1931. *Datblygiad yr Iaith Gymraeg*, Cardiff.

——, 1942. 'The Sentence in Welsh'. The Sir John Rhŷs Memorial Lecture, *Proceedings of the British Academy*, pp. 259–80.

——, 1943. *Yr Elfen Ladin yn yr Iaith Gymraeg*, Cardiff.

Lloyd-Jones, J., 1928. *Enwau Lleoedd Sir Gaernarfon*, Cardiff.

Loth, J., 1892. *Les mots latins dans les langues brittoniques*, Paris.

Meillet, A., 1908. *Les dialects indo-européens*, Paris.

——, 1908. *Introduction a l'étude comparative des langues indo-européennes*, Paris.

——, 1925. *La méthode comparative en linguistique historique*, Oslo.

Morgan, T. J., 1950. 'The Welsh Language', *Chambers's Encyclopaedia*, XIV, pp. 518–20.

——, 1952. *Y Treigladau a'u Cystrawen*, Cardiff.

Morris-Jones, John, 1913. *A Welsh Grammar Historical and Comparative*, Oxford.

——, 1918. 'Taliesin', *Y Cymmrodor*, xxviii, London.

——, 1921. *An Elementary Welsh Grammar*, Oxford.

——, 1931. *Welsh Syntax*, Cardiff.

Parry, Thomas, 1955. *A History of Welsh Literature*. Translated from the Welsh [with an appendix on the twentieth century] by H. Idris Bell, Oxford.

Parry-Williams, T. H., 1923. *The English Element in Welsh*, London.

Pedersen, Holger, 1909–13. *Vergleichende Grammatik der keltischen Sprachen*, 2 vols., Göttingen.

——, 1925. *Le groupement des langues indo-européennes*, Copenhagen.

Richards, Melville, 1938. *Cystrawen y Frawddeg Gymraeg*, Cardiff.

Royal Commission on Ancient and Historical Monuments in Wales and Monmouthshire, 1937. *An Inventory of the Ancient Monuments in Anglesey*, London.

Strachan, John, 1909. *An Introduction to Early Welsh*, Manchester.

Thomas, R. J., 1938. *Enwau Afonydd a Nentydd Cymru*, i, Cardiff.

Thurneysen, Rudolf, 1946. *A Grammar of Old Irish.* Revised and enlarged edition, translated from the German by D. A. Binchy and Osborn Bergin, Dublin.

Vendryes, Joseph, 1911–12. 'La place du verbe en celtique', *Mémoires de la Société de Linguistique de Paris*, xvii, pp. 337–51, Paris.

Whatmough, Joshua, 1949–51. *The Dialects of Ancient Gaul*, Michigan.

Williams, Ifor, 1938. *Canu Aneirin*, Cardiff.

——, 1939. 'When did British become Welsh?', *Transactions of the Anglesey Antiquarian Society and Field Club*, pp. 27–39.

——, 1945. *Enwau Lleoedd*, Liverpool.

——, 1960. *Canu Taliesin*, Cardiff.

Williams, Stephen J., 1952. *Beginner's Welsh*, 2 parts, Tonypandy (fourth edition).

——, 1959. *Elfennau Gramadeg Cymraeg*, Cardiff.

DICTIONARIES:

Geiriadur Prifysgol Cymru: A Dictionary of the Welsh Language, Cardiff, 1950– (proceeding in parts).

Anwyl, Bodvan J., 1937. *Spurrell's Welsh–English, English–Welsh Dictionary*, Carmarthen (eleventh edition).

Evans, H. Meurig, and Thomas, W. O., 1953. *Y Geiriadur Newydd: The New Welsh Dictionary*, Llandybïe.

——, 1958. *Y Geiriadur Mawr: The Complete Welsh–English, English–Welsh Dictionary*, Llandybïe–Aberystwyth.

XI

PLACE-NAMES

GWYNEDD O. PIERCE

HISTORICALLY, the evidence of place-names tends to be corroborative rather than primary. This is especially true when there is a scarcity of adequate early and contemporary source-material as is the case in respect of the region here surveyed. It is not always enough merely to identify an element in a place-name which is known, for example, to be Scandinavian in origin etymologically. It might be assumed that such a name is evidence of Scandinavian settlement, but this evidence alone is not going to convince the historian completely. *Homri* occurs as the name of a farm in the parish of St. Nicholas, near Cardiff, and the earliest form adduced so far for this name is *Horneby*, 1382–3. The earliest form available for what now survives in the Cardiff street-name *Womanby Street* is *Hundemanby*, *c.* 1280, and *Langby*, later *Lamby*, on the Monmouthshire side of the Rhymney estuary cannot, as yet, be attested earlier than 1401. These names have as their final element, in all probability, ON *bȳ*, *býr*, 'farmstead, village', and forms virtually identical with the first two examples in *Hornby* of the North Riding of Yorkshire and Lancashire, and *Hunmanby* of the East Riding of Yorkshire, tend to confirm their Scandinavian origin, but when the known fact that the South Wales seaboard was subject to Norse raids since at least the ninth century is taken into consideration, the disadvantage of being unable to attest these names earlier than the thirteenth to fifteenth centuries becomes apparent. The historian would like to know precisely when these settlements were made, but he is not likely to derive that information from the existing place-name evidence. We cannot, therefore, be clear as to the exact meaning of the suffix *-by* in these names because the evidence of place-names in England, in the *Danelaw*, shows a considerable semantic development with a range from 'newly developed or cultivated land' to 'hamlet, village' and with intervening stages in sense-development, and in ME the word had been taken over as *bi*, *by*, 'village, town', and used in literary works in that sense. All these stages are important to the historian. *Langby* is attested late enough to be a ME name if we theorize, as we must, on the basis of the earliest form adduced, in spite of the likely assumption that it was probably earlier than the fifteenth century in origin. Such precision is not usually required, on the other hand, for names like *Sker* (*Bla*(*c*)*kescerre*, 1153–83, probably ON *sker*, 'skerry, rock'), *Flatholm* and *Steepholm*, the two islands which stand outside Cardiff in the Bristol Channel (ON *holmr*, 'island') and others like them.

A similar uncertainty exists with regard to one place-name element which, more than any other, is almost symbolic of the Anglo-Norman occupation of the Vale of Glamorgan and the coastal area of Gwent, namely OE *tūn*, originally 'an

enclosure', and subsequently 'a farmstead, estate, manor, village', and appearing generally as a suffix, *-ton*. This development in meaning occurred particularly after the element gained precedence over OE *hām*, and it began to be used extensively in south-west England as the Anglo-Saxon hold extended gradually westwards. By the Norman period it could mean 'estate, manor' or 'farm, farmstead' in names like *Bonvilston* (after Simon *de Bonville*, thirteenth century), *Wrinston* (*Wrenchestun*, *c.* 1262), *Laleston* (*Lagelestun*, 1147–83), *Candleston* (*Cantlowstoune*, 1545, preserving a form of the family-name *de Cantilupe*), *Flemingston*, *Colwinston* (*Col*(*e*)*winestun*(*e*), 1139–49), *Sigingstone* (*Siginestone*, *c.* 1260, the home of Hugh *Sigin*), *Cosmeston* (*Costantinestun*, *c.* 1262), all in the Vale of Glamorgan; and in Gwent, *Osbaston* (*Villa Osberti*, *c.* 1070, *Osbertston*, 1345), *Ifton* (*Yveton*, 1314), *Itton* (*Edeton*, 1291), *Mounton* (*Monketowne*, 1535), *Harpson* (*Herberdeston*, 1306), or *Wolvesnewton* (*Wolvesneuton*, 1311, the 'new' *tūn* connected with the *Wolf* family; Ralph *le Wolf* held the manor in 1314). There are also several names of the type *Norton*, *Sutton*, *Weston* (OE *norð*, *suð*, *west*) in the area, and one *Easton* at least, now in the rather improbable form *Yniston* (OSM) which is *Eston*, fifteenth century, a farm at the top of Leckwith Hill, south-west of Cardiff (locally pronounced *Nishton*, the prefixed *n*- being the remains either of the Eng. preposition *in*, ME *atten*, as in *Nash*, Glamorgan and Monmouthshire, ME *atten ashe*, later (*atte*) *nash*, 'at the ash-tree', or its Welsh counterpart *yn*, as in *Narberth*, Pembrokeshire, originally *Arberth*). As can be seen from the above examples, however, but a few are attested at an early enough date to be certain of the exact significance of the suffix *-ton* in them. Names of the type *Norton*, *Sutton*, etc. suggest, indeed, that the suffix was also used in its earlier sense of 'a farm' at much later dates, ranging even into the modern period, as a mark of anglicization. A knowledge of local history is more than a prerequisite in order to arrive at a reasonable assessment. The modern form *town*, which has lost its earlier meaning, is used in many places attached to a personal name or surname to signify recent urban additions to pre-existing urban areas, such as *Wattstown*, *Tylorstown*, etc., in the Rhondda, and even *Palmerstown* and *Morristown* attached to Cadoxton (Barry) and Penarth, respectively, in the Vale of Glamorgan.

Moreover, *tūn* was also used within the area with ecclesiastical connections, together with the more likely OE element *stōw*, originally 'place' and 'meeting place' (a good example of its use in this sense being *Chepstow*, which was *Chepestow*, 1308, etc., and is OE *cēap-stōw* 'market-place') and later in the developed sense of 'holy, consecrated place'. Either one of these elements, and in some cases both, supplanted an earlier Welsh *llan* or *merthyr* in the more anglicized districts. It may be sufficient to repeat here that the primitive sense of Welsh *llan* 'enclosure' became particularized in the sense of an enclosure dedicated to a saint's name, containing cells, and subsequently a church. Later the equation of *llan* with 'church' became common, and in some areas in Wales even with the village which grew around, or in the vicinity of, the church. However, in Welsh place-names the majority of *llan*-names have as their second element either a saint's name or a word which indicates the location, and it should be noted that *llan*, being feminine in gender, causes the following element to undergo soft initial mutation where the initial consonant is a mutable consonant. Thus *llan* + the saint's name *Cadog* takes the

form *Llangadog* (corrupted under Eng. influence to *Langattock*, for example, in Monmouthshire), or *llan* + the river-name *Taf*, to signify its location, appears as *Llandaf*, anglicized to *Landaff*. A superficial glance at the Ordnance Survey maps of the area will suffice to show that many *llan*-names retain their original forms, but in other cases the later renderings in English, along the lines already mentioned—one hesitates to say that they are all translations—have gained circulation. Thus *Bishton*, Monmouthshire, is for an earlier W *Llangadwaladr* (*Lancatgualatir*, Lib. Land.[1], *Bysshopston Lanathelwather*, 1440) and records the fact that it was a *tūn*, here probably 'manor', of the bishop of Llandaff. *Bishopston*, in the Gower peninsula, has a similar association, being the older W *Llandeilo Ferwallt*. But *tūn* is used to render the Welsh *llan* whilst retaining some vestige of the original Welsh second element, a fact which is more difficult to explain. Thus *Dixton*, Monmouthshire, is for an earlier W *Llandydiwg* (*Lann tydiuc*, Lib. Land., *Dukeston* 1291, presumably a shortened form of *(*Ty*)*diwg's-tūn*).

As already suggested, the use of OE *stōw* to render W *llan* is a more likely proposition, on grounds of similarity of meaning. We have no record of an early Welsh form of the name *Dewstow*, Monmouthshire, but the first element is probably W *Dewi* (David) and an original W *Llanddewi* is not unlikely. The name may be compared with *Dewchurch* (*Lann deui ros cerion*, Lib. Land.), *Bridstow* (*Lann sanfreit*, *Lannsanbregit*, ibid.), and *Peterstow* (*Lann petyr*, *lann petir*, ibid.), over the border in Herefordshire. *Wonastow*, Monmouthshire, is a rendering of what would in Modern Welsh be *Llangynwarwy* (*Lanngunguarui*, Lib. Land.), pronounced locally as *Llanwarw*. *Stow Park* and *Stow Hill* in Newport, Monmouthshire, probably refer to the pro-cathedral church of the Welsh saint *Gwynllyw*, now the centre of the see of Monmouth (corrupted by English influence to *St. Woollo's*). It may be as well in this connection, as a slight diversion, to refer to the patrimony of *Gwynllyw*. One means of indicating a personal connection in an early territorial Welsh name was the addition of the suffix *-wg* to the personal name, as in *Morgannwg* (Morgan(t)) the alternative name for *Glamorgan* (W *Gwlad-forgan*). In the case of *Gwynllyw* + *wg* we get *Gwynllŵg* as the name, broadly speaking, for the low-lying land between Cardiff and Newport. It is this form which has been corrupted to *Wentloog* by non-Welsh elements of the population in order to connect it with the old regional name *Gwent*.

Dingestow, Monmouthshire, is a rendering of W *Llanddingat* (Giraldus Cambrensis wrote *Landinegath*, *c*. 1191), but the form in Lib. Land. is *merthir dincat* (in Modern Welsh *Merthyr Dingat*). The equation of Welsh *llan* and *merthyr* in this instance is significant. There is a Welsh word *merthyr* 'martyr', and as it appears, superficially, to be compounded in Welsh place-names with a saint's name, such locations have been erroneously regarded as the scene of the martyrdom of the saint indicated. In place-names, however, *merthyr* is derived from Latin *martyrium* which

[1] *Liber Landavensis: The Book of Llan Dâv*, ed. J. Gwenogvryn Evans, Oxford, 1893, being a collection of early documents relating to the diocese of Llandaff, some of which are in OW orthography. The compilation is twelfth century (except where otherwise stated) but many forms of place-names included must be earlier than that date.

has originally the meaning 'a saint's burial place' or a place consecrated to his bones, and is paralleled by Breton *merzer* and Cornish *merther*. Its use in place-names differs but very little from W *llan* and even OE *stōw* in its derived sense, hence *Merthyr Tydfil*, Glamorgan, is dedicated to the female saint *Tudful*, and *Merthyr Dyfan*, near Barry, Glamorgan, to *Dyfan* (cf. the genitival form *Dobagni*, *Dovagni*, as a personal name on an inscribed stone at Letterston, Pembrokeshire). An interesting example is *Merthyr Mawr*, near Bridgend, Glamorgan, the saint here being *Myfor*, *Mofor* (the form in Lib. Land. is *merthir mimor*, in OW orthography) corrupted to *Mawr* in later years and often mistaken for the common Welsh adjective *mawr* 'big, great'. The same saint's name is perpetuated, with regular initial mutation and subsequent loss of the mutated consonant, in *Llanofer*, *Llanover*, Monmouthshire (*Lanmouor*, *c.* 1348, Lib. Land., *Lameveir*, *Lamavor*, 1376, Cal.Inq.P.Mort., xiv, 164). A further interesting ecclesiastical connection is indicated in the name now generally written as *Baseleg*, near Newport, Monmouthshire. The correct Welsh form is *Basaleg*, and it is directly derived from the Latin *basilica*, the only known example of its kind in Wales.

The substitution of OE *tūn* or *stōw* for W *llan* is accompanied in other examples by the supplanting of one of the OE elements by the other. In *Tythegston* (W *Llandudwg*), *Michaelston-le-pit* (W *Llanfihangel-y-pwll*), and *Michaelston-super-Ely* (W *Llanfihangel-ar-Elái*), all in the Vale of Glamorgan, the earliest attested English forms of the names have *stōw* as the final element, being *Tethegstowe*, 1258, *Michelstowe*, *c.* 1291, and *Mihelstowe*, 1368, respectively. Here *-ton* has ousted the original English final element probably because of the similarity of the names to the large number of *-ton*-names in the vicinity, but it is far more difficult to explain away the presence of *-ton* in parish-names like *Peterston-super-Ely* and *Michaelston* (Cwmafan), Glamorgan, and *Michaelston-y-Vedw*, Monmouthshire, where no early forms in *-stow* can, as yet, be attested, and where *-ton* seems to be used directly, coupled with a saint's name (and biblical saints at that).

All Welsh *llan*-names in the area, on the other hand, are not always what they seem to be. *Llan* did supplant two or three original Welsh elements, but reference will be made here only to one instance. *Llancarfan*, Glamorgan, in spite of its early medieval fame as the centre of the cult of the Welsh saint *Cadog*, is not a true *llan*-name. The original form, rendered in Modern Welsh, was *Nantcarfan* (*Carbani Uallis*, *Caruani Vallis*, *Nant Carban*, etc., Lib. Land.) being Welsh *nant*, now 'stream, rivulet', earlier 'valley ravine' through which the stream ran, and probably in that sense here + an Old Welsh personal name *Carfan*, in all probability (cf. the genitival *Corbagni* which occurs as a Brythonic personal name on an inscribed stone in Carmarthenshire) which became the name of the stream flowing through the valley. The same substitution also occurred in the name *Llantarnam*, Monmouthshire, originally *Nant Teyrnon*, and *Llanthony*, Monmouthshire, originally *Nant Hodni*, *Nant Hoddni*; *Hoddni* and its metathesized form *Honddi*, *Honddu*, occurring elsewhere in South Wales as a river-name, the first element of which (*hodd-*) Sir Ifor Williams compares with the Welsh adjective *hawdd* 'happy, pleasant'. The Welsh name for *Brecon* is *Aberhonddu*, where the first element is W *aber* 'estuary' when it occurs on

the coast, but 'confluence' where it occurs inland, as in this instance, and in such Glamorgan names as *Abercynon*, *Aberaman*, *Aberdare* (*Aberdâr*), etc., and *Abersychan*, *Abergavenny*, *Abertyswg*, *Abertillery* (*Abertyleri*), etc., in Monmouthshire.

The second element in these names is a river-name, and river-names are, of course, among the oldest names in existence, having parallel forms throughout the length and breadth of Britain and Celtic Europe. We can only refer here to a few of the largest rivers in the area. The *Usk*, more correctly the Welsh *Wysg*, which flows through Newport, Monmouthshire, is connected etymologically with the Devon *Exe*, and its primitive form is reflected in the latinized names of the well-known Roman fortresses built on the banks of both rivers, *Isca Silurum* (Caerleon) in Monmouthshire, and *Isca Dumnoniorum* (Exeter). The name goes back to an Indo-European root-form which probably gave the Latin *piscis* 'fish' and signifies 'a river abounding in fish'. The *Wye*, which flows into the Severn near Chepstow, is probably a 'winding river' (W *Gwy*, cf. W *gŵyr* 'bent, winding', verb *gwyr-o* 'to bend'). The *Rhymney*, forming for part of its course the boundary between Glamorgan and Monmouthshire, may well be a 'boring river' (cf. W *rhwmp* 'auger, gimlet', a boring instrument), whilst the *Ewenny*, near Bridgend, is perhaps named after a Celtic goddess *Aventi-* (*Aventio* being the form in a seventh-century list known as the *Ravenna Cosmography*; see note on books *infra*). The *Taf*, which flows through Cardiff, has etymological connections with the London *Thames* and the Cornish *Tamar*, etc., and all may derive from a common root-form meaning 'dark (coloured), black'. This is also, basically, the second element of the name *Cardiff* itself, being Welsh *caer* 'enclosed stronghold, fort, fortress, etc.' + the form *tyf*, mutated initially to *dyf* as a mark of its genitival connection with the first element in the compound. Early forms such as *Kairdif*, 1106, *Cayrdif*, 1126, and the even earlier *Villae Cardiviae*, 1081, etc., show this quite clearly. *Tyf* is probably from an oblique form of the primitive **tam-os* (> *Taf)*, such as the genitive form **tam-i* (by ultimate *-i* affection). The English form *Cardiff* is therefore nearer to the original than the Modern Welsh form *Caerdydd* (not evidenced earlier than the sixteenth century) which came into being by a well-attested Welsh colloquial change of *-f* to *-dd*.

The river-name *Rhondda* is a metathesized form of an earlier *Rhoddni*, *Rhoddneu*, etc., and may have in its first syllable a derivative from the primitive root which would give a Welsh **rhawdd*, seen in the verb *ad-rawdd* (Mod.W *adrodd*) 'to speak, utter, relate, etc.' and the noun *ymadrawdd (ymadrodd)* 'speech', cognate with Irish *rádim* 'I speak, talk', an element which may tend to give the inhabitants of the Rhondda the basis for a just claim to regard their river as the original 'babbling brook'. The *Ely*, which has its estuary adjacent to that of the Taf between Cardiff and Penarth Head, is in Welsh *Elái* (accented on the second syllable), earlier *Elei* (three syllables), and has a parallel in Brittany in the river-name *Ellé*, earlier found in a latinized form *Elegium*. Sir Ifor Williams tends to connect this with an Indo-European root-form **leg-* 'dripping, oozing, slow-flowing' seen in Welsh *llaith* 'wet, moist' and perhaps English *leak* and *lake* (OE *lacu* 'stream, water-course'; ME *lake* 'lake, pool' is taken to be derived, through OFr. *lac*, from Lat. *lacus*).

It will be appreciated that only a fraction of the place-names of the district has been discussed in the foregoing note, but it is hoped that they may be sufficient

to demonstrate some of the influences which have fashioned the toponomy of the area. Precise chronological information is difficult to achieve from place-name evidence, one good reason being that place-names are not inert, fossilized remains of bye-gone days but, to make a dubious comparison, 'living organisms'. They are still undergoing a certain amount of development because of the linguistic factor which is involved, and even if the historian is not always completely satisfied, the student of language is certainly grateful for much philological and semantic knowledge which might not as readily come his way from any other source.

BIBLIOGRAPHICAL NOTE

Most of the information on the meaning of such place-names in the area as have been studied may be found in B. G. Charles, *Non-Celtic Place-Names in Wales*, London, 1938; idem, *Old Norse Relations with Wales*, Cardiff, 1934; Sir Ifor Williams's note on *Usk* and *Exe* in Aileen Fox, *Roman Exeter*, Manchester, 1952, pp. 5–6, and his many notes on early Welsh texts edited by himself over the years, as well as his notes on individual names in I. A. Richmond and O. G. S. Crawford, 'The British Section of the Ravenna Cosmography' in *Archaeologia*, Vol. XCIII, 1949. A vast amount of information is packed into Sir Ifor's slim *Enwau Lleoedd*, Liverpool, 1945, and the standard work on Welsh river-names is R. J. Thomas, *Enwau Afonydd a Nentydd Cymru*, Cardiff, 1938. Much useful information can still be gleaned from Egerton Phillimore's copious footnotes to the text of *The Description of Pembrokeshire, by George Owen of Henllys*, ed. Henry Owen, Vols. I–IV, Cymmrodorion Record Series No. 1, London, 1892–1906. There is a survey of the *Place-Names of Cardiff* by the late Thomas Jones in Publication No. 2, 1950, of the *South Wales and Monmouth Record Society*.

Anyone wishing to pursue a study of non-Celtic place-names must now, perforce, consult Vols. XXV and XXVI of the English Place-Name Society's publications, these being A. H. Smith's *English Place-Name Elements*, Cambridge, 1956. Welsh elements and words are fully explained in the new standard Welsh dictionary of the University of Wales, *Geiriadur Prifysgol Cymru*, in progress since 1950, and issued in parts periodically.

XII

THE LATIN LITERARY TRADITION

A. O. H. Jarman

IN the twelfth century A.D. the region gave to medieval Europe one of its major writers of creative literature in the Latin language. Geoffrey of Monmouth, author of the *Historia Regum Britanniae*, was born towards the end of the eleventh century and is believed to have belonged to a family or community of Bretons who had settled in Monmouth after the Norman conquest of England. He appears to have spent the greater part of his adult life at Oxford, where his name appears on a number of charters between 1129 and 1151, and where he was probably a canon of St. George's. It was there in 1136, or possibly a little later, that he completed and published his *Historia*. This work brought him great fame, but official recognition did not come until 1152 when he was consecrated bishop of St. Asaph in North Wales. It is improbable, however, that he ever visited his diocese, which was at that time under Welsh control, while he was entirely dependent on the Normans for his preferment. He died in 1155.

The *Historia Regum Britanniae*, or 'History of the Kings of Britain', is a substantial work in chronicle form purporting to give the history of the Britons from the time of Brutus, who according to legend had flourished over a thousand years before Christ, to the death of Cadwaladr in the seventh century A.D. It therefore covers a period of some seventeen or eighteen centuries, of which between a half and two-thirds belong to prehistory. The story begins with a lengthy account of the career of Brutus, a Trojan prince, who after the fall of Troy is said to have rallied the scattered remnants of his people and to have led them through many perils in Greece, North Africa and France. Ultimately he brought them to Britain, which took its name from him, and where he is credited with being the founder of civilized society. The thousand odd years between the reign of Brutus and the invasion and conquest of Britain by the Romans are filled by Geoffrey with an imposing, but entirely imaginary, succession of monarchs, of whom the best-known today is Lear, whose story is here told for the first time in literature. The campaigns of Julius Caesar against the Britons are described in some detail, but subsequently the relationship between Britons and Romans develops more as an affair between equals than as the rule of the conquerors over the vanquished. After the end of the Roman period the events of the reign of the unfortunate Vortigern are related fully, including the landing of Hengist and Horsa in Kent, the Treachery of the Long Knives and the discovery of the prophet Merlin. Shortly afterwards the *Historia* reaches its climax in its account of the reign of Arthur. This occupies one-fifth of the entire work, and on it Geoffrey lavished all his powers of narrative and description. King Arthur, who in earlier Welsh tradition had been a figure of folklore and magic, is here transformed into a mighty feudal monarch, holding a magnificent

court at Caerleon-on-Usk and conquering all who dared to oppose him in Great Britain, Ireland, Scandinavia and France. Ultimately he defeated the Emperor of Rome himself, but while he was beginning the crossing of the Alps in order to add Italy to his conquests he was called home by news of the treachery of his nephew, Modred, who had usurped his throne. The traitor fled before the king until, in the general slaughter of the battle of Camlan, both Arthur and Modred fell. After this catastrophe the story of the Britons continues in a more subdued vein during a final inglorious century and ultimately comes to an end with the occupation of England by the Saxons.

Work of imagination though the *Historia* is, the material out of which it was constructed was not for the most part invented by its author. The sources used by Geoffrey were many and various and are still imperfectly known. In his prologue Geoffrey himself disclaims all originality and explicitly declares that his book was a translation made by him into Latin of an 'ancient book in the British tongue' which had been shown to him by Walter, Archdeacon of Oxford. It is uncertain whether by 'British' Geoffrey meant Welsh or Breton, but, whichever it was, this 'original' was never produced and the question of its existence was for centuries furiously disputed. The consensus of opinion among modern scholars rejects Geoffrey's claim that his work derived from such a single, unitary source, although, of course, it is not denied that he could have had access to written sources, possibly in Welsh or in Breton, that have since been lost. Walter, Archdeacon of Oxford, was a historical person, contemporary with Geoffrey, but it is impossible to tell whether or not he was a party to Geoffrey's deception. Among Geoffrey's sources the compilation known as the *Historia Brittonum* ('History of the Britons') of Nennius must have figured prominently in some form or other. This consisted of a collection of traditional material put together about the beginning of the ninth century and containing accounts of the lives and exploits of such legendary or semi-historical figures as Brutus, Vortigern, Ambrosius and Arthur, which Geoffrey incorporated in a highly expanded and embellished form into his own *Historia*. Similarly, his debt to Bede's *Historia Ecclesiastica* as well as to many other sources, classical, Biblical and medieval, has been demonstrated, and there is no doubt that he drew also on the resources of saga and popular folktale as well as on his own powerful and fertile imagination. In later times he would perhaps have been a writer of acknowledged historical fiction, but, being a twelfth-century cleric writing in Latin for an aristocratic and learned audience, he had virtually no choice but to cast his story into the chronicle form acceptable to the age and offer it to the world as true history. So authoritative was his manner and so refreshing his style, compared with the common run of chronicles in that period, that his *Historia* was accepted as an authentic account of early British history by all except a small minority of critics during the remaining centuries of the Middle Ages.

Although his *Historia* may here and there contain some scraps of genuine history, Geoffrey must of course be judged not as a historian but as a creative and imaginative writer. It is indeed difficult to believe that, privately, he himself would have dissented from this view. There has been much speculation among modern scholars about his real motive in writing the *Historia*. Some, for instance, have

attempted to relate it closely to political developments during the reign of Henry I. Others have urged that political motives should not be looked for in a work such as the *Historia* and that Geoffrey was primarily, if not exclusively, one who enjoyed telling a good story. Probably his motives were somewhat mixed. However much of a conscious literary artist he might be, he could not escape from the rather complex facts of his position as a Breton, brought up in south-eastern Wales, writing for a Norman audience in England about the past glories of the Welsh people. The period in which Geoffrey lived was one of military conflict between the Welsh and the Normans, and his work does not in fact offer any comfort or hope of victory to the former. On the other hand, his *Historia* is full of pride in the alleged achievements of the Brythonic 'race' in the distant past. A classical origin is claimed for the ancient Britons through Brutus, for Geoffrey thought of the Trojans as Greeks. The language spoken by the Trojans he describes as *curuum grecum*, or 'distorted Greek', which he no doubt equated with *Cymraeg* (for *Cam Roeg* as in the Welsh versions of the *Historia*). Long before the Christian era he makes the ancient British kings Brennius and Belinus conquer and occupy Rome. After the separation of the Welsh and Breton peoples, which occurred in the fourth century A.D. according to Geoffrey, those remaining in Britain are treated as a degenerate remnant. Subsequently, whenever the insular Britons were hard pressed by their enemies, they inevitably turned to their Armorican cousins for help. This view of former Welsh–Breton relationships was not only satisfying to Geoffrey but also was no doubt acceptable to the Normans, who had many Breton followers at the time of their conquest of England. Furthermore, it was pleasing to the pride of the Normans in England to be made aware of the ancient martial traditions of the land they had conquered. This satisfaction Geoffrey's book gave them, while at the same time it gave people of his own kin reason for pride in their own ancestry in remote times, however pitiful an appearance they might make on the contemporary scene. For in Wales Geoffrey's unfavourable opinion of the latter-day Welsh does not seem to have been noticed, and his *Historia* in a short time attained an immense popularity. This is shown by the fact that it was translated into Welsh by three different translators and that some sixty manuscript copies still survive of these versions or of texts deriving from them. In the later centuries of the Middle Ages Welsh poets would sometimes seek to sustain the national spirit of their countrymen, in face of defeat and degradation, by referring to the prowess of their ancestors recorded in the Brut, as the *Historia* was called. Later, during the Renaissance, when modern historical criticism began its onslaughts upon the *Historia Regum Britanniae*, Welsh scholars such as Sir John Price and Humfrey Lhuyd considered it their patriotic duty to defend the veracity of the Brut against all who denied it. Belief in the genuineness of Geoffrey's history became an article of faith in Welsh patriotism for some two or three hundred years, and the subject was debated among scholars until the late eighteenth or early nineteenth century.

In the field of medieval European literature the widespread influence of the *Historia* was principally due to the section devoted to Arthur. Indeed, Geoffrey's two outstanding specific contributions to the literature of Europe are his portrait of Arthur and his court, and the story of Lear. Earlier references to Arthur in

'historical' sources such as Nennius and the *Annales Cambriae* had been meagre, while in saga and traditional verse in the Welsh language he was portrayed as a beneficent giant, a slayer of monsters, a conqueror of the otherworld. Some traces of the Arthur of folklore remain in Geoffrey's account of him, but the general picture is that of a contemporary feudal ruler, and this conception of Arthur passed through the work of Geoffrey's popularizers, such as Wace and Layamon, into the main stream of European vernacular literature during the twelfth and early thirteenth centuries. The material contained in the Arthurian romances had, of course, many other sources besides Geoffrey, but there can be no doubt that the widespread vogue of Arthurian literature in the later Middle Ages, as well as the regal conception of Arthur himself, are in a very large degree to be attributed to the influence of the *Historia Regum Britanniae*.

In 1148–50 Geoffrey published his second work, which was very different in character from the *Historia*. This was the *Vita Merlini*, a poem of over 1500 lines, avowedly a work of fancy and imagination. Geoffrey had already introduced Merlin to the European literary scene in his *Historia*, in which he is portrayed as a wonder-child possessing prophetic powers, and later as a powerful magician. In the *Vita Merlini*, Merlin is a king who becomes mad in battle and acquires prophetic powers after fleeing to live a wild life in the woods. The two portraits differ appreciably, the discrepancy being due to the fact that in the *Vita Merlini* Geoffrey used elements from traditional Welsh saga of which he was not aware when he wrote the *Historia*. It is typical of Geoffrey that the inconsistency seems not to have bothered him in the least, and perhaps typical of the age in which he lived that the difficulty was soon resolved by the adoption of the view that there had in fact been two Merlins. Among much varied and interesting material contained in the *Vita Merlini* is the earliest account in literature of the wounded Arthur's voyage to the 'Island of Apples known as the Fortunate Isle' to receive the healing ministrations of Morgen and her sisters. The *Vita*, however, did not achieve the success of the *Historia* and it only survives in one complete manuscript text. In contrast, the popularity of the *Historia* is attested by the fact that some two hundred manuscript copies of the Latin text still exist. In the last five lines of the *Vita Merlini* reference is made to Geoffrey of Monmouth's major work and the Britons are called to honour him, for he has made their deeds celebrated throughout the world:

> Duximus ad metam carmen: vos ergo Britanni
> Laurea serta date Gaufrido de Monumeta;
> Est etenim vester, nam quondam prelia vestra
> Vestrorumque ducum cecinit, scripsitque libellum
> Quem nunc Gesta vocant Britonum celebrata per orbem.

XIII

THE WELSH LITERARY TRADITION

G. J. Williams

EAST Glamorgan and Monmouthshire, a region which includes a part of the old province of Morgannwg as well as the old province of Gwent, remained, to a great extent, Welsh-speaking until the last decades of the nineteenth century. Although this part of Wales fell into Norman hands before the end of the twelfth century, the language survived, except, possibly, in a few areas in Gwent, and in parts of the Vale of Glamorgan. A study of place-names, of the charters, and other sources, seems to confirm this, although much work remains to be done before a satisfactory account of the fortunes of the language in this area in the early Middle Ages can be given.

Blaenau Morgannwg, the hilly regions to the north, remained Welsh after the Norman Conquest, and for this reason by the fourteenth and fifteenth centuries the descendants of the Norman and English settlers in the Vale had become Welsh-speaking, a good example of the effect of the vigorous survival of the language in one area on its revival in another. In many cases, this may have happened at a much earlier period. Welsh poets were welcomed in the homes of the gentry, the Turbervilles, the Stradlings, the Bassets, the Gamages, the Flemings, and were given statutory fees for their songs of praise, and their elegies. It is known that some of these families became ardent supporters of the literary life of Wales and of Welsh learning. From then on, until the second half of the nineteenth century, Welsh remained as the first language of the vast majority of the inhabitants of the county of Glamorgan (except the Gower Peninsula, which was not a part of the old Morgannwg), and a high proportion of these were, to all intents and purposes, monoglots. But there was a recession in the Vale in the second half of the last century, and by today dialecticians have to rely on small communities of native speakers in those parishes which border on the uplands.

The history of the language in the industrial belt is rather different. Welshmen from every part of Wales flocked to these new towns and villages of the *Blaenau* throughout the nineteenth century. Welsh was the vernacular of all these industrial districts (as it is today in parts of west Glamorgan and in Carmarthenshire), and workers who came from England and Ireland found no difficulty in learning it. Towns like Merthyr Tydfil, Aberdare and Pontypridd, and the mining villages of the Rhondda Valley, have played a notable part in the cultural life of Wales until our own day. But these areas began to be anglicized before the end of the century, although the full effect of this process was not felt until fairly recent times. There has been a recession, but the language has by no means disappeared. In most of the villages and towns there are flourishing Welsh chapels, and literary societies where lectures on Welsh subjects can still draw big audiences. The National

Eisteddfod held in Aberdare in 1956 received the enthusiastic support of all sections of the community. But the recession has caused serious concern, and a special effort has been made by the Glamorgan Education Committee to teach Welsh in all primary and secondary schools. Indeed, further steps have been taken in recent years. Several primary schools have been established where Welsh is used as a medium of instruction. The outstanding success of this venture is a fact of great significance, and there is now a demand for Welsh secondary and grammar schools, which will, in all probability, be established in the fairly near future. This should lead later on to the establishment within our National University of a college in which Welsh would be the medium of instruction.

Even in the border county of Monmouthshire, Welsh remained as the common vernacular in most parts until the second half of the last century. But the southern fringe of the county bordering the Bristol Channel began to be anglicized in the seventeenth century, and by 1700 there were no native speakers in Chepstow. And in all probability, Welsh disappeared in some areas on the eastern fringe during the eighteenth century. But in the other parts it remained, and one keen student of dialects remarked, about 1800, that he had found a higher percentage of Welsh monoglots in Monmouthshire than in any other county in Wales. Indeed, Sir Joseph Bradney, the learned author of the *History of Monmouthshire*, states that there were people on the Herefordshire border until about 1860 who could not make use of English devotional books. Then came a period of rapid decline in the rural areas, although the industrial valleys remained Welsh-speaking for many years after this, and were well known throughout Wales as the home of famous writers and preachers. Indeed, there is a flourishing Welsh community in Rhymney and the surrounding districts today. The great success of the National Eisteddfod held in Ebbw Vale in 1958, an all-Welsh festival, should not be overlooked.

But whatever may be the result of the great efforts that are being made to restore the position of the language, nothing can save the old dialect of Gwent and Morgannwg, a rich dialect which is of the greatest interest to all Welsh scholars. In very many areas the last of the old men and women who could speak it in its purity have died, and in many others only a few old people remain. Even where the language continues to flourish, the number of those who have inherited the vocabulary and certainty of the monoglots is steadily diminishing, and we have to rely on the old. Scholars have realized that a detailed survey of this dialect with its rich vocabulary is a matter of the greatest urgency, and much excellent work has been accomplished in recent years.

The works of poets who may have lived in Gwent and Morgannwg in pre-Norman days have all disappeared—at least, no one can prove that any poem which has survived was composed in these Welsh kingdoms. But there are old Welsh texts which scholars maintain were written in Llandaff. The earliest text is a memorandum written, in all probability, towards the end of the eighth century, and is preserved in a manuscript of the Gospels now in the Cathedral Library at Lichfield. This manuscript is of Welsh provenance, and at the time this memorandum was written it belonged to a church dedicated to the sixth-century Welsh

Saint, Teilo, and it has been generally held that this must have been Llandaff, the most important of his churches. But today, some scholars are of the opinion that the Teilo dedication is a deliberate forgery of the Llandaff clergy in the early years of the Norman period, and that this copy of the Gospels belonged to the church of Llandeilo Fawr in the modern county of Carmarthen. Place-names which occur in other entries in this manuscript seem to confirm this view. The *Book of Llandaff*, written about 1135–40, however, contains a great collection of Latin charters and other documents connected with that church. In many cases the land boundaries are given in Welsh, and that is also true of Teilo's 'Privilegium'. So there are Welsh documents which were written in the first half of the twelfth century relating to the church of Llandaff which is today within the confines of the city of Cardiff.

It is impossible to speak with any certainty of the part played by the men of Morgannwg and Gwent in the literary life of Wales in the early Middle Ages. This was a period of great activity, when the bards sang in the halls of the Welsh princes, the period of the Arthurian romances, when the *cyfarwyddiaid* (the story-tellers) told the old legendary tales, the period when so many Latin and French texts were translated into Welsh. Scholars are agreed that many of the manuscripts which contain this prose literature were written in South Wales monasteries, and that most of the texts contain forms and expressions which strongly suggest that the authors and translators spoke a South Wales dialect. We cannot be more precise until scholars have made a detailed study of all the Welsh dialects and of the history of the dialects. It is known that, at a later date than this, some of the Glamorgan gentry asked monks and priests to translate Latin and French texts. A close connection may have existed between the Norman families of the Vale and the *cyfarwyddiaid* of Morgannwg, some of whom may have been bilingual. The place of that great man of Gwent, Geoffrey of Monmouth, in the development of the Arthurian romances is discussed elsewhere.

This is the period of the great court poetry in Gwynedd, Powys, and Deheubarth, when the struggle for independence led to a great poetic revival, and when the poets (as one historian puts it) 'transferred the passion of the people into song'. But, as far as is known, not one of the great odes (*awdlau*) of this period was written either in Morgannwg or in Gwent. There were certainly poets singing in the halls of the descendants of the old princes of Morgannwg, and it is interesting to note that, according to the genealogical manuscripts of the heraldic bards, many of the poets of the fifteenth and sixteenth centuries could claim that they belonged to these old princely families. It is more than probable that a vast corpus of this early medieval poetry has disappeared. The work of a Glamorgan poet who flourished in the early years of the fourteenth century shows that he had inherited the same traditions and the same discipline, and had received the same bardic training and education as his fellows in Gwynedd and Powys and Deheubarth. They were the custodians of the cultural traditions of the Welsh nation, and these they handed on to their successors.

For in the fifteenth century the bardic life of Morgannwg emerges from the obscurity of the Middle Ages. This is not true of Gwent—at least, no one can prove

that any of the major poets between the fifteenth century and the seventeenth were natives of Gwent, although poets from other parts of Wales were welcomed in the homes of the gentry throughout the province. There are today in our public libraries large collections of the works of the Glamorgan poets of this period, many of them written by professional scribes, and some by the poets themselves. They formed a professional body. They were the custodians of the cultural traditions of the nation, and their patrons were the gentry, the *uchelwyr*, who were generally keenly aware of their responsibilities. This professional body formed a highly organized hierarchy. No one could be admitted unless he had received formal training, and the teachers, the *penceirddiaid*, had to testify to the attainments of their pupils. They had to master all the intricacies of Welsh metrics, the four and twenty strict metres, and *cynghanedd*, that complicated system of consonantal correspondencies and internal rhyme which had been perfected in the fourteenth and fifteenth centuries. They also had to master the old literary language which had been taught in the bardic schools throughout the centuries. They had to learn the traditional lore of their profession, and they were the recognized authorities on the genealogies of the noble families. They were supported by the gentry, and received statutory fees for their songs of praise and their elegies. This bardic system maintained an unbroken continuity until the seventeenth century when it finally disintegrated. There are, in manuscript, hundreds of poems composed by the Glamorgan bards. They went to the castles of St. Donat's, Coety and Raglan, to the abbeys of Neath and Margam, to famous houses which are now in ruins or have completely disappeared (such as Gwernyclepa, near Newport, the home of the most renowned of Welsh bardic patrons, Ifor Hael, 'Ifor the Generous', whose fame had spread throughout Wales). Very often, the homes of these patrons remain as farmhouses, a fact which local historians tend to ignore. Many areas in Glamorgan and Monmouthshire are rich in associations of this kind. Walking through this Welsh countryside can be a most interesting, and often a most exciting, diversion for the literary historian. Of course, many of these poets went on circuit to the other provinces, and poets from North Wales and West Wales often came to Morgannwg and Gwent to sing the praises of the *uchelwyr*, and to write their pedigrees in their genealogical manuscripts. Only a small part of this great collection of poems, poems which are of the greatest interest, not only to students of literature, but also to all Welsh historians, has been published.

It has already been stated that the bardic system disintegrated in the seventeenth century. But the old traditional learning was not entirely forgotten, and in the first half of the eighteenth century there arose a new generation of scholars who began to revive the old traditions. This meant an intensive study of old manuscripts, of Welsh metrics and the literary language, and an effort to regain the masterly craftsmanship of the bards. This movement spread to Glamorgan and Gwent. In Glamorgan, farmers and craftsmen, clergymen and Nonconformist ministers, began to study the old metrical system, the history and traditions of Wales, and to collect manuscripts. One of these clergymen published a Welsh–English dictionary so that young poets could regain the rich vocabulary of the *penceirddiaid*, and another compiled a monumental English–Welsh dictionary, so that writers could have an

adequate vocabulary to discuss all subjects in Welsh—'a small tribute to the pre-eminence of my native language'. This literary and scholarly activity, this patriotic fervour, helps us to explain the extraordinary career of the strangest character in the literary life of our nation—Edward Williams, born in Llancarfan, within a few miles of Cardiff, in 1747. He is generally known by his bardic name, Iolo Morganwg. He was a stone-mason, and this literary renaissance had a most remarkable effect on an abnormal and perverted mind. He was an excellent poet, and as he had made a close and sustained study of old Welsh manuscripts, he became the greatest authority of his day on the history of Welsh literature and, indeed, on most aspects of Welsh history. He was a man of exceptional ability, an authority on such subjects as folklore, geology, botany, and agriculture, but a man whose mind was dominated by his dreams of a glorious past, and by an urge to rewrite the history of his nation. This is, undoubtedly, one of the most curious psychological problems in the history of literature. He wrote dozens of poems which he attributed to the old poets, including the greatest of them, Dafydd ap Gwilym, and their authenticity was accepted until the present century. He manufactured hundreds of documents of various kinds, and those which were printed—only a small fraction of the enormous collection which still remains in manuscript—were accepted by most literary historians until the end of the last century, and even then his honesty was not questioned. He invented the famous Druidic 'Gorsedd of the Bards of the Island of Britain', which is still held every year during the National Eisteddfod week. This, of course, is the direct result not only of the idea which had conditioned Welsh thought since the sixteenth century, namely that the Welsh bardic tradition was Druidic in origin, but also of the great interest taken in Druidism after William Stukeley and other romantic antiquarians had given such a fascinating picture of those ancient priests who had, as was generally believed in the eighteenth century, worshipped in Stonehenge, Avebury, and in all the stone circles. This affected Englishmen as well as Welshmen. 'The Ancient Order of Druids' was founded in London by an Englishman—a Society which still survives. And Iolo Morganwg began to maintain that the 'Ancient British' Druidic institution had been kept alive in his native Glamorgan throughout the centuries. He invented an elaborate ceremonial, and all was accepted by a nation which had believed for centuries that the Welsh bards were the direct descendants of the Druids and that they had inherited their learning. But we should remember that the Gorsedd forms but a minute part of the vast edifice built by this remarkable stone-mason. He is probably the most successful and the most marvellous forger—if that is the correct term to use—in literary history, a forger of genius, whose dreams have coloured the imagination of succeeding generations of Welshmen, even until our own day.

One result of the Literary Revival of the eighteenth century was the establishment of Welsh societies in London with the avowed intention of encouraging Welsh literature and Welsh learning. This movement spread to Wales in the early years of the nineteenth century, and received a great welcome in the new industrial areas of Glamorgan and Monmouthshire. Places like Merthyr Tydfil, Aberdare, Tredegar, Rhymney, etc., became centres of great activity. Welsh societies were formed, and the eisteddfod, the old bardic congress, which had by now become a popular

competitive festival, soon formed a notable feature of Welsh life in these towns and villages, and aroused a general interest in poetry, and especially in the old traditional strict metres. Classes were formed to study the literary language, and dictionaries and grammars of various kinds began to appear. The strict metres, the product of the old aristocratic society, became the delight of craftsmen, shopkeepers, publicans, coal-miners and industrial workers of all kinds. There were long discussions in the mines and iron-works on the intricacies of *cynghanedd* and the strict metres. All the bulky volumes on Welsh history and Welsh literature, and the ten volumes of the Welsh Encyclopaedia (of which there were two editions), which appeared in the second half of the nineteenth century—the most extraordinary period in the history of the Welsh press—received a great welcome in these industrial towns and villages. This helped to keep alive the old traditional learning in days when Wales did not possess an educational system and national institutions of higher learning. The literary life of these industrial valleys produced one of the great poets of modern Wales, William Thomas (Islwyn), born in the Sirhowy valley in Monmouthshire in 1832, whose long poem *Y Storm* ('The Storm'), which he wrote before he was twenty-four, is considered by modern critics to be, in spite of its unevenness and diffuseness, one of the great masterpieces of modern Welsh literature.

But any account of the literary life of this region would not be complete without referring to the most distinguished of the ladies of Gwent—Lady Llanover (1802–96), the wife of Sir Benjamin Hall ('Big Ben'), Baron Llanover. Although she was of English origin she learned Welsh, and became an enthusiastic supporter of those scholars and poets, clergymen and gentry, who had established Welsh societies. The mansion of Llanover, in the heart of Monmouthshire, where she and her husband welcomed their English aristocratic friends, statesmen and church dignitaries, foreign scholars and diplomats, became a Welsh home, where all the servants had to speak Welsh, and a cultural centre, where scholars and literary men could meet to consider such questions as publishing the great manuscript collections, the promotion of Welsh scholarship, and the use of Welsh in all spheres of life, the foundation of a Welsh public school, and the organization of those colourful eisteddfodic festivals at the neighbouring town of Abergavenny, which represent a most important stage in the work of transforming the eisteddfod into a national festival of the arts. This is a most fascinating story, and should find an honoured place in any study of the growth of national consciousness and nationalist sentiment in nineteenth century Wales. One could maintain that this was the great period in the literary life of Monmouthshire.

In this brief survey it has only been possible to refer to some of the main features of this literary tradition. It should be emphasized that it was a Welsh tradition, and that no one can hear and interpret the voice of the past in this region unless he is acquainted with the language of almost all its inhabitants for a period of nearly fifteen hundred years.

XIV

THE ENGLISH LITERARY TRADITION

R. G. Thomas

MY first reaction to the title of this section was one of scepticism: Did such a tradition exist and, if it did, where was the clear path through the tall bracken and trailing brambles of controversy which had grown around the use of the title 'Anglo-Welsh literature'? A second, tempting, reaction was even more difficult to silence: Why not develop in detail the growth and spread of the English language in this region from Doomsday Book—or even earlier!—until 1959, using the published works of five and a half centuries as milestones along this path of progress? Unfortunately, neither reaction squared easily with the facts known so far.

This is a much neglected field of research; the more plausible picture is as variegated as Housman's 'coloured counties'. Probably an English tradition of sorts has existed longest in the Vale of Glamorgan, most firmly established in a few towns; parts of Breconshire have certainly produced some notable English authors; since before 1800 Monmouthshire was the home of an ever-increasing area of culture based on the English language but with its own distinctly local flavour which suddenly reached maturity about sixty years ago. Again the boroughs of Cardiff, Newport and (although it is outside the region) of Swansea could receive special treatment and, even more so, the mining valleys whose tradition—if that is not too grandiose a term for the culture suddenly forced into violent growth by industrialization—has occasioned the works of a remarkable crop of writers since 1930.

Obviously, those provisions of the Acts of 1536 and 1542, which made it illegal to conduct any part of the King's official business in Welsh, form the necessary starting-point for any significant discussion of the English tradition in Wales. Once the Tudor gentry educated their sons in English schools and in the English language, one section of the community was placed in touch with the main stream of English literature. The process of assimilation is shown to be complete in the works of Sir John Stradling (of St. Donats, 1583–1637): his Latin epigrams and epitaphs are written mainly for well-known Elizabethan courtiers and writers; his translation of Lucian reflects a typical Elizabethan activity; and although his *Divine Poemes* anticipate the theme of Milton's two epic poems, they also follow the current fashion for imitating Du Bartas. In fact, so unmistakable is his Englishness that his writings could be used as adequate illustrations of the trends and fashions of ideas and literary taste among late Elizabethan and Jacobean writers. There is no indication that he shared his grand-nephew Sir Edward Stradling's 'singular knowledge in the British language and antiquities'.

Henry Vaughan, the Silurist (of Newton-on-Usk, 1621–95), also writes in a completely assimilated English manner. He is sensitive to the changes of literary taste in the second half of the seventeenth century, and while Vaughan is powerfully influenced by the poetry of George Herbert, much of his verse is written in the shadow of poets as diverse as Ben Jonson, Marvell, Cowley, and even Milton. He was, perhaps, the greatest English poet that Wales has produced before Dylan Thomas and, like Thomas, he writes in a personal way without any trace of fussy Welshness. Apart from a few poems, the reader must seek closely for hidden references to Vaughan's native Breconshire. His twin brother, Thomas, the alchemist (1621–66), is believed to have acted as model for at least part of Samuel Butler's Ralpho, squire to Hudibras: another example of the easy and fluent manner in which members of the younger branch of an old Welsh family fitted into the English literary and cultural scene. Of less distinguished lineage, but from the same county, came James Howell (of Llangamarch, 1594–1666) who is now remembered for his *Epistolae Ho-elianae: Familiar Letters*; the son of a curate he gained the favour of Charles I and, like the Vaughans, had been educated at Jesus College, Oxford.

A more detailed account of the subject would have to trace the relationship between that English tradition which lies behind the many Civil War pamphlets written by Quakers and Dissenters from the region and the late seventeenth and early eighteenth century Grub Street habit of writing comical pseudo-'Welsh' satirical pamphlets. This habit persisted until the 1720s when, on and off the English stage, the Scot and the Irishman replaced Taffy as a comic butt for the then rapidly crystallizing father-figure of John Bull. When Thomas Gray's Pindaric ode, *The Bard*, was published (1757), Wales, with her ancient legends and poetry, her picturesque scenery and curiously presented history, had taken a firm hold on the imagination of English writers. The Cambro-Briton had pushed Fluellen and Taffy into the wings.

Gratifying as this mid-eighteenth century shift in taste might be, the resulting poetry produced by numerous versifiers from the region and published in a stream for over a hundred years by local printers and publishers—frequently in conjunction with London firms—makes very mixed reading. Sir Charles Hanbury Williams (of Pontypool Park, 1708–59), verbal wit, mordant satirist, and friend of Henry Fielding and Lord Chesterfield, seems to have left no chastening influence on his compatriots. The large number of poems by Monmouthshire and Vale of Glamorgan men which can be read in the two Cardiff libraries alone are sufficient in number to constitute a tradition. Most of them are downright trivial, unctious and banal to modern ears, but they are no better or worse than most of the local verse published in the Border counties. In fact, a diligent reader of the vast output of minor English poetry published between 1750 and 1850 will recognize these poems as part of a decayed but truly English tradition of well-bred topographical verse. Even Welsh poets like Islwyn and Ieuan Ddu tried their hands at English poetry, as earlier in the period Iolo Morganwg had begun his published career with two volumes of *Poems, Lyrical and Pastoral* (1794).

During the same period, the growing taste for novels which, in Wales as well as England, was fed by the circulating libraries, coincided with an avid demand for tales with a Welsh background, however improbable it might be! Possibly Lady Charlotte Guest's perennial, magnificent and influential translation of the *Mabinogion* (1838–49) derives obliquely from such a demand, but her work, when compared with the numerous double- and three-decker novels that still survive,[1] is like a genuine Jacobean oak chest placed by the side of a dealer's pre-war reproduction piece. Two non-fictional prose writers from the region, Dr. Richard Price (of Tynton, 1723–91) and David Williams (of Watford, Caerphilly, 1738–1816), belong more to the intellectual life of London in the later eighteenth century than to Wales. They are mentioned here as two of the better known[2] products of the growing, anglicising influence of Nonconformity in preparing the ground for an English tradition lower down the social scale. The very existence of this tradition was later obscured by the large numbers of immigrants from West Wales to the industrial parts of east Glamorgan and Monmouthshire; its significance for individual writers has not yet been properly assessed, although a great deal of evidence awaits sifting in the tabulated sections of the many mid-nineteenth century reports into the 'state of Wales'.

The result of such reports—no less than the establishment of an English based educational system at primary, secondary and university level—brings our rapid survey close to the twentieth century, with its genuine 'Anglo-Welsh' contribution to English literature. This, the best known part of the English tradition will here receive a brief treatment, though many of the works cited merit a closer critical scrutiny.[3]

Two of the earliest writers of distinction came from Monmouthshire: Arthur Machen (of Caerleon, 1863–1947)—poet, translator, novelist, critic and autobiographer—and W. H. Davies (of Newport, 1871–1940)—lyric poet, tramp, and autobiographer. A younger man, Gwyn Jones (of Blackwood, 1907–)—novelist, short story writer, founder of *The Welsh Review* and translator of Welsh and Icelandic classics—is happily still Professor of English at Aberystwyth. All three are unmistakably sons of Gwent and seem to find the inspiration for their best work in their native county: Machen in the superb evocation of his early life in *Far Off Things* (1922) and *Things Near and Far* (1923); Davies in his poems and in the prose that deals with his walks in South Wales (*Autobiography of a Super Tramp* (1908)); and Gwyn Jones, in numerous short stories and in the novel *Times Like These* (1935), which record the distinctive English dialect of West Monmouthshire as well as the very essence of life in a mining community in the 1920s. A fourth writer, D. G. James (of Griffithstown, 1905–), a philosophical and literary critic—now Vice-Chancellor of the University of Southampton—shows in his work how thoroughly

[1] *Bleddyn: A Welsh National Tale* or *A Romance of the Ancient Monastery of Neath*, for example.

[2] Price was an influential moral philosopher and economist; Williams is best known as the founder of the Royal Literary Fund.

[3] The authors and works mentioned specifically in this section are used as illustrations of trends: the list is by no means exhaustive and represents less than a tithe of the material available in Cardiff alone. The whole subject will receive fuller treatment elsewhere.

assimilated to English tastes and standards were the scholars educated at twentieth century Monmouthshire grammar schools. When it appeared in 1937, his first critical study, *Scepticism and Poetry*, marked a new development in critical thinking about the Romantic poets and the later plays of Shakespeare.

Cardiff was slower in making its contribution to English literature: only four of its native writers have reputations outside Wales. Howard Spring (1889–), journalist and novelist, has spent much of his working life in the North of England. Similarly, the Cardiff born R. S. Thomas (1914–), whose poetry has won increasing critical acclaim since 1948, finds the marrow and very bone of his poetry among his parishioners in Mid- and North Wales; his observation of their life and his own acquired knowledge of the native Welsh language, have done most to nourish his crabbed and acidly etched view of the problems of rural Wales. Dannie Abse (1924–), a young Jewish doctor turned novelist and poet, is still finding his true medium: and although his early days in Cardiff form the subject of his first novel, *Ash on a Young Man's Sleeve* (1952), his inspiration seems to come from outside Cardiff. The same is true of the late Dr. Kathleen Freeman (1897–1959): a fine product of the local educational system, she began adult life as a university lecturer in Greek and gradually allowed her hobby of writing to dominate her life. First and foremost a bold and scholarly interpreter of the Greek way of life, she found time to write novels under her own name and many detective stories as 'Mary Fitt', as well as contributing a weekly review column to the *Western Mail* for many years after the war.

Before discussing the best interpreters of industrial life in the Glamorganshire mining valleys, two writers should be named: Wil Ifan and Huw Menai. Both are bilingual and both have local fame as occasional poets. But whereas Wil Ifan's personal English verse is an additional ornament to his Welsh writing, Huw Menai has, since the nineteen-twenties, seemed about to carve an important niche for himself as a prose writer and poet, without quite being able to sustain his promise. He will stand as an exemplar and forerunner of those 'valleys men' of this century who deliberately chose and cultivated the English language as their only flexible medium for expressing an essentially Welsh way of life.

This is the field in which Jack Jones (of Merthyr, 1884–), has excelled. Three of his many novels, *Rhondda Roundabout* (1934), *Bidden to the Feast* (1936), and *River out of Eden* (1951), give forceful and almost photographic pictures of industrial Glamorgan; the colloquial force of the native idiom, too, disguises the author's painstaking research. But *Unfinished Journey* (1937), the first part of his autobiography, represents the high point of the development of Jack Jones's gift of evoking the very breath of a way of life. Glyn Jones (of Merthyr Tydfil, 1905–) is a younger writer from the same area who has enjoyed a grammar school and college education. He, too, is at home in the native tongue and gets some of his best effects from the interplay of two languages which lies behind the dialogue of his characters. *The Blue Bed and Other Stories* (1937) is a classic of the remarkable development in British short story writing since 1926 and, having lately turned to novel writing, he will, it seems likely, use to the full his remarkable poetic gifts for evoking the sensuous

side of experience. Another teacher, like Glyn Jones from the top of a mining valley, Idris Davies (of Rhymney, 1910–53), began as a poet and later tried the novel. Faber and Faber published his *Gwalia Deserta* (1938) and T. S. Eliot has commended his power of conveying the exact sense and feel of a given place at a given time. He is the best commentator on the decayed life of the very earliest industrial villages, and few of his contemporaries can deny the power of his satire, the exactitude of his observation, nor (in his later verse) the agony of his perception.

Rhys Davies (of Porth, 1903–) and Gwyn Thomas (of Porth, 1913–) are two novelists and short story writers who write against a Rhondda background. Davies made a strong impression on literary London in the nineteen-twenties, became a friend of D. H. Lawrence and, in time, a lover of France. *The Dark Daughters* (1947) and *Boy with a Trumpet* (1949) revealed a still developing talent, but more recently *The Darling of Her Heart* (1958) shows that Anteus-like he still draws literary strength from his native soil, though the Rhondda valley about which he writes has long ceased to exist. A similar gap between literary fiction and human fact exists in Gwyn Thomas's successive novels where the chiaroscuro effect derives from the author's comic intention. For in Thomas's best novels, *The Alone to the Alone* (1947), *Where Did I Put my Pity* (1946) and *All Things Betray Thee* (1949), we enter a cloud-cuckoo-land created partly from the juxtaposition of a heavily latinate vocabulary and native Rhondda idiom and partly from the application of the broad categories of Freudian psychology to the obviously typed Rhondda characters of the 1926–39 era of depression. Thomas is beginning to imitate his own mannerisms, particularly in his *Punch* sketches, but behind it all lies his deep understanding of Spanish literature and the passion of his social pity.

As one contemplates the best-selling impact of prose works by Jack, Glyn and Gwyn Jones, and by Rhys Davies and Gwyn Thomas over the last thirty years, it becomes obvious that a firmly established English literary tradition now exists in this region. No poet of the stature of W. H. Davies has yet appeared,[1], but one feels that the shadow of Dylan Thomas's powerful, individual talent will have to be exorcised before a younger generation of poets and dramatists will be able to speak to the next few decades with an authentic and personal voice.

[1] *Raiders' Dawn* (1942), the first volume of poems by Alun Lewis (of Aberdare, 1915–44), seemed to suggest that another poet as original as Dylan Thomas—if somewhat more astringent—had come out of South Wales; but, in the same year, Lewis published a volume of short stories (*The Last Inspection*) and by the time of his death in India he seemed to be finding his personal voice in prose rather than in verse. [See *Letters from India* (1946) and *In the Green Tree* (1948).]

XV

EDUCATIONAL INSTITUTIONS

THE UNIVERSITY COLLEGE OF SOUTH WALES AND MONMOUTHSHIRE

ANTHONY STEEL

(With acknowledgments to J. F. Rees, William H. John and the Western Mail Ltd.)

ON 24th October, 1883, Cardiff was *en fête*. There was a general holiday to celebrate the opening of the new University College. Lord Aberdare, the first President of the College, delivered an inaugural address in the Public Hall, Queen Street. A procession of the Mayor and Corporation, members of the Council and the Court of Governors of the College, the Principal and Senate, the children of the schools in the town and many others, proceeded from the Town Hall in St. Mary Street by way of Queen Street to the old Infirmary buildings in Newport Road. The formal opening was followed by a luncheon in the Drill Hall where speeches were made by Henry Richard, John Rhys and the famous trade union leader, William Abraham, better known to his generation as 'Mabon'. Nature did her best to warn the orators that the future was not to be quite as rosy as they predicted. It rained in torrents.

The College had come into being as the result of the report of a departmental committee presided over by Lord Aberdare. It recommended that a College should be established 'in Glamorganshire for South Wales' (a College had been opened at Aberystwyth in 1872 and had had a precarious existence), and that it should be aided by a parliamentary grant of £4,000 a year. The committee anticipated that there would be a difference of opinion about the appropriate site for the College. The respective claims of Cardiff and Swansea were strongly pressed, and to resolve the difficulty the matter was referred to three arbiters. They found unanimously in favour of Cardiff.

The College was launched on its career with a sum of £12,000 raised by voluntary subscriptions and the promise of the Government grant of £4,000 a year already mentioned. It thus became the first University College in Wales to be founded with the assurance of firm support from State funds. The old Infirmary buildings in Newport Road were rented from the Cardiff Infirmary authority for £400 a year. Around the main building a number of temporary wooden sheds were erected as lecture-rooms (some of them are still in use to-day!). Viriamu Jones, who although only twenty-seven years of age had been for nearly two years Principal of Firth College, Sheffield, was appointed Principal. It was a most fortunate choice. Between 1883 and his untimely death in 1901, he not only laid the foundations of the College but also played a leading part in the development of secondary education in Wales and in the formation of the University of Wales.

The small original staff included W. P. Ker, A. Seth (Pringle-Pattison) and T. F. Roberts. In the first session 151 students were enrolled—109 men and forty-two women. An analysis of the list illustrates the fact that there was very limited provision in Wales at that time for secondary education. Some forty students came from educational institutions in England and ten others qualified by private study. For the foundation of the College preceded the passing of the Welsh Intermediate Act of 1889. Cardiff thus became the first Welsh College to which women were admitted on the same terms as men. They were not slow to take advantage of the opportunities offered them, the best scholarship in the first entrance examinations being carried off by a woman. This was most gratifying to Lord Aberdare, who had enlightened views on the subject of women's education. He doubtless encouraged his wife to work for the establishment of the women's hostel at Cardiff (opened in 1885 as Aberdare Hall) and he was delighted when his daughter, the Hon. Isabel Bruce, became first Principal of that institution.

The new University College reflected the contemporary religious discord for, in the interests of educational progress, the report of 1881 had made it clear that the Principal should be a layman and that there should be no religious teaching in the curriculum. And finally, while it was essentially a Welsh institution, it reflected the ideal of true university teaching, for which, as Lord Aberdare said, 'the one ruling thought should be to select the ablest, the most gifted, the most vigorous man'. In this, even then, the College ran counter to the views of some Welshmen who maintained that Welsh Colleges could be satisfactorily run only by 'true-born Welshmen', and who were prepared to tilt even at Lord Aberdare by reminding him of his Scots ancestry.

There was no significant increase in numbers for the first ten years. Then there was a rapid increase. At the outbreak of the First World War there were more than 800 students. In the early years they were prepared for the external degrees of the University of London in Arts and Science. A movement was initiated in 1891 to unite the three existing Welsh University Colleges—Aberystwyth, Bangor and Cardiff—in a federal university which would grant its own degrees. After much deliberation a scheme was adopted and a draft charter prepared. A Royal Charter was granted to the University of Wales in 1893.

As early as 1886 the Council of the College contemplated the beginning of medical education but failed to get Government assistance for the scheme. In 1894, however, it had collected enough money to begin the teaching of anatomy and physiology, and the main building was raised a storey to provide accommodation for the new departments. This was the genesis of the involved and troubled story of medical education in Cardiff. *Sunt lacrimae rerum.* Students were able to complete their pre-clinical courses and then proceed elsewhere (usually London) for their clinical work. After 1906 they could qualify for the Welsh University degree in Medicine in this manner. But naturally there was a desire to complete the whole course of study in Wales. This would involve considerable expenditure.

The College also made an attempt to establish a School of Mining. A department was formed in 1891 with Professor (later Sir) William Galloway as the head.

Owing to pressure of professional work as a consultant he resigned in 1902. An effort was then made by Principal E. H. Griffiths to place the teaching of Mining in the College on a more satisfactory basis, but it met with failure. The coal-owners combined to set up a Mining School of their own at Treforest.

The growing demand for teachers as the Welsh educational system developed opened up new possibilities. A Day Training Department was instituted at the College in 1891. At first a two-year course was offered and the standard for admission was not high; but step by step advances were made until it became usual for the students to pursue courses for a degree. There is no doubt that the Training Department contributed considerably to the increase of student numbers. The provision of the 'normal grant' by the Board of Education enabled many with restricted means to enter College. It also tended to divert to teaching some who would have preferred another career in which, indeed, their particular capabilities might have found more congenial outlets. In 1891, too, the College, in association with certain local authorities, formed a Training College of Domestic Arts which found its home in St. Andrew's Place six years later. To the same period belongs the building of Aberdare Hall, as we have already seen, as a hostel for women students. It was provided and managed by a committee independent of the College, but closely associated with it.

The federal system of the University of Wales was found in practice to impose restrictions, sometimes irksome, on the conduct of the individual Colleges. They had to surrender some of the autonomy they had previously enjoyed. As they were jointly responsible for degree courses and examinations, this involved the setting up of a University Senate. It was to consist of all the heads of departments of the three Colleges. It was an unwieldy body in which the more officious often dominated set debates; for academic persons often find it more congenial to prolong discussion than to arrive at a conclusion. A Royal Commission was appointed in 1916 to inquire into the organization and work of the University of Wales and its three constituent Colleges. Its members were impressed by the case against the University Senate and recommended that it should be abolished. In its place the present Academic Board was formed, mainly representative of the faculties of the Colleges. This was a major change in the 'federal' structure of the University. In the nomenclature of political science it would be more appropriate to call it a confederation. The Colleges enjoy such a high degree of freedom from control that they are becoming quasi-universities.

The Royal Commission had to grapple with the vexed question of medical education. Its recommendation was that the Medical School should be organized as a separate constituent College of the University. A precedent was found in the College of Medicine at Newcastle which was a constituent member of the University of Durham. (It may be remarked that a Royal Commission in 1935 recommended that the College of Medicine at Newcastle should be amalgamated with Armstrong College to form the present King's College there!). The Council of Cardiff College refused to accept the solution. In particular it was not prepared to hand over the departments of Anatomy and Physiology. Another difficulty was that the Institutes

of Physiology and Preventive Medicine, erected through the munificence of Sir William James Thomas at Newport Road, were the property of the College. The Medical School would require the use of these buildings. In the event the Medical School was carried on as an integral part of the College. A Board of Medicine and a Faculty of Medicine were organized to administer medical education under the control of the College Council. It was admittedly elaborate machinery for the management of a relatively small school. But worse was to follow.

The Royal Commission had recommended that the 'unit' system should be applied to the new School. This was something of a novelty at the time and the attempt to adopt it at the Royal Infirmary, where the major part of the clinical teaching had to be done, led to friction. The future historian will find it hard to explain the quarrel. It was not so much a clash of principles as of personalities, and those who did not know the men cannot appreciate what happened. The crisis came when the Infirmary authorities refused to admit the students, and the College had to arrange for them to go to hospitals in London and elsewhere. Some kind of compromise was inevitable. This was effected in 1931. The College retained the pre-clinical teaching (including the departments of Anatomy and Physiology) while the clinical teaching passed to the Medical School as a constituent part of the University with its own Council and Senate and a Provost at its head. A new agreement was arranged with the Royal Infirmary. Much tact was required at first in the initiation of this scheme, but like many anomalies it worked when there was a common will to make it do so. The College acquired the old Infirmary buildings (which it had hitherto rented) in 1895 and subsequently purchased the freehold of nearly all the property on the 'island site' bounded by Newport Road, West Grove, The Parade and the old Rhymney Railway approach. Here the Institutes of Physiology and Preventive Medicine, already mentioned, were built.

As leases fell in, development continued. The Department of Engineering, now about to be absorbed in a £400,000 new building, was begun as early as 1896, with a small extension in 1949. Plans to rehouse the old Department of Mining were set in hand in 1943, and the present magnificent building, which also accommodates the much newer Department of Industrial Relations, was occupied only last year. Not much now remains to be planned for the 'Old College' in Newport Road, but it must be put on record that the present ambitious programme could never have been contemplated without the magnificent support given by industry to the Engineering Development Fund started by Mr. G. H. Latham, the President of the College. Over £400,000 was contributed in the winter of 1957–8 by twenty-one firms, especially Richard Thomas and Baldwins Ltd., The Steel Company of Wales, Guest Keen and Nettlefolds, British Nylon Spinners and Whitehead Iron and Steel Co., who provided about four-fifths of this large total between them.

Another most important step was taken early in the present century when the College secured from the Cardiff Corporation five acres in Cathays Park on a lease of 999 years at a pepper-corn rent. It meant that the future of the institution would be definitely centred there. It also meant that the College authorities were committed to a standard of building which involved great expense. The necessary funds

at that time had to be raised by public appeal. Fortunately, generous benefactors came forward, the chief of whom was the late Lord Glanely, President of the College. The Administrative and Arts block was opened in 1909 and the Tatem Laboratories for Chemistry and Physics in 1930. The cost of building and equipment, however, left a debt which, when the industrial depression set in during the 'thirties, made further progress impossible.

Since the conclusion of World War II the University Grants Committee has been enabled to adopt a much more generous attitude with regard to grants for capital expenditure. The north wing of the College was 'completed' in 1954—though a still further extension is now planned—and the whole south wing should be ready in a year's time: part of it has already been occupied for two years by the Department of Zoology. It may be added that in 1920 the College was granted for future development the triangular piece of land of about three acres north of the present buildings in Cathays Park. A badly needed Arts block was started in the far corner of this triangle in the present year, and it is hoped that in due course this will be supplemented by new pre-clinical buildings and a new College library.

Reference has already been made to the provision of residential accommodation for women students, but the men had lagged behind. It was felt that the amount of travelling which many of them were obliged to do was a serious handicap, especially on the social side of College life. A small, but much appreciated, contribution to the solution of this problem was made by a former Bishop of Llandaff when he gave the use of St. Teilo's Hall, Roath, to the College as a residence for thirty-five students. More recently Llandaff House, Penarth, which is also the property of the Church in Wales, has replaced St. Teilo's with approximately the same amount of accommodation; but much greater developments have occurred during the past five years. With the assistance of the University Grants Committee, the College has not only acquired two large houses with extensive grounds adjacent to each other on Penylan Hill, but has already developed one of them into a hostel for nearly 200 students, known as University Hall. The second house will soon be subject to a similar development and has been converted in the meantime into a temporary annexe for a further twenty-two students. Aberdare Hall, too, has grown to 133 students, for substantial additions were made in 1939 after the committee, which had hitherto managed it, had voluntarily placed itself under the control of the College Council.

From the earliest days of the College students formed a great variety of societies, but they had no place of their own for their meetings. After the end of the First World War some active spirits among them decided to build a Union as a war memorial. A small beginning was made by the purchase of a house in Park Place. This proved to be quite inadequate. Consequently, in 1931 a pageant was promoted in Cardiff Castle grounds which proved so successful that a hall with kitchen, committee rooms and a billiards room was built on the same site. The enlarged Union, however, suffered serious damage through enemy action in 1941. In 1954 the buildings in Dumfries Place, which were acquired by the College as long ago as 1894 and had been put to a variety of uses in the intervening years,

were adapted and furnished (again with the generous help of the University Grants Committee) as an admirable centre for the students' social activities. They are already, unfortunately, becoming too small. However, it has recently been found possible to provide additional facilities—for staff as well as students—on the site of the old Union in Park Place.

The same story of small beginnings may be told of the College playing fields. The oldest was Cae Syr Dafydd, in Llandaff Road. Then some eight acres were purchased at Caerau. A Rugby pitch was found for the medical students at Rookwood. Now all these have been superseded by the extensive and well laid-out playing fields at Llanrumney with an excellent pavilion. They were formally declared open by the late Lord Aberdare on 19th May, 1955.

Important changes have taken place in the provision for the training of teachers. As the result of the McNair Report, a Collegiate Faculty of Education has been established. It consists of the Principals of the Training Colleges of Barry, Caerleon, Cardiff and of Domestic Arts, together with representatives of the local education authorities concerned. The Professor of Education at the University College is Dean of the Faculty. A Collegiate Centre of Education has been opened at 34 Cathedral Road, where provision is made for conferences and lectures and generally for teachers to meet one another.

As a result of the Education Act, 1944, a change has taken place in the management of the Training College of Domestic Arts. It is now under the joint control of all the local education authorities of South Wales and Monmouthshire, but in view of services rendered by the University College in the past the scheme makes provision for a substantial representation from the University College Council, and for full membership of the students in the University College Union. The accommodation of this Training College in St. Andrew's Place had long been considered inadequate, and it became particularly so when the course was recently extended to three years. Efforts were made in the inter-war years to raise money for new buildings. By 1955 the Ministry of Education had agreed to finance the building of a completely new College with its hostels at Llandaff, and this building was completed and occupied last year.

The University College may claim to have initiated technical education in the area. Viriamu Jones, not it must be said with the complete approval of his academic colleagues, induced the College Council to enter into agreements under the terms of the Technical Instruction Act, 1889, with Cardiff Corporation, Glamorgan County Council, Monmouthshire County Council and Newport County Borough. The College was to provide evening courses in Science, Commerce, Music and Art. This was the origin of the Associated Authorities which still have special representation on the College Council. These arrangements came to an end in 1916 when the local authorities assumed full responsibility for technical education. The former Cardiff Technical College, now the Welsh College of Advanced Technology, has grown into a major institution. It has fostered departments of graduate status. The University College has succeeded, despite difficulties which arise from the federal nature of the University, in getting two of these

departments—Architecture and Pharmacy—recognized. Students in these departments may qualify for degrees in the University of Wales after spending an initial period in the University College.

This rapid sketch of the evolution of the provision of facilities for higher and professional education in Cardiff has had to omit much. Student numbers have now grown to over 2,000, and new Chairs have been created since 1949 in Spanish, Archaeology, German, Biochemistry, Applied Mathematics, Electrical Engineering and Mechanical Engineering. But nothing has been said of the research conducted in so many fields—scientific, historical, literary and social—and of distinctions gained by many students in so many walks of life. To attempt such a chronicle would be a prodigious task. Suffice it to say that the orators of 24th October, 1883, had no conception of what would be achieved by the institution they then launched upon a career in which so many difficulties would be encountered and so much devoted service given to surmount them.

To-day Wales can recall with pride the pioneers of her educational system, and particularly the work of the first President of the University College at Cardiff. There Lord Aberdare is duly honoured; his coat of arms crowns the new south wing, while his statue looks across Cathays Park to the College which is his really lasting memorial. Associated with his name must be that of Principal Viriamu Jones. Men of vision, they recognized then what all recognize now—that the future well-being of a nation rests on the strength and vitality of its educational institutions—and they gave due prominence to this belief in the College motto, *Nerth Gwlad ei Gwybodau*—'the strength of a country is its learning'.

THE WELSH NATIONAL SCHOOL OF MEDICINE

A. TREVOR JONES

The School of Medicine is a constituent School of the University of Wales, administratively distinct from the four constituent Colleges, with its own Council and Senate. It shares with the University College, Cardiff, the responsibility for medical education, the College undertaking the pre-clinical part and the School the clinical part.

Although the School was established only as recently as 1931, and is thus the youngest medical school in the country, medical education in Cardiff goes back to the last century, when in 1893 Departments of Anatomy and Physiology were set up in the University College of South Wales and Monmouthshire. These were recognized by the University of London for its pre-clinical examinations, and an addition to the Charter of the University of Wales in 1904 gave it power to confer degrees in Medicine. It was not, however, until 1921 that medical students were able to complete their course in Cardiff, and until that year had to proceed to London for their clinical experience. A Chair in Pathology and Bacteriology had been established before the war, and this was followed after the war by Chairs in

Hygiene and Public Health, Medicine, Surgery and Obstetrics and Gynaecology, and with the co-operation of the Cardiff Royal Infirmary it was possible in 1921 to provide full clinical training.

For some years after 1921 the Medical School remained part of the University College of Cardiff, but as a result of an arrangement which had been reached between the University and the College, the independent School, with its own Charter, came into existence in 1931, the pre-clinical departments remaining at the College.

It was necessary, and to be expected, that there should be many links between the various bodies which all have their part to play in medical education. The University College, the Medical School and the Teaching Hospitals are all bound together by a series of formal and informal ties which, over the course of years, have produced out of this apparently complicated pattern a harmonious and serviceable system. To the observer who is interested in results rather than constitutional niceties, the arrangements for medical education in Cardiff follow closely those found in other provincial universities.

One of the aspects of the teaching facilities at Cardiff has, from the beginning, been the establishment of whole-time 'units' under the directorship of clinical professors. The full-time staff all hold honorary appointments at the Teaching Hospitals, which now include Llandough Hospital in addition to the Royal Infirmary. Alongside these 'units' are the consultant staffs of the hospitals who are all recognized clinical teachers, and are responsible for a large part of the bedside teaching of the undergraduate. In fact, it would be difficult to distinguish the responsibility of the full-time staff and the hospital staff in their relations either to patients or to students. The aim of the School has been to integrate, to the fullest possible extent, the activities of both; and this policy has been reflected in the location of the school departments which are mostly situated in hospitals with the closest association with the wards. Moreover, it is intended that this integration will be carried out, to an extent hitherto never achieved, in the new Medical Teaching Centre which has been planned for Cardiff.

In its short period of independent existence the School has rapidly extended its arrangements both for teaching and research, and in recent years Chairs of Pharmacology, Anaesthetics, Child Health and Bacteriology have been established, bringing the total of professorial departments up to ten, and catering for an intake of sixty-five medical students a year. In addition, classes are provided for post-graduate students in Tuberculosis and Chest Diseases, and in Public Health; and regulations of the University provide for diplomas to be conferred in those subjects. The School is also responsible for instruction leading to the Certificate for Health Visitors.

The advent of the National Health Service Act has brought changes which have had their impact on medical schools in Cardiff as elsewhere. The Teaching Hospitals, the Royal Infirmary and Llandough Hospital have been united under a Board of Governors who provide under the Act 'facilities for teaching and research', and upon which the Medical School is strongly represented. In addition there are

several other hospitals in the Cardiff area which are recognized clinical institutions, among which should be mentioned Sully Hospital for Chest Diseases, Whitchurch Hospital and the Lansdowne Hospital for Infectious Diseases. These hospitals come under the aegis of the Welsh Regional Hospital Board and, in so far that they provide facilities for teaching, their relationship to the Medical School is a close one, but in a wider field the School has been able to exert influence on the hospital services throughout Wales, thus implementing the intentions of the Act which arranged the hospital regions throughout the country in such a way that they were associated with a 'University having a school of medicine'. In its task of reorganizing and planning the specialist services in Wales, the Hospital Board has called upon the School in many ways, the most effective, perhaps, being the appointment of many members of the professorial staff to act as Consultant Advisers. In that capacity the staff have continued to visit hospitals in all parts of the region and are in touch with the varied developments which are going on in places far removed from the teaching centre. The School also plays its full part in the clinical research activities of the hospital service, and is well represented on a committee which encourages research projects in hospitals throughout the region.

In yet another way the School is in touch with the hospital service because the Medical Act 1950 requires newly qualified practitioners to spend a year's residence in hospitals; the School is the official body which approves the posts for this purpose and the staff make inspections of the Regional hospitals and keep in touch with their graduates who are performing duties in these posts. All these opportunities combine to bring the School into the general picture of the hospital service, and thus, it is hoped, able to bring its teaching into line with the requirements and needs of the community.

In this connection special mention may be made of two of the earliest endowments, namely the David Davies Chair of Tuberculosis and the Mansel Talbot Chair of Hygiene. The first was linked with the work of the Welsh National Memorial Association, which for many years conducted the campaign against tuberculosis in Wales. The Professor has always held the position of Adviser to the Association, and this practice was continued when the Regional Board inherited the responsibilities under the National Health Act; it is a good illustration of the way in which a university department can reinforce the work of a social service. Similarly, the Department of Hygiene has always worked closely with the local health authorities. The Departments of Child Health and Obstetrics and Gynaecology have also had many points of contact with the local authorities with mutual benefits to these subjects and the services to the community.

The School is also fortunate in being able to co-operate closely with the public health laboratory service of the Medical Research Council, and the Director is the Professor of Bacteriology; mention should also be made of the Pneumoconiosis Research Unit of the Medical Research Council at Llandough Hospital, which in recent years has extended its field of study into the epidemiology of many other diseases found in the community; much of the work which is being carried out there has been in partnership with the School, for the subjects studied are necessarily

Plate XXIV.—The new Medical Teaching Centre for Wales. The architect's impression.

of common interest. Another department which has always worked in collaboration with the School is the Neuropsychiatric Research Centre at Whitchurch Hospital, which has only recently been transferred to the Medical Research Council.

While these points of contact with the outside medical world have been stressed it should not be forgotten that all the departments in the School carry on their own researches vigorously in many directions, for it is believed that an active programme of investigation brings with it a lively interest in teaching. There is no attempt, either individually or collectively, to separate the two main functions of the Medical School, which are teaching and research.

This account of the activities of the School in Cardiff would be incomplete without some mention of its plans for the future. Much of the work of the past years has been carried out in institutions widely separate from each other, and in buildings which are out of date. Plans are now on foot for the building of a new Teaching Centre on a site of fifty-three acres, which is not too far removed from the University College where the new pre-clinical departments will be built. Here will be a hospital of 800 beds in which the Medical School departments will be integrated in the manner above mentioned. There will also be a Dental School and Hospital, together with the necessary residential accommodation for students, nurses and other staff. 'This immense project' (as it has been termed by the Minister of Health) is at present the subject of an architectural competition, and it is hoped that during 1960 the architect responsible for the winning design will be instructed to proceed with the detailed plans, and that building will start in the near future.

THE DEVELOPMENT OF TECHNICAL EDUCATION

ALEXANDER HARVEY

In many areas the existing provision for further education stems directly from a Mechanics Institute. While such an Institute was established in Cardiff in 1841, it closed down about 1856, so that there appears to be no connection between it and the technical classes which commenced in January, 1866. The Public Libraries Act of 1855 made these classes possible, one of its objects being the establishment of Science and Art Schools, and the classes which started in 1866 were sponsored by the Library Committee, paid for out of the Library rate and housed in the Library premises (then situated in St. Mary Street). Some forty part-time students enrolled for these first classes, and the subjects taught were Geometry, Machine Drawing, Building Construction, Mathematics and Art.

The available accommodation soon proved inadequate, and in 1870 the classes moved to rooms in the Royal Arcade. Above the fireplace in the restaurant of David Morgan Ltd. there is a plaque which reads 'The School of Science and Art now the Technical College was established in this room 1st July, 1870, and remained here to 24th July, 1882'.

When the present Library building in the Hayes was erected in 1882, the Science and Art School moved there, but its stay was not of long duration. The Technical Education Act of 1889 made provision for the setting up of Technical Instruction Committees: Cardiff established such a committee in 1890 and the Science and Art School then left the Library Committee. The new committee immediately made arrangements for the Science and Art School to be operated by the recently established University College, and for the next few years the Principal and Registrar of the University College acted as the two senior officers for the Science and Art School.

In 1892 the classes actually left the Library building, to be rehoused in premises belonging to the University College. Huts on Newport Road housed some of the work, whilst a building in Dumfries Place (now used as a Students' Union) was the main centre for a number of years. At this period (around 1900) about 1,000 students were attending the various classes.

Eventually the Cardiff Corporation realized that full and separate provision must be made for this work. Following a report by Sir Philip Magnus in 1907, the Corporation took over responsibility, appointing Charles Coles as Superintendent of Technical Instruction. Further Education in Cardiff owes a great debt to Mr. Coles. He surveyed and reorganized the work and urged the necessity for building a major technical college in Cardiff. This idea was accepted, the original building in Cathays Park being commenced in 1914 and completed in 1916. It came into full use in 1919, with Mr. Coles as Principal, and a large range of full-time professional courses was offered.

The ensuing period, up to the outbreak of war in 1939, was one of steady development. Immediately prior to the war the college had about 750 full-time students in attendance and some 5,000 part-time students. It had become an important regional college, drawing students from all parts of South Wales and Monmouthshire, with a number from England and abroad. Much of the work was of university standard, and students were being presented in considerable numbers for University of London external degrees, especially in Engineering. Apart from this there was also a link with the University of Wales, in that degree schemes for Architecture and Pharmacy had been formulated and the College was associated with the University in connection with both of these schemes.

The war years held up further development, but much work was done in furtherance of the war effort. Nearly 5,000 men and women were trained in full-time courses. The major contributions came from the Engineering Department (1,460 fitters and turners for the Army, 970 women machinists for the Ministry of Labour) and from the Physics Department (783 radio mechanics for the Navy).

The ending of the war brought fresh problems, with demands for new courses such as Catering, and large numbers of men and women returning from the Forces to complete their interrupted education and training. The number of students rapidly became almost double the pre-war number, the number of full-time students reaching 1,384 in 1947, while the part-time figure climbed to 7,700 in 1949. Further accommodation had to be found as a matter of great urgency, and two disused

schools were brought into use. Crwys Road School was taken over to provide accommodation for the new course in Catering, and to house the Building Department with its large complement of craft students, while a little later St. John's School, in the Friary, was used to house the Art Department.

At this point, just after the war, the College was essentially an 'omnibus' college, catering for all work from the most elementary to the most advanced. At one end of the range were two schools, the Reardon Smith Junior Nautical School and the Building School, providing schooling for boys aged 13 or 14 to 16. At the other end of the range were the fifty or so graduates taking degrees in Architecture, Chemistry, Economics, Engineering and Pharmacy. No other institutions in Cardiff, apart from a number of evening institutes operating in school buildings, were in the further education field.

It became clear that a breakdown was necessary, with new institutions to take over sections of the work, thus leaving the original College to concentrate upon advanced work. During the six years from 1948 to 1954, the Cardiff Authority founded new institutions. The Cardiff College of Music and Drama took over certain part-time classes in Music and introduced full-time courses, and the Art Department (already mentioned), which had been housed in the Friary, became a separate College of Art in 1950. The Llandaff Technical College was opened in 1954 as a contributory college to take over the elementary part-time work in Science and Technology from the original Cardiff College of Technology and Commerce, and the Reardon Smith Nautical College, providing a one-year residential pre-sea course, was established in 1955 and replaced the Reardon Smith Junior Nautical School. It was also envisaged that a further contributory college would be built to take over the elementary work in Commerce.

These developments would result in all elementary work being removed from the College, together with certain specialized work, such as that in Art, Drama and Music. By 1956 all of the projects, save that for a contributory college of Commerce, had been carried through. This had eased the College accommodation problem considerably, and had enabled the College to concentrate practically all of its efforts upon advanced courses.

In 1956 the White Paper 'Technical Education' Cmd. 9703 appeared, which, amongst other developments, envisaged the designation of a small number of institutions as Colleges of Advanced Technology. Such Colleges were to concentrate wholly on advanced work. The Cardiff College of Technology and Commerce, as it was then known, was selected as one of the eight colleges to be designated. The designation took effect in 1957, when the College became known as the Welsh College of Advanced Technology.

In spite of the transfer of elementary and other work referred to earlier, further work had to be removed in order that the College could fit into the new pattern. Thus, the work in Bakery and Catering was detached. This work was already housed in the school building in Crwys Road so that its removal was an easy matter, and the courses in question are now provided by a new institution—the College of Food Technology. Work in Dressmaking, etc., was transferred to the College of Art,

whilst the General Certificate of Education courses (Ordinary and Advanced) were transferred to the Llandaff Technical College. Unfortunately, it has not proved possible as yet to provide a contributory college for the elementary commercial work. Some of this has been transferred to the Llandaff Technical College, but it is hoped that this second contributory college will commence building in the near future.

In spite of the transfers which have taken place, the development of new courses and the higher standard of accommodation required for advanced work has resulted in very heavy pressure on the available accommodation. It has proved necessary to build a new block, and this is scheduled for completion in September 1960. Three departments are being housed in this new block, those of Chemistry, Navigation and Pharmacy. In the case of Chemistry, special provision is being made for work in plastics and rubber, and with radioisotopes. In both this and the Pharmacy Department, good provision has been made for research activities. The accommodation for Pharmacy has been substantially increased, in order to cope with the increasing demands which are being made for pharmacists. The new block also includes a complete (and self-contained) suite of rooms for the Students' Union, together with a large hall and refectory. The cost of the building is £640,000.

The transfer of the three departments to the new building will allow of the remaining departments expanding within the existing building, and plans have been prepared for reconstruction of this after the new building has been occupied. The departments which will remain in the present building include Applied Physics, Architecture, Building, Commerce and Administration, Electrical Engineering, Engineering, English and Adult Studies, and Mathematics.

The present period, while the pattern of the Colleges of Advanced Technology is emerging, is one of rapid transition with each college adapting its existing courses and devising new courses to meet the particular needs of the region which it is its first duty to serve. So far as the Welsh College of Advanced Technology is concerned the changes vary considerably from department to department. Thus, in the case of departments such as Architecture, Navigation and Pharmacy, no radical changes have been necessary, those which have been made being required by the natural development of the subject. On the other hand, departments such as Chemistry and Engineering, which formerly provided full-time courses leading to the external degrees of London University, have had to be largely re-orientated. Sandwich courses (which had been run on a small scale since 1921) have been developed, some leading to the new Diploma in Technology, others to a Higher National Diploma. So far the College has been recognized for the Diploma in Technology in Applied Physics, Electrical Engineering, Mechanical Engineering and Production Engineering, while other courses are being prepared.

Finally, harking back to the White Paper, referring to colleges of Advanced Technology, it was claimed that they were 'of crucial importance to the future of technical education in this country'. The colleges, however, at any rate in their new dress, are still in their infancy, and it will be some years before their contribution becomes noteworthy. However, in the section dealing especially with Wales, it was said that 'leaders of the educational and industrial life of the Principality must

regard selected colleges as common possessions to be developed to the highest level of academic efficiency in their own fields'. It should be recorded that much good will has been shown the College and much help given—by industrialists, by university staffs, by education authorities and many others. The co-operation shown augurs well for the future.

THE COLLEGE OF DOMESTIC ARTS

EDNA M. DAVIES

The Training College (originally called the South Wales and Monmouthshire Training School of Cookery) was established in 1891 by a committee of enthusiastic educationalists elected for that purpose by the Council of the University College, Cardiff, and acting on the maxim so frequently expressed by Principal Viriamu Jones that 'the impress of the University should be put on all educational efforts'. It began its work in the cookery centre of the Higher Grade School for the training of students for the Teachers' Diploma in Cookery, granted by the Training School. With increasing numbers, it was found necessary to transfer the School to the Stacey Road Hall, where it remained for three years. During that period departments of Laundrywork and Dressmaking were added for the training of teachers in those subjects. Then, in 1897, expansion necessitated a move to more central and suitable premises at 6 St. Andrew's Place, and in 1899–1900 the Board of Education recognized the Training School and made arrangements to examine students for the Teachers' Diploma in Cookery. By 1906 the School had outgrown the new premises and three adjoining houses were added to the original building, involving considerable alterations and additions. Quoting from 1906 records, 'This is the only School of its kind in the Principality, and the only one in the United Kingdom that is a department of a University College'. In 1907 the departments of Cookery, Housewifery and Dressmaking commenced in the larger, better equipped, premises and a new building was added for the department of Laundrywork.

The 'Coming of Age' celebrations took place at the University College in Cathays Park in 1912. Up to that year, the management of the Training School had been in the hands of the University College of South Wales and Monmouthshire, but it was then transferred to a Joint Committee of representatives of five education authorities of South Wales and Monmouthshire.

The opening of a hostel for students in 1920 in Cathedral Road laid the foundations of residential accommodation.

In 1929 the College, at the suggestion of the Board of Education, was again taken over by the University College and the Local Education Authorities of Breconshire, Cardiff, Cardiganshire, Carmarthenshire, Glamorgan, Merthyr, Monmouthshire, Rhondda and Swansea. During the period from 1929–39, there was extensive reorganization of the existing accommodation at 6 St. Andrew's Place, and in 1932 another house in Cathedral Road was acquired for the residence

of students. A new refectory was opened in 1934, various departments were extended and replanned, and residential training in Household Management was inaugurated for all students. This final course in Household Management co-ordinated all the subjects involved in the training. By 1937 it had been only too evident that the extension of the teaching of Domestic Arts, as planned and envisaged, was hindered by the inadequate premises—described in 1907 as 'commodious and luxurious'—and plans were initiated for the erection of a new college at Cae Syr Dafydd, Llandaff Road.

The war years postponed this project, and post-war conditions modified these original plans. During the war years the Golden Jubilee Celebrations were held at the University College in 1941.

A further hostel was opened in 1941 and, in 1950, the Training College acquired and equipped a house in Cardiff Road, Llandaff, for training in Home Management for intending teachers of Housecraft. Three flats, suitably furnished, allow students to practise Home Management under varying conditions of accommodation, equipment and income.

In September 1947 the Training College came under the management of a Joint Education Committee of all the education authorities in South Wales and Monmouthshire, together with co-opted members nominated by the University College of South Wales and Monmouthshire. It is this committee which in 1959 sees the completion of the work of those University College pioneers in education who, by their vision and foresight, founded this College sixty-eight years ago.

The new buildings in Llantrisant Road, Llandaff, include the teaching block, accommodation for approximately 150 residents, four flats for practice in household management, together with residence for the Principal; student amenities for living and their social life have been given careful thought, and the development of community living with the desired educational and social background should form the basis of a study of home and community. The erection of these new buildings marks the beginning of a new era in the teaching of the Domestic Arts in Wales.

THE CITY OF CARDIFF TRAINING COLLEGE

WALTER T. JONES

The City of Cardiff Training College was opened in 1950 to provide third-year supplementary courses for qualified teachers. These courses were in Art and Crafts, and Physical Education, in both of which subjects there was a serious shortage of specialist teachers, particularly in the new secondary modern schools. The buildings, a converted military camp, were adequate and were very pleasantly situated in Heath Park. When an arrangement was made whereby practising teachers were admitted to specialist courses, while still in receipt of their salary, recruitment of students steadily increased, and the governing body felt that the time had come for extending the scope of the work. Approaches were therefore made to the

University of Wales School of Education, and after considerable negotiations permission was given by the University to begin in 1956 a full course of training leading to the Teacher's Certificate. The usual subjects of this certificate course were to be offered but all students had to specialize in Physical Education. It was hoped that most would remain in College for three years and would, in their third year, take the supplementary course in Physical Education. Two changes resulted from this change of status, viz. the College was to take men students only, and secondly there was no room for the third year course in Art and Crafts. Fortunately that course could then be accommodated at the Cardiff College of Art to which it was transferred.

The intention of the University of Wales School of Education was that the newly recognized College should be the forerunner of a Welsh National College of Physical Education to be established as soon as the Ministry of Education would give its consent. Approval in principle was given by the Ministry. The full course soon proved to be very attractive, and students from the Welsh grammar schools and from many parts of England applied in increasing numbers for admission to the course which would give them the highest possible qualifications as specialist teachers of Physical Education. Between 1956 and 1959 the entry doubled and nearly all students wished to stay for three years. It was equally gratifying to find that a very satisfactory number of students wished to take a second main subject such as History, Mathematics, Welsh, Geography, Art and Crafts, in addition to their compulsory main Physical Education. On completing their course the students found no difficulty in obtaining appointments in grammar, comprehensive or secondary modern schools in England as well as in Wales.

With the rapidly increasing number of students and the widening of the curriculum it became apparent that the temporary buildings were soon to become inadequate, and the governing body began negotiations with the Ministry for inclusion of a new College in its building programme. Such negotiations had not proceeded very far when the National Advisory Council for the Training and Supply of Teachers reported in 1958 on the subjects of the three-year course and the necessity for greatly increasing the supply of teachers. The Ministry did not feel able to accept the whole of the National Council's recommendations, but did agree that 12,000 additional teachers must be obtained by 1962 and then trained by the Colleges annually. The Welsh Training Colleges were to be given a share. There were very protracted and difficult meetings inside the Welsh Area Training Organization and between the University and the Ministry. There were problems relating to the number of additional students to be allocated to Wales and to which Colleges were to be expanded. Eventually the Ministry, in January 1959, made its decision that 850 extra places were to be given to Wales and that a new College was to be built in Cardiff. In England and Wales as a whole only three new Colleges were to be built, and Cardiff was to be one of the three.

In consultation with the University of Wales School of Education the Ministry decided that the new College to be built in Cardiff should be a mixed college of 150 men and 250 women students and that it should be ready for occupation in September 1962. Of the 150 men, ninety would specialize in Physical Education

and would take it to the Advanced Main level. The new College would be the only one in Wales at which this level of Physical Education could be taken. This was a slight departure from the original idea of having a National Physical Education College in Wales, but it retained within the framework of a general Training College the strong element of Physical Education training. The women students would not take Physical Education to this high level as that course was to be held at Barry Training College.

A very full range of subjects will be offered in the new College. The Main Courses will be available in English Literature, Welsh, History, Geography, Mathematics, Music, Biblical Studies, and in some Sciences such as Biology, Anatomy and Physiology and Nature Study. The College has also been designated as one of the two Colleges in Wales which will be permitted to offer an Advanced Main Course in Art and Crafts. After a series of preliminary meetings with the Ministry, plans for the new College were agreed, and a site of over thirty acres chosen at Cyncoed.

The new College, which will have been begun by the early summer of 1960, should be one of the best planned and attractive colleges in England and Wales, and should give the staff and students the conditions under which the new three-year course of training can develop and produce teachers better trained and equipped for their profession than has hitherto been possible.

EDUCATION IN CARDIFF

Robert E. Presswood

The history of education in Cardiff reflects the development of the city as a community. A century ago the population was 6,187, and one or two church schools provided elementary education. The Cardiff School Board was established in 1875, and having a duty to provide elementary education for all children it is not surprising that the period 1875 to 1902 was one in which many schools were built. The Cardiff School Board was responsible for providing eighteen schools while the Church of England added six to those provided earlier in the century, and to meet the needs of the Catholic population six Roman Catholic schools were built. During the period of the School Board the population of Cardiff increased from 39,675 in 1875 to 164,333 in 1902, as the coal-exporting trade was developed.

During this period the need to provide a separate opportunity for more gifted pupils was realized, and two higher grade elementary schools at Howard Gardens—the forerunners of the present Lady Margaret High School for Girls and the Howardian High School for Boys—were built in 1885. The passing of the Welsh Intermediate Education Act 1889 resulted in two schools being built, viz. the Cardiff High School for Girls 1895 and the Cardiff High School for Boys 1898.

The Education Act 1902 brought the end of the School Board, and the provision of educational facilities became the direct responsibility of the local

authority acting through an Education Committee. Additional elementary schools were provided as the population increased, and in 1905 the higher grade schools became municipal secondary schools. Similar schools for boys and girls were provided in Canton in 1907. The wider powers of the education authority were used to develop technical and commercial education, and in 1916 the Cardiff Technical College was opened in Cathays Park.

The years between the wars brought additional elementary schools, and the Cathays High Schools for Boys and Girls were provided in 1930, when the Cardiff Extension Act was negotiated. The Heathfield House High School for Girls and St. Illtyd's College for Boys were provided by the Roman Catholic authorities in 1930.

Thus, by 1944, the general pattern of education in Cardiff was reflected in a 30 per cent entry to grammar school education in high schools, a range of 'all-age' elementary schools, a central technical college supported by evening institutes and adult education classes, and the ancillary services of education. During the second war period, eight nursery schools were provided, the youth service was established, and the school meals service introduced.

At the beginning of the post-war period, the Cardiff Authority was faced with two important questions of policy. The first was to reorganize education so as to provide separate primary and secondary education for all pupils in accordance with the Education Act 1944. The second was to provide for an increasing population and for children residing on new housing estates. Reorganization came in 1950 when eighteen secondary modern schools were established. It was inevitable that existing school buildings should be used, but it soon became clear that children benefited greatly from the separate organization of primary and secondary schools. At this time the Fitzalan Technical High School was provided. It was realized, however, that the full benefits of secondary education would only be possible with the facilities available in modern buildings. As a result of the school building programme, twenty-two primary schools and twelve secondary schools have been built and two additional schools are in course of erection.

The provision of schools by the local education authority is supplemented by other schools. The Howell's School for Girls is a direct grant school founded in 1859. The fifty per cent free place entry is shared equally by the Cardiff and Glamorgan Authorities. In addition, there are twenty independent schools.

The post-war period has also brought important developments in further education. A separate College of Art has been established, while advantage has been taken of the gift of Cardiff Castle to the city to use part of it as a College of Music and Drama. The need to extend technical education has resulted in the Llandaff Technical College which provides a wide range of courses which are linked with the work of the Welsh College of Advanced Technology. This College has had a major extension in Cathays Park. A separate College of Food Technology has been provided. Another interesting feature of further education is the Reardon Smith Nautical College, which provides a year's residential pre-sea training for prospective merchant navy officers.

In recent years, Cardiff has had an opportunity of providing a training college for teachers, the history of this development being outlined separately.

The Education Act 1944 re-emphasized the need to provide educational facilities for handicapped children. This has been done in Cardiff by providing three schools for educationally sub-normal children—a primary school and separate secondary schools for boys and girls. The Greenhill Open-Air School, which was acquired by the Education Committee in 1926 and opened in October 1927, has been reconditioned by providing new class-room units. It has been extended to provide for partially-sighted children, and a centre has also been provided by the training and treatment of spastic children. There are two hospital schools for physically handicapped pupils. Partially deaf children are also given attention in Cardiff. Blind and deaf children are provided with residential education on the recommendation of the Principal School Medical Officer. Home tuition is made available for children who cannot attend school and speech therapy classes are available. The school medical service is available for all children.

Reference has already been made to the Youth Service which has expanded considerably recently. Assistance is given to voluntary organizations, while a number of youth centres are provided by the education authority in schools. Many adults attend classes in evening institutes, three community centres and other organizations.

It is a feature of education in Cardiff that attention and encouragement is given to the Welsh language. Instruction is given after ascertaining parents' wishes and, as a result, 80 per cent of the children receive instruction in the Welsh language. A primary school in which all instruction is through the medium of Welsh was established in 1949.

While important developments have taken place, there is still need for further progress. It is hoped that all outmoded schools will be replaced or reconditioned during the next five-year period and that an additional College of Further Education to provide for commerce, food technology and women's work will be built. An immediate development of psychological and educational interest will be the provision of a diagnostic centre for the observation of children who are on the border-line of ineducability. The Authority have the whole arrangements for secondary education under review, and with the abolition of the 11-plus examination in mind have sought the views of teachers and parents.

THE CARDIFF NATURALISTS' SOCIETY

H. Morrey Salmon

The Cardiff Naturalists' Society will, in seven years' time, celebrate its centenary, since it was founded in the year 1867 at the instigation primarily of Robert Drane, F.L.S. (1833–1914), in whose memory, sixty years later, a tablet was placed upon the entrance to No. 16 Queen Street, Cardiff, by the Society, recording that here he had lived and here the Society had been founded.

Twenty years previously an earlier scientific society had been formed in Cardiff and subsequently a second one, but both had ceased to exist by 1863. A museum collection begun by the first of these societies had, however, been maintained in being and later became the nucleus of the town Museum after the Cardiff Corporation adopted the Libraries Act, when the Free Library Committee appointed, in December 1863, a sub-committee to 'manage and arrange the Museum'. Interest in this Museum appears to have lapsed, however, after the middle of 1865.

Meanwhile, Robert Drane, who had come to live in Cardiff in 1855 and had contributed both specimens and his active help to the Museum, was clearly dissatisfied with its lack of progress. So, it is recorded, he called together at No. 16 Queen Street two friends of like interests, Philip S. Robinson and R. Rhys Jones, and put to them his idea of forming a society to help the Museum.

As a result of their discussions others were consulted, and a preliminary meeting was held in the Museum on 29th August, 1867, when those present constituted themselves a committee of the new Society, with William Adams, C.E., F.G.S., President; William Taylor, M.D., Vice-President; and Philip S. Robinson, Hon. Secretary. Rules were drawn up and the first general meeting was held on 11th September, 1867, when twenty-four members were present. At the end of the Society's first year, in September, 1868, the membership stood at seventy-six, with three honorary members, one of whom was the then Marquess of Bute. Among the names of the seventy-six members, twenty-six are marked as being the original Promoters of the Society. Robert Drane became the first life member.

The early meetings of the Society were held, by permission of the Corporation Library Committee, in the Museum room, and thus began the close association of the Society with the Cardiff Museum which was maintained until the establishment of the National Museum of Wales, with which institution it has always had a very close connection and most cordial relations. Many functions of the Society are held in the Museum; the use of the Court Room has been granted for the Society's Council meetings, and the general meetings of the Society are held in the lecture theatre. Many members of the Society serve, or have served, upon the Court, Council and committees of the Museum, and members of the staff of the Museum have always closely associated themselves with the activities of the Society over the years.

With the University College, also, there have always been the most cordial relations; in particular, it may be mentioned that for considerably over half a century there has existed a very close association between the Department of Zoology and the Society's Biological and Geological Section. The present Hon. Secretary of the Society is a member of the College staff, and the Director of the Museum and the Principal of the College are *ex-officio* members of the Council of the Society.

In its Memorial to the Privy Council on 23rd March, 1905, urging the location of the National Museum at Cardiff, it was recorded that the Society was then the largest scientific society in Wales; that the foundation of the present Cardiff Museum had been due to the Society; and that its support and enlargement had been one

of the main objects of the Society's existence. It can, therefore, justly be claimed that the ideals and labours of the Society during the years 1867–1907 came to fruition in the National Museum of Wales, founded by Royal Charter in 1907 and formally opened by the late King George V on 19th March, 1927, the year of the Cardiff Naturalists' Society's Diamond Jubilee.

While the establishment of the Museum was the keynote of the Society's early activities, as well, its original Rule 3 laid down the objective of 'practical study of Natural History, Geology and the Physical Sciences', but as early as in the first Presidential Address in March 1868 we find Archaeology referred to, also, as one of those matters 'our Society professes to become acquainted with'. Apart from fieldwork and research by individual members, this objective has been pursued by the establishment of specialist Sections within the framework of the Society's activities, and as early as 1875 the first, a Geological Section, was formed. This and two other early Sections had relatively short lives, but in 1887 a Biological and Microscopical Section came into being which, five years later, was redesignated Biological and Geological, and under this title has had a continuous active existence until the present time. Branching from it in 1946, a strong and active Ornithological Section was formed. Archaeology has always been a major activity of the Society, and this Section has been in existence since 1894, with only one early and very short period of quiescence; the Society and this Section have carried out many important excavations, notably those at the Roman fort, Gelligaer (1899—1900–1) and Breach Farm, near Cowbridge (1937). A Photographic Section came into being in 1911 and a Junior Section, covering all aspects of the Society's work, was formed in 1920. All these Sections are in active existence at the present time.

An annual volume of *Transactions* has been published continuously since that for the first year, 1867–8, excepting that, owing to the exigencies of war years, two or more annual records had to be condensed into one volume, so that the latest volume, LXXXVII, now in print, will be relative to the 91st year of the Society's existence.

In these *Transactions*, besides containing the records of the meetings and other activities of the Society and its Sections, there have been published many papers by members based on original research; papers read to the Society and Sections, etc., as well as *Lists* of the fauna and flora, and records of the geology, archaeology and history of the county of Glamorgan.

Originally the Society's area was conceived as only that part of Glamorgan eastward of the Ogmore river, later altered to a landward radius of thirty miles from Cardiff but, for many years, for all practical purposes it has regarded the whole of the county as within its purview; indeed, it has frequently gone much farther afield, e.g. in the publication of the 'Mammals of Breconshire' in vol. XXXIX and the 'Birds of Monmouthshire' in vol. LXX, and in this connection it should not be forgotten that the first scientific records of the recently declared National Nature Reserve, Skomer Island, Pembrokeshire (brought about by the efforts of the West Wales Field Society) were made by members of the Cardiff Naturalists' Society, in particular by Robert Drane, who first noted and recorded in the

Transactions, vol. XXXIII, the island's unique vole, *Clethrionomys skomerensis*, and that the safeguarding of the sea-bird colonies on Skomer and Grassholm were assured for many years by the fact that these islands were leased by the late J. J. Neale, J.P., of Penarth, a member of the Society from 1885 until his death in 1919, and twice its President.

Although the county lists of the flora and fauna, as originally published, are now somewhat out-of-date, they have been kept up-to-date by the annual publication in the *Transactions* of botanical, entomological and ornithological notes. An annual record of meteorological observations made in the Society's district was a feature of the *Transactions* from the first volume in 1867 until 1949, when it was discontinued.

The Society has, for a great many years, conducted an almost world-wide exchange arrangement with societies publishing like journals, and has thereby acquired a library of some 7,000 volumes which is housed in the library of the National Museum of Wales and is there available for reference.

The present activities of the Society include general meetings during the winter, in the course of which lectures are delivered at members' meetings by members of the Society or others, and public lectures by persons of standing or note upon subjects germane to the Society's aims. Field meetings are held between spring and autumn. The Sections' activities are, broadly, on similar lines.

Finally, the association of the Society with the British Association for the Advancement of Science began eighty years ago when a delegate was sent to the meeting at York. The Society joined the Conference of Corresponding Societies when it was instituted in 1885 and has regularly sent a delegate to the annual meeting ever since.

The following are the more important papers on, and lists of, flora and fauna, published in the Society's *Transactions*, later than the 'Bibliography' in the *Handbook, British Association, Cardiff*, 1920:

Vol.			
L	1917	The Lepidoptera of Glamorgan	H. M. Hallett
LI	1918	The Freshwater Fishes of Glamorgan	H. E. Salmon
		The Diptera of Glamorgan	J. W. Yerbury
LIII	1920	A Preliminary Moss-Flora of Glamorgan	P. W. M. Richards
LV	1922	A Contribution to the Spider Fauna of South Wales	A. R. Jackson
LVIII	1925	The Birds of Glamorgan (prepared by a Committee of the Society)	
LIX	1926	The Non-Marine Mollusca of Glamorgan (with 'additions', vol. LXII, 1929)	J. D. Dean
LX	1927	The Hymenoptera Aculeata of Glamorgan	H. M. Hallett
LXII	1929	The Neuroptera of Glamorgan	H. M. Hallett
		The Orthoptera of Glamorgan	H. M. Hallett
		The Paraneuoptera of Glamorgan	F. Norton
LXIII	1930	The Sawflies of Glamorgan	H. M. Hallett

LXIV	1931	The Ichneumonidae of Glamorgan . . .	F. Norton
LXVI	1933	Additions to the Coleoptera of Glamorgan .	J. R. le B. Tomlin
LXVIII	1935	Seals on the West Coast	H. M. Salmon
LXX	1937	The Birds of Monmouthshire	G. C. S. Ingram and H. M. Salmon
LXXIX	1943–8	The Ticks of Glamorgan	D. R. Arthur
LXXX	1948–50	Additions to the known Spider Fauna of Glamorgan, Carmarthenshire, Monmouthshire, etc.	D. R. Arthur
LXXXI	1950–2	Insects and Spiders collected in Glamorgan, 1952	E. C. M. d'A.-Fonseca and J. Cowley
LXXXIII	1953–4	Hymenoptera Aculeata in Monmouthshire .	H. M. Hallett

THE NATIONAL MUSEUM OF WALES

D. DILWYN JOHN

When the British Association last visited Cardiff in 1920, the National Museum of Wales was still in the hands of the contractors, and members were invited to apply to the Clerk of Works or to the foreman on the site if they wished to visit the unfinished building. Those who come in 1960 will be welcomed to a considerable and imposing edifice housing well-established departments of Geology, Botany, Zoology, Archaeology and Art, and a recently-formed Department of Industry. The Department of Folk Life, which originated in the building as an off-shoot of the Department of Archaeology, subsequently moved to St. Fagans to become the Welsh Folk Museum. Within the last ten years a Museum Schools Service has been developed which, among other activities, carries specially prepared exhibits from the Museum to secondary schools in all parts of Wales and Monmouthshire.

Despite this growth the building remains half-complete. The Charter of Incorporation of the Museum was granted in 1907 and building began in 1912, but because of delays caused by the war the first part was not opened to the public until 1922. The East Wing with the Reardon Smith Lecture Theatre (named after Sir William and Lady Reardon Smith, among the Museum's most generous private benefactors) was added in 1932, and there has been no extension since that time. More than half the cost of building was met by public subscription, and the remainder by the State. In the conditions which exist to-day, it cannot be expected that the cost of future extensions will be met in a similar way and it has, indeed, been recognized as a State responsibility. The Museum Council is hoping that permission will soon be granted for more building. The Fifth Report of the Standing Commission on Museums and Galleries, published in May 1959, has for the third time pressed the claim for a West Wing, which it regards as vital to the interests of the Museum; it is required to provide more exhibition and storage space for the five established Departments and to allow for the full development of the newly-formed Department of Industry.

The purpose of the Museum is to picture on the one hand the natural background which Wales has provided and now provides for human life, and, on the other hand, man's activities in Wales in the past and to-day. In dealing thus with a wide range of subjects, covering Nature and Man, the Museum is a comprehensive one; in another sense, in that it is the National Museum *of Wales*, specially concerned to illustrate the Welsh aspects of its subjects, it is restricted. It fulfils its purpose in part through its collections on display and in reserve, but since those who conceived the Museum intended that it should 'teach the world about Wales and the Welsh people about their own Fatherland', its service is not confined to those who can visit the Museum in person. It reaches a much wider public by its publications and by the extramural activities of its staff, fields in which its contributions are outstanding in character and amount.

The collections of Cardiff's former municipal museum, the Welsh Museum of Natural History, Arts and Antiquities, formed the nucleus of the national collections in 1912. Some measure of the rate of growth since that time is shown by the increase of the herbarium from 3,500 to 193,000 specimens, and in that of the collection of British butterflies and moths from 20,000 to more than 100,000. The 'Cardiff Collections' as they were called were a good, but small, beginning; those which exist to-day are large and representative, though by no means exhaustive, and they are still being freely added to by the gifts of a public, not confined to Wales, which has become actively interested in the institution, by purchase, and as a result of work in the field by members of the staff. In all departments the specimens which are exhibited are, of course, only a small part of the entire collection.

The emphasis in the galleries is upon Welsh interest. The archaeological exhibits are all of Welsh provenance except for a small number from over the Border and from Ireland, which are included for comparative purposes. The natural history is, in the first place, that of Wales, and where general lessons have to be taught Welsh material is used in preference to other material if it serves equally well; for example, the Department of Geology, in illustrating the work of wind, uses three-cornered stones, the *Dreikanter* of the Germans, not from African or Asian deserts, but from Welsh sandhills. The new Department of Industry, as it develops, will find a sufficiently wide field in the Wales of yesterday and to-day, for it will illustrate the past history and present status of the industries of Wales, especially those that have originated in materials of Welsh origin or in which Wales has made contributions in the realm of technology. The visitor to the Art galleries, recently so splendidly enriched by the Gwendoline Davies Bequest of French nineteenth-century paintings and Old Masters, may not at first feel the Welsh character, but it is there: in the eighteenth-century gallery particular honour is paid to the eminent Welsh painter, Richard Wilson; Swansea and Nantgarw porcelain is shown in association with paintings in the nineteenth-century galleries; and so on. The Welsh material is seen in a wider setting, and it remains true that the primary purpose of the Art Department is the acquisition of works by Welsh artists and craftsmen, portraits of Welshmen, and pictures of Welsh scenes.

The National Museum is rarely without a temporary exhibition, and there are often two or more being shown at one time. There were twenty-three in the past

year. The majority are of pictures, but some are scientific, including many specimens and entailing long preparation by the departments which sponsor them. The most recent of this kind was *Paper and its Uses*, while others have dealt with *Tin through the Ages*, *Coal in Science and Industry*, *Weeds and Weed Control*, *Insects and Man*, and *Wild Life Preservation.* Such exhibitions allow for the full illustration of themes which could not be dealt with in the permanent galleries, and the National Museum is fortunate in having the Circular Gallery, specially provided for temporary exhibitions, in which to show them. They are accompanied by handbooks which have an independent value when the exhibition is over.

By far the greater part of the collections are, as has been said, in reserve: they are study collections for the staff and are available for visiting scholars. Without them, and the data which are collected at the same time as the specimens, the publications of the Museum could not have been prepared. The latter, too, reflect the Welsh interest, the Museum's concern with a defined province, as the titles of many of them show. The following are examples from among those now in print: *The Slates of Wales*, *The Evolution of the Bristol Channel with Special Reference to the Coast of South Wales*, *The River Scenery at the Head of the Vale of Neath*, *Welsh Flowering Plants*, *Welsh Ferns*, *Some Welsh Fungi*, *Changes in the Fauna of Wales within Historic Times*, *Wales and the Sea Fisheries*, and *The Brown and Black Rat in Wales.* On the humanistic side there are *The Prehistory of Wales*, *The Early Christian Monuments of Wales*, a *Catalogue of Oil Paintings*, and *A Survey of Portraits in Welsh Houses.* Some have a wider scope: *Pattern and Purpose*, the Museum's most recent publication, is, as its sub-title makes clear, *A Survey of Celtic Art in Britain* as a whole; the *Personality of Britain* is a general study of Britain as an environment for man, and places Welsh antiquities in their true perspective as elements and manifestations of cultures which were spread over a much wider area than Wales.

The Museum is a State-aided institution receiving an annual grant-in-aid from the Treasury, and it also receives the product of a halfpenny rate from the City of Cardiff; but there is one important side of its work, developed within the last ten years, which is paid for in another way. It is the Museum Schools Service, financed by the local education authorities of Wales and Monmouthshire by an arrangement which became possible under the Education Act of 1944. The Museum Council eagerly accepted the opportunity it gave of regularly serving the schools of Wales and of extending its influence throughout the country. The Museum Schools Service Committees are composed of representatives of the local authorities and of educational interests in Wales, as well as of the Museum Council.

The Service is confined to secondary schools, of which there are just over 400, and by far its most important activity is its loan service, a means of taking the Museum to the schools.

There are five Schools Service Officers, one each for the departments of Geology, Botany, Zoology, Archaeology and Art. Lack of space has made it impossible to extend the Service to the Welsh Folk Museum, and the Department of Industry is far too recently formed to take part in it, but it is hoped that both will do so in time. Each officer is assisted by a craftsman and an already large collection

of loan exhibits which is continually being added to has been built up. Every eligible school has copies of the catalogues of available exhibits and material, and each is invited to participate in an allocation every term. The proportion of schools which takes part has steadily risen as the Service has developed and is now well over half the whole number, and in any one term there are now more than 5,000 exhibits distributed throughout Wales and Monmouthshire, delivered and collected in the Museum's vans. The officers visit the schools as frequently as possible in order to ensure that the Service provides what the teachers need and that the loaned material is used to the best advantage.

The Service, with its staff of seventeen, its workrooms and storerooms, is accommodated in the Museum with great difficulty owing to shortage of space. A reception room for school classes could only be provided by adapting for the purpose what had been an exhibition gallery. Fortunately one opposite the entrance to the Museum could be made available as the centre for this intramural work of the Service. Although not specifically designed to help the Museum, there are pleasing signs that the Schools Service is doing so, for, since it started, more children have brought or sent specimens to the Museum than ever before and they have done so with greater discernment, while a new awareness of the Museum has come about in parts of Wales which are distant from Cardiff.

In 1923 a scheme was drawn up whereby the smaller museums of Wales might be affiliated to the National Museum to their mutual advantage. It was the first arrangement of its kind in these islands, and nineteen museums are now affiliated.

In its short history the National Museum has taken over and thereby ensured the future of two institutions which were in existence long before it. In 1921 the trustees of the Turner House, Penarth, transferred the building and its contents to the National Museum. James Pyke Thompson had built it in 1888 to share his collection of pictures with the public, and he had named it in homage to J. M. W. Turner. It is now a branch art gallery of the National Museum at which frequent temporary exhibitions, as well as selections from the national collection and from the Pyke Thompson collection, are shown.

A still older institution was merged with the National Museum when in 1930 the Monmouthshire and Caerleon Antiquarian Society invited it to take over the Legionary Museum of Caerleon which it had built in 1850 to exhibit local antiquities. It is now a branch of the National Museum devoted to showing objects found in the excavations of the Roman legionary fortress. The exhibits in it were recently completely re-arranged and include finds from recent excavations.

THE WELSH FOLK MUSEUM

IORWERTH C. PEATE

The Welsh Folk Museum at St. Fagans, four and a half miles from the centre of the city of Cardiff, was opened to the public in July 1948. Its primary purpose is to illustrate the life and culture of the Welsh nation: its method of doing

so is broadly similar to that of the great folk museums of Scandinavia and north-western Europe. The Folk Museum is the natural outcome of the pioneer work of the National Museum of Wales since its inception in 1907 in the collection of folk material and in ethnographical research. This work of collection and research (begun in the late years of the nineteenth century by such friends of the then Cardiff Municipal Museum as the late T. C. Evans, *Cadrawd*, and T. H. Thomas) was first organized by the late William Evans Hoyle, the first Director of the National Museum, and actively encouraged by its third Director, Sir Cyril Fox. In 1932 a sub-department of Folk Culture was instituted in the National Museum: this became a full Department of Folk Life in 1936, and in 1943 the Museum Council declared that a folk museum with an 'open-air' park was one of the chief needs of post-war reconstruction.

The opportunity came in 1946 when the Earl of Plymouth offered St. Fagans Castle and its eighteen acres of gardens and grounds as a centre for a Welsh Folk Museum. An additional tract of eighty acres of adjacent park land was also secured. A Welsh Folk Museum Fund was opened and through the generosity of individuals, and of local and county authorities in Wales, a sum of over £100,000 was collected by the end of 1958. It is this Fund which has made possible the development of the Welsh Folk Museum from 1948 onwards.

Since its modest opening in 1948 as a constituent unit within the general framework of the National Museum of Wales, the Welsh Folk Museum has grown steadily (its staff now numbers over fifty persons). It will ultimately consist of (1) a modern block of buildings which will include exhibition galleries and store-rooms, a library, a theatre for lectures, plays and music, a shop, students' rooms, restaurant and offices, and (2) a fully representative open-air section.

Plans have been prepared for the modern block of buildings, but as this entails an expenditure of about £400,000 it has been found impossible so far to erect more than a very small part of the proposed block. The first floor of this part, ultimately intended for storage, is used temporarily for the exhibition of a small cross-section of the Welsh folk collection. After intensive fieldwork throughout the second quarter of this century this national folk collection has now reached considerable proportions and the need for adequate exhibition and storage space is most pressing. It is hoped that funds will be found to continue with the building of the Museum block in the immediate future.

In the meantime, work during the Folk Museum's first ten years has been concentrated on the development of the open-air section. A sum of over £25,000 was spent in restoring St. Fagans Castle and its gardens as an exhibit to illustrate the setting of a Welsh nobleman's life during the past four hundred years. The house, built about 1570–80 on the ruins of a medieval castle, has rooms furnished in sixteenth–seventeenth century style: others illustrate the eighteenth and nineteenth centuries. Late nineteenth-century additions are used to house (1) an exhibition of costume in Wales, (2) a small restaurant for the convenience of visitors, and (3) wood-turners' and basket-makers' shops. Some of these accretions to the

manor house will be rehoused when space in the modern block becomes available.[1] The gardens include a herb garden of sixteenth-century type, a formal garden, a sunken lawn with examples of topiary, a mulberry grove and a rose garden. The St. Fagans Castle vines are well known, a considerable quantity of grapes being sold every summer. Below the terraces is a series of fish-ponds stocked with carp, bream and tench.

The buildings removed to St. Fagans may be listed briefly. All of them have been presented to the Folk Museum by generous donors.

(1) Esgair Moel Woollen Factory, near Llanwrtyd, Brecknockshire. This building was erected about 1760 and developed as the business expanded in the nineteenth century. Its last textile worker died in 1947, and the building was rapidly deteriorating in 1949 when it was offered, with all its machinery, to the Folk Museum. It was removed completely, re-erected, the machinery placed in working order, and opened to the public in 1951. It is now in full production, and is staffed by two textile-workers.

(2) A timber-framed cruck barn, about 1550–1600, from Stryt Lydan, near Penley, Flintshire, opened to the public 1950.

(3) Abernodwydd, Llangadfan, Montgomeryshire, a timber-framed farm-house, about 1600, last occupied about 1935 and later used as a cattle-shed. Opened to the public 1955.

(4) Kennixton, Gower, Glamorgan. A substantial stone farm-house, built and added to between 1630 and 1730. This house was evacuated in 1939 when a new farm-house was built nearby. Its removal to St. Fagans meant the handling of 400 tons of stone several times: it was opened to the public in 1955.

(5) Capel Pen-rhiw, Dre-fach, Vale of Teifi, Carmarthenshire. This was an old building converted into a Unitarian chapel in 1777, its original pews, gallery (early nineteenth century) and pulpit being rescued. Opened to the public in 1956.

(6) Cilewent, Dyffryn Claerwen, Radnorshire. A typical long-house of possibly medieval date, renovated in 1734 and occupied until 1954 when a new farm-house was built nearby to replace it. Opened to the public 1959.

(7) Hendre-rwydd-uchaf, Llangynhafal, Denbighshire. A Vale of Clwyd cruck-built house with a central hearth and late fifteenth-century features. Removed to St. Fagans but not yet re-erected.

(8) Llainfadyn, Rhostryfan, Caernarvonshire. A typical Caernarvonshire *croglofft* cottage set on a plinth of large boulders: internal slate partition and furniture 'platform'. Removed to St. Fagans, but not yet re-erected.

The specialized work of dismantling and re-erecting these buildings is carried out by a small team of skilled workers. Experience has shown that it is essential that the men who dismantle the buildings shall also re-erect them. No work is let out on contract and none of the material handled by any persons other than members of the staff, under the supervision of the Curator. When a house is to be dismantled, two or three members of the Museum staff, an Assistant Keeper and the foreman being two of them, visit the building and remain at work in it for a period of two

[1] Until this is the case, the Castle—although an exhibit—has also to serve as the administrative headquarters of the Folk Museum, housing the curatorial and clerical staff.

to four weeks. Their task is to prepare a series of scale-drawings and full notes on all details of construction, number all individual timbers and stones, marking corresponding numbers on the plans, and to prepare a detailed report on the setting of the building, e.g. the farmyard, site and type of trees, garden plans, walls and ditches, etc. During this stage it is generally possible to work out the evolution of the building throughout the centuries, most remaining problems being solved when the building is actually in course of demolition. At the same time, a detailed photographic survey is also carried out. The men are then joined by a mason and a labourer and demolition begun. The surveying and dismantling of none of the eight buildings referred to above have taken more than three months' time. For the transport of the materials to St. Fagans, a reputable heavy-haulage firm is employed, the loading and unloading being carried out by Museum workers.

At the Museum end, the site of the 'new' building has to be decided upon, care being taken to ensure that ground levels, approaches, etc., are as similar as possible to those on the original site. Exact reproduction of the original site is, of course, impossible, but the orientation of each building, the approach road, lane or path, the disposition of the garden, etc., can be reproduced. All the timbering is carefully inspected, all doubtful pieces being rejected, and the remainder treated for the elimination of woodworm. The re-erection work is then undertaken by the Museum team with the assistance of other members of the staff.

The choice of buildings as exhibits in a folk museum is, of course, of great importance. The offer of a house as a gift can be made unexpectedly or may be the result of long and patient negotiation. Certain types of Welsh houses—and the same is true of other countries—demand a place naturally in a folk museum, in view of their social and architectural significance and of their rapid disappearance from the countryside because of new conceptions of hygiene, etc. Such is the long-house occupied by beast and man alike, the cows being separated from the dwelling end by a transverse passage only. Modern dairy requirements and the present standard demanded for the sale of milk have finally condemned this type to sudden extinction. Yet from Neolithic times to the twentieth century it has played an important part in the social structure of north-western Europe. Twenty years ago a small selection of interesting Welsh long-houses was noted and their fate during the intervening years followed carefully. When the new Claerwen reservoir in Radnorshire was opened, it appeared obvious that one of these houses would soon disappear. A new dwelling-house was built by the owners, Birmingham City Corporation, and the old house presented to the Welsh Folk Museum.

A valuable folk-museum exhibit may present a mean and unattractive appearance when seen in its final decrepit condition: it needs imaginative vision to picture it re-erected in its former glory on the Museum site. The Esgair Moel woollen factory was such a building. It had lost its white-wash almost completely, its walls were disintegrating and its stone-tiled roof had been replaced many years ago by thin Welsh slates. When it was first inspected, some friends dismissed it contemptuously as a miserable shack. But once re-erected, it has proved to be one of the most attractive features of the Welsh Folk Museum, and represents there a rural industry which has been of exceptional importance in the Welsh past.

The Caernarvonshire cottage represents a type discussed by Hughes and North.[1] The size of the stones at the base of the walls is enormous, their bottom course standing forward a little, increasing the effect of stability. The *croglofft*, a loft above the sleeping end only and reached by a ladder from the living-room floor, is still characteristic of all the western counties from Anglesey to Pembroke but is also found inland (as in east Montgomeryshire). It is hoped to find later an example for the Folk Museum of the simple one-roomed cottage with no internal division or loft. Typologically, this is the earliest form of habitation still surviving in this island.

Nonconformist chapels suffered greatly in Wales as in England during the nineteenth century. Down to about 1820–30 on the Welsh moorland these were simple, severe, barn-like structures reflecting indeed the experience of the early congregations which had their meetings in barns, the 'granaries of God'. Few of these early meeting-houses escaped unscathed from the fashions of the nineteenth and early twentieth centuries. One such is Capel Pen-rhiw, now re-erected at the Welsh Folk Museum. This chapel with its two doors (it was formerly customary for men and women to sit apart during services) and the pulpit between them in the middle of the long front side, has interesting box-pews made for the chapel and a gallery round three sides, held on wooden pillars. Such galleries were a feature of Nonconformist chapels, the aim being to increase accommodation without adding unduly to the size of the building, particularly where the purchase of land was difficult (owing to the prejudice of most landowners against the early Nonconformists) and funds unobtainable. Note also the enclosed communion-place. The complete design is honest and straightforward and has none of the defects of most Victorian Gothic chapels.

The value of bringing together to a national centre examples of ancient buildings (which would otherwise be destroyed) of architectural and social significance cannot be overestimated. They can provide, in the words of a Swedish author, 'a deep well of living waters invigorating the soul of the nation'. This is one of the aims which the Welsh Folk Museum has set out to achieve.

Those who had worked in the field of Welsh ethnography had long felt that essential as was the collection of evidence illustrating Welsh national culture, it was not enough if a complete picture of the traditional ways of life in Wales was to be obtained. In recent years, therefore, a department in the Welsh Folk Museum has been developed to deal with oral traditions. By this is meant a survey of all the dialects of Wales, including a study of the vocabularies of the home, the farm, crafts, etc., folk-song, folk-lore, folk-beliefs and customs in general. The twentieth century has brought catastrophic changes to the countryside—the development of bus transport to hitherto inaccessible areas, the mechanization of agriculture with the consequent disappearance of the terminology relating to human labour and horse-drawn implements, and the development of sound radio and television with their universal attractions in areas formerly secluded and self-sufficient. No record

[1] Hughes, H. Harold and North, H. L.: *The Old Cottages of Snowdonia* (1905).

of a traditional way of life now subjected to such a transformation can be even remotely complete if it is restricted merely to a picture of the material past. Old people who represent the last speakers of local dialects or the last practitioners of dying crafts or techniques have to be interviewed and recorded so that the skills already represented in the Museum by material objects can literally speak to future ages. Much has already been achieved in a brief space of time, but the work is extensive and onerous and will need a considerable team of workers if it is to be successful. A large modern house near the Castle gardens is now being converted to serve as a centre for the Oral Traditions Survey. This will contain a laboratory, studio, an archive of recordings of dialects, etc., and general facilities for research workers.

In the same way, the element of change in living communities demands constant sociological study and the Welsh Folk Museum aims at the study of rural and urban communities in Wales so that its record of Welsh ways of life may be reasonably complete.

This, then, is the achievement and intention of the Welsh Folk Museum. Situated on the western fringe of the capital city, it is easily accessible to a population of over one and a half million people. It receives an annual maintenance grant from the State, and in its capital development has received liberal help from the authorities of all the thirteen counties of Wales (including Monmouthshire) which it primarily serves. It is proud, too, to maintain the motto of its mother-institution, the National Museum of Wales, 'to teach the world about Wales and the Welsh people about their own fatherland'. As part of its wider duty, its staff maintains close contact with workers in the same field in England, Ireland and Scotland, in Scandinavia and Europe and in America. Its publications include Sir Cyril Fox's and Lord Raglan's *Monmouthshire Houses*, Mr. Ffransis Payne's *Yr Aradr Gymreig*, and Mr. Trefor M. Owen's *Welsh Folk Customs*. Others on various aspects of Welsh ethnography are envisaged.

D0528527